Students a~~~

Staff & P~~~

JOHN SHAW BILLINGS
AET. 58

detail of portrait by Cecilia Beaux
(National Library of Medicine)

SELECTED PAPERS

OF

JOHN SHAW BILLINGS

———◆———

Compiled, with a Life of Billings, by
FRANK BRADWAY ROGERS

MEDICAL LIBRARY ASSOCIATION
1965

Medical Library Association Publication No. 2

Copyright 1965

Medical Library Association

Free use of the material in this book is granted, provided that acknowledgment of the source is made.

Library of Congress Catalog Card Number: 65-23107

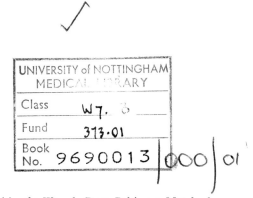

Printed by the Waverly Press, Baltimore, Maryland

Contents

Preface

One hundred years ago John Shaw Billings took over the direction of the Library of the Surgeon-General's Office, U. S. Army. This book is issued in celebration of that anniversary.

It has been a task at once easy and difficult to assemble these papers from sources widely dispersed and often almost inaccessible to the reader of today; easy, because the papers hold many things important for our own time, and because I had available the five volumes of reprints bound in turkey red, their paper now disintegrating, in the collection of the National Library of Medicine; difficult, because the corpus from which the selection was made is very large, and the winnowing-out process brought many twinges of regret. In general, it will be evident that I have included mainly the papers on medical bibliography, in which Billings' fame is most enduring, and some papers in which the autobiographical element is prominent. In addition, I could not resist the inclusion of "Scientific Men and Their Duties" and "Ideals of Medical Education," which deal with more general themes.

I have not presumed to edit Billings. Sometimes I have rearranged the typographical format in what I conceive to be a way which facilitates easy grasp of the data, as in the long lists of "Medical Journals of the United States," but in the same article I have not altered the variant pattern of the Ohio section—it is interesting evidence that, then as now, a man had to rely on the contributions of his staff members. All articles are presented in their entirety, except for minor deletions in "The Card Catalogue of a Great Public Library," the excerpt on Hollerith cards, and the article on "Medicine in the United States." This last is of some concern, for the article had a large impact, and the effect, however undeserved, of turning much criticism toward Billings; it is, however, full of maps and diagrams and statistical matter which are unsuitable for reprinting in a book of this sort.

In the bibliography of Billings' writings, originally prepared in 1915 by Miss Hasse for Garrison's memoir, I have corrected some errors, and can only hope that in the process I have not created others, as in the course of the extensive stylistic changes I have introduced. I have followed Miss Hasse's practice in not listing the official publications of the Library of the Surgeon-General's Office, under Billings' supervision, as part of the Billings corpus, but serious students of his life should not forget the prefatory and other materials to be found in the many volumes of the *Index-*

Catalogue and the *Index Medicus* and in the *Annual Report of the Surgeon-General, United States Army,* for the Billings years.

When I conceived of this book at the beginning of 1957, I intended to include the bibliography, and undertook some work on it, only to drop it later as it began to appear that it might have to be sacrificed as a means of keeping the book down to reasonable size. In the last months, at the urging of the Publication Committee of the Medical Library Association, I have again taken up the matter of bibliographical revision. For additions to the bibliography I am particularly indebted to Dr. Dorothy M. Schullian, who discovered and confirmed the attribution of many of the new items which originally had been published anonymously; to Miss M. Ruth MacDonald, who helped check against the *Index-Catalogue,* and in other ways; and to Dr. Jean Curran. I also here record my indebtedness to colleagues in Bethesda, Washington, New York, and London for their helpful assistance in gathering material and in tracking down obscure bibliographical and biographical points.

There are many repetitions in Billings' writings—favorite metaphors, favorite stories, particularly felicitous ways of stating a problem—as one might expect from a man who was in constant demand for the presentation of public addresses. But the honest, straightforward, and easy style is always there, too, and reveals the man in all his great serenity of spirit. Billings has much to teach us, and not only about bibliography.

In the preface to the last volume of the *Index-Catalogue* which he edited, Billings described his efforts as a "labor of love." So has the compilation of this work been for me, and I hope it will be of some usefulness as the National Library of Medicine embarks upon its next hundred years.

Frank Bradway Rogers

Denver
University of Colorado Medical Center
14 March 1965

The Life of John Shaw Billings

Billings, John Shaw. B. April 12, 1838, son of James and Abby Shaw Billings, in Cotton Township, Switzerland County, Indiana; moved to Rhode Island in 1843, returned to Allensville, Indiana, in 1848. Bachelor of Arts, Miami University, Oxford, Ohio, 1857. Doctor of Medicine, Medical College of Ohio, Cincinnati, 1860; demonstrator of anatomy, 1860–61. Entered Medical Corps, U. S. Army, 1861; 1st Lieutenant to Lieutenant-Colonel; field service with Army of the Potomac. M. Katherine Mary Stevens, September 3, 1862; C. Mary Clare, Kate Sherman, Jessie Ingram, John Sedgwick, and Margaret Janeway B. Assigned Surgeon-General's Office, Washington, December 31, 1864. Librarian, Library of the Surgeon-General's Office, 1865–95. Professor of Hygiene, University of Pennsylvania, Philadelphia, 1895–96. Director, New York Public Library, 1896–1913. D. New York City, March 11, 1913.

The portrait of John Shaw Billings which hangs in the National Library of Medicine shows him vested in the scarlet gown which he wore on the occasion of receiving the degree of Doctor of Civil Law at Oxford in June 1889. At the time of receiving this honorary degree, Billings was fifty-one years old, and for the moment was staying at the home of his friend, Sir Henry Acland. In the afternoon, after the ceremonies, the Aclands took Billings for a picnic on the river, carrying along a kettle and boiling tea on the bank. Billings sat, tired and silent, until Acland's young daughter insisted that Billings must tell the children a story. Billings promptly and very solemnly began:

"A travelling showman, going around with a Biblical panorama, thus described one of the pictures, 'This, ladies and gentlemen, is a picture of Daniel in the Lion's Den and—you will be able to distinguish Daniel *from* the lions because he carries a green cotton umbrella' " [1]

It is a revealing incident. Billings was musing on the past, reflecting on the long course of a lifetime which had led to a scarlet vestment and drinking tea on the banks of the Cherwell. He was thinking of another summer, 32 years earlier, and another Oxford, in southwestern Ohio near the Indiana border, where he had graduated second in his class from Miami University in 1857. He was penniless and hoped to obtain employment as a tutor so as to be able to pursue the study of medicine. Instead, he took

---

Address by Dr. Rogers at the National Library of Medicine, Bethesda, Maryland, June 17, 1965.

[1] Letter from Miss Acland to F. H. Garrison, quoted in Garrison's *John Shaw Billings; a memoir* (New York, Putnam, 1915) p. 389.

a job with an itinerant exhibitor of lantern slides and toured the midwest delivering a rapid-fire running commentary on the startling scenes his employer flashed before an enthralled backwoods citizenry.

In 1858, at the age of twenty, he had matriculated at the Medical College of Ohio, founded by Daniel Drake 40 years earlier in a booming Cincinnati that was then the largest metropolis west of the Alleghanies. As Billings later described it,

"...I graduated in medicine in a two years' course of five months' lectures each, the lectures being precisely the same for each year...In those two years I did not attend the systematic lectures very regularly. I found that by reading the textbooks, I could get more in the same time and with very much less trouble. I practically lived in the dissecting room and in the clinics, and the very first lecture I ever heard was a clinical lecture..."[2]

He lived in the hospital, cleaning out the dissecting rooms and doing all sorts of odd jobs. At St. John's he was known to the nursing sisters as "St. John of the Hospital," because of his melancholy mien and his austere ways. The austerity was forced upon him by his financial condition; all one winter he budgeted his food bills at 75 cents a week, which went largely for milk and eggs.

He took his medical degree in 1860 and stayed on at the school as demonstrator of anatomy, one of a faculty of nine. A newspaper advertisement shows the fees for six months of lectures at the College, October through February, as $105. Billings considered going into private practice with his surgical professor, George Blackman, now remembered chiefly for his re-editing of Mott's edition of Velpeau.

But at the end of that February of 1861 dark events were brewing. Threats had been received against the life of the President-elect of the United States; in Philadelphia he boarded the regular sleeper to Washington, and Pinkerton men sat with drawn revolvers in the dark berths to either side of where he slept. Lincoln was inaugurated on March 4, and in April the guns fired on Fort Sumter. It was Billings' twenty-third birthday.

He took the examination for admission to the Medical Corps of the United States Army and passed first on the list. He served a preliminary period as a contract surgeon, then was appointed First Lieutenant and Assistant Surgeon in April 1862 and placed in charge of Cliffburne Hospital in the old cavalry barracks on the hill above Georgetown. At the end of August he was transferred to Philadelphia as executive officer of the hospital there and, a few days later, was married to Miss Kate Stevens. At the end of March 1863 he reported for duty to Dr. Jonathan Letterman, Medical Director of the Army of the Potomac, then encamped near Fred-

---

[2] *Boston Medical and Surgical Journal* 131: 140–2 (1894).

ericksburg. The Rappahannock river was crossed on April 28 and 29, and Billings performed his first surgery in the field as Hooker engaged Lee in the battle of Chancellorsville on May 2 and 3. Two months later he was with the Second Division of the Fifth Corps at Gettysburg; Dr. Curran has given us an account of how Billings established his regimental aid station at the base of Round Top.[3] Following the Draft Riots in New York City later in July, Billings was sent to New York with the Seventh Infantry, which pitched camp on Fifth Avenue just above Forty-ninth Street. He was reassigned to hospital duty on Bedloe's Island in New York harbor, and then in February 1864 was placed in charge of an extraordinary expedition to Haiti, to rescue 371 survivors of a group of freed slaves who had been resettled there and swindled in the process. At the end of March 1864 he again joined the Army of the Potomac, still bogged down between the Rapidan and the Rappahannock. As Medical Inspector for the Army, he roamed a wide front and lived through the Wilderness and Spottsylvania, Cold Harbor and the siege of Petersburg. By summer he was invalided back to Washington, and in the fall of 1864 was assigned for duty at the Surgeon General's Office. His field service was over.

In the wonderful biography of Billings which Garrison has left us, there is a long series of remarkable letters from Billings to his wife, covering in a vivid way the period of his duties in the field. Of these we note two short but typical fragments:

"July 9, 1863, Hospital near Gettysburg ... PM. I am covered with blood and am tired out almost completely, and can only say that I wish I was with you tonight and could lie down and sleep for 16 hours without stopping. I have been operating all day long and have got the chief part of the butchering done in a satisfactory manner ..."

"April 17, 1864. Nothing new or important yet ... Yesterday I went up to Culpeper, saw Major Dent, who inquired very specially after you, was introduced by him to General Grant and took dinner with the General and his staff. I *like* Genl. Grant. He is a thoroughbred gentleman and suits me exactly ..."

The war over, Billings settled down to a routine of office duties. Curiously, he was worried at first that he would not have enough to do to occupy his time; he began the study of German, as he had once studied Latin and Greek as a boy, and undertook to teach himself something about microscopical studies. A contemporary[4] describes Billings' duties as "arid drudgery among invoices and receipts, requisitions and bills of lading, treasury drafts and auditor's decisions. His days were filled with routine office work, with questions of bookkeeping and pecuniary responsibility,

---

[3] J. A. Curran, "Billings at Gettysburg." *New England Journal of Medicine* 269: 23–7 (1963).

[4] Alfred A. Woodhull.

with the supervision of checks and balances." He was detailed to the Secretary of the Treasury in 1869–70 to inspect the condition of the Marine Hospital Service, and prepared a reorganization plan which set that service, later renamed the Public Health Service, on a new course. During the period 1870–75 he prepared long reports on Army hospitals and Army hygiene. He planned a new hospital for the Soldiers' Home in Washington, he became active in the affairs of the American Public Health Association, and was for a short time vice-president of the ill-starred and short-lived National Board of Health. He was a founding member and later President of the Cosmos Club and of the Philosophical Society of Washington. He was elected a member of the National Academy of Sciences, and served as its treasurer from 1887 to 1898.

The wonder is that in the midst of all these activities, his major task for the 30 years from 1865 to 1895 was the direction of the Library of the Surgeon General's Office. The Library, which had occupied a few shelves behind the Surgeon General's desk since the days of Joseph Lovell and Andrew Jackson, numbered about 1,800 volumes at the close of the War. When Billings arrived, the man and the opportunity met. Years later, in a commencement address at his old medical school, Billings described what he had first envisioned in Cincinnati in 1860, while preparing his thesis on the surgical treatment of epilepsy.

"In the thesis just referred to, it was desirable to give the statistics of the results obtained from certain surgical operations as applied to the treatment of epilepsy. To find these data in their original and authentic form required the consulting of many books, and to get at these books I not only ransacked all the libraries, public and private, to which I could get access in Cincinnati, but for those volumes not found here (and these were the greater portion), search was made in Philadelphia, New York and elsewhere to ascertain if they were in any accessible libraries in this country.

"After about six months of this sort of work and correspondence I became convinced of three things. The first was, that it involves a vast amount of time and labour to search through a thousand volumes of medical books and journals for items on a particular subject, and that the indexes of such books and journals cannot always be relied on as a guide to their contents. The second was, that there are, in existence somewhere, over 100,000 volumes of such medical books and journals, not counting pamphlets and reprints. And the third was, that while there was nowhere, in the world, a library which contained all medical literature, there was not in the United States any fairly good library, one in which a student might hope to find a large part of the literature relating to any medical subject; and that if one wished to do good bibliographical work to verify the references given by European medical writers, or to make reasonably sure that one had before him all that had been seen or done by previous observers or experimenters on a given subject, he must go to Europe and visit, not merely one, but several of the great capital cities in order to accomplish his desire.

"It was this experience which led me when a favourable opportunity offered at the close of the war, to try to establish, for the use of American physicians, a fairly complete medical library, and in connection with this to prepare a comprehensive catalogue and index which should spare medical teachers and writers the drudgery of consulting ten thousand or more different indexes, or of turning over the leaves of as many volumes to find the dozen or so references of which they might be in search." [5]

Billings had to acquire and train a staff, he had to obtain the books, and he had to find housing for both. For a staff he had a dozen civilian employees, many of them former army hospital stewards; only a single member of the staff had had a college education. But they were dependable and reliable, and Billings trained them in the rudiments of bibliographic procedure for which at that time there were as yet no nationally accepted standards. To get the books, exchanges were instituted with medical societies and institutions, begging letters were written to private individuals at home and abroad, duplicates were amassed for subsequent swapping. Wrappers were printed in two languages, English and Japanese, and sent to Japan to facilitate mailing of journals from that newly opened country. Billings sent one of his clerks to copy the list of journal titles which had been compiled by Dr. Joseph M. Toner of Washington; he wrote to Dr. Thomas Windsor of Manchester, instituting a series of exchanges and gifts which were to form the backbone of the Library's historical collections; he was constantly on the prowl in the libraries of his friends, as Oliver Wendell Holmes and James R. Chadwick would later testify. He was lucky enough to receive a fund of some $85,000, the proceeds of the sale of properties left over from disbanded hospitals, and he used the money to triple the collection. It was the lone instance of having money available in any considerable amount; in later years the annual sums available to Billings for operating the Library would reach $10,000.

In 1867 the Library found quarters in the old Ford Theatre building on Tenth Street. That building of tragic memory, originally a Baptist church before Mr. John T. Ford converted it for theatrical performances, had been purchased by the government for official use. For a while Billings and his staff remained at the Surgeon General's Office at Fifteenth Street and Pennsylvania Avenue, where the books were accessioned and processed before being carted over to Tenth Street. By 1880 the collections had grown to such a size that the need for a new building was imperative. Billings organized an intensive building campaign. Congress was bombarded by letters from physicians across the country; funds were appropriated in 1885; and the new building at the corner of Seventh Street and Independence Avenue was completed in the fall of 1887, at a cost of $200,000. The ground floor of the building was occupied by a section of the Adjutant General's Office; the east wing was occupied by the Army Medical Museum, which had been formally placed under Billings' charge in 1883; and the west wing with its four-tiered cast-iron bookstack was occupied by the Library. From high clerestory windows the light filtered down through

---

[5] *Cincinnati Lancet-Clinic* 20: 297–305 (1888).

stack floor gratings; on late winter afternoons the aid of a candle was sometimes needed to find the books on the lower shelves of the first stack level.

The growing collection had to be organized and cataloged. Small pamphlet catalogs had been printed in 1864 and 1865; the book catalog of 1868 lists over 6,000 volumes. The book catalog of 1872 ran to 431 pages, listed over 13,000 volumes, and was provided with a subject index. The catalog of 1873–74 was published in three volumes, and listed 50,000 titles of books and pamphlets. Then, in 1876, the *Specimen Fasciculus of a Catalogue of the National Medical Library* appeared. The title alone is noteworthy; "National Medical Library" appeared prominently in 28-point type; indeed, the letterheads of the Library during this period bore the same legend. The *Specimen* set forth in dictionary order both books and periodical articles—the books listed by author and by subject, the periodical articles by subject only, in a single alphabet. On this plan, the first volume of the *Index-Catalogue of the Library of the Surgeon General's Office* appeared in 1880. The first series of the *Index-Catalogue* was to be completed in 16 volumes, in the year of Billings' retirement.

The rise of the periodical form of publication of scientific literature had been spectacular during the middle third of the nineteenth century. Billings recognized the importance of this new form and strove to cope with it. He had clothesbaskets full of journals delivered to his home in Georgetown, where he worked at night at the job of checking the items in each issue which he wanted indexed. Returned to the Library, the journals were processed by the Library clerks, who copied out the titles on cards which measured 4¼ x 6⅛ inches. The next step sent the cards to Billings or to his great assistant, Dr. Robert Fletcher, who had joined the staff in 1876; they penciled a single appropriate subject rubric across the top of each card, which was then filed to await its proper sequence in the publication of the *Index-Catalogue*. Duplicate cards of current materials were made, and these were published, beginning in 1879, in the monthly *Index-Medicus*, for which the financial arrangements were handled on an extra-governmental basis. Thus Billings provided a bibliographic service for current awareness, along with another service designed primarily for retrospective search.

With all this activity, reference services were not neglected. Billings and his small staff somehow found the time to answer as many as two thousand inquiries per year. Billings also instituted a forerunner of today's interlibrary loan system; physicians outside of Washington, on depositing $50.00, were allowed to borrow books from the Library, and the records show that William Osler, Howard Kelly, William Halsted, Reginald Fitz, Walter Reed, Rudolph Matas, and George Crile were among those who took advantage of that privilege.

That Billings possessed extraordinary reserves of physical stamina, as well as intellectual capacities, is shown by the fact that during this same period, beginning in 1875, he was closely involved in the development of the new Johns Hopkins Hospital and Medical School. Billings' plans were chosen for the new hospital, which was begun in 1877 and opened in 1889. No matter that those plans tolerated no elevator shafts, no matter that they provided for thick coats of asphalt on the floors, in deference to the still prevalent idea that foul miasmas arising from the soil should be prevented from spreading, the plans represented a fresh new point of view and a departure from the old block buildings or rambling wooden pavilions of the past. And they embodied new ideas in medical education: there was to be a separate out-patient dispensary, first-class physiological and pathological laboratories, and a graded series of accommodations for private patients. During this time Billings was the chief medical adviser to Daniel Coit Gilman, the President of the new university. He arranged the curriculum for the new school: he insisted that its purpose must be to train investigators as well as practitioners; he was instrumental in bringing in Welch and Osler as the nucleus of the first staff. He placed emphasis on the keeping of proper records, financial and clinical; he taught courses in the history of medicine, commuting back and forth from Baltimore to Washington by train. He was giving his lectures on medical history elsewhere, as well—in Boston, in New York, and on some of his numerous trips abroad.

His interests in public health and vital statistics led to a position as consultant for the tenth, eleventh, and twelfth U. S. Censuses between 1880 and 1912, and he published voluminous reports of his findings. He stressed the necessity for morbidity as well as mortality statistics; he strove to get agreement on a standardized classification for reporting purposes. Of special interest to us of the present day, when the furor over machine methods of bibliography is at a peak, is the fact that it was a suggestion of Billings to Herman Hollerith, made over some chicken salad at Billings' home, which led to the development of punched-card tabulation. As Hollerith later wrote:

"... and so it happened that one Sunday evening at Dr. B tea table he said to me there ought to be a machine for doing the purely mechanical work of tabulating population and similar statistics ... After studying the problem I went back to Dr. Billings and said I thought I could work out a solution for the problem and asked him would he go in with me. The Dr. said no he was not interested any further than to see some solution of the problem worked out." [6]

---

[6] Letter of August 7, 1919; quoted by J. Fraser Muirhead in his article "Doctors afield; John Shaw Billings," *New England Journal of Medicine* 268: 778–9 (1963). See also Frederick J. Rex, Jr., "Herman Hollerith, the first 'statistical engineer'." *Computers and Automation*, August 1961, pp. 10–3 [with an important bibliography of Hollerith].

He went abroad often, buying books, visiting medical military installa-
tions, speaking at medical convocations, representing his country. His address at the International Medical Congress in London in 1881 was an
enormous success and drew world-wide attention to the problems of a growing medical literature and to medical bibliography. In 1886 he was invited
to speak before the British Medical Association, and his frank address on
the state of American medicine, kindly and humorous and forthright
though it was, drew some criticisms in this country and some disapprobation from organized medicine that did not abate for many years thereafter.

In 1895, after 30 years' service at the Library, President Cleveland
granted his retirement from the Army, and he accepted a post as Professor
of Hygiene at the University of Pennsylvania, at the insistence of his old
friend, William Pepper, whom he had advised for some years. It was not
an entirely happy move; Billings was a public health man of the old school,
the statistician and the sanitary engineer, and did not feel too much at
home in the direction of the type of laboratory investigations then becoming prominent. He attracted capable people, however, and gave them their
heads. At the end of November 1895 a great banquet was held in Billings'
honor in Philadelphia, and the medical community turned out in force.
The toastmaster on this occasion was Billings' old friend, Weir Mitchell;
Osler and DaCosta and Jacobi and Chadwick and Fletcher were there, and
spoke of Billings' achievement. Osler read a message of congratulations
from Surgeon General Sternberg, and announced that Billings' portrait
was to be painted and presented to the Library. Billings was given a silver
box, and inside it was a check for $10,000, which had been subscribed by
friends in England and the United States.[7] Billings responded in his usual
eloquent fashion, and was magnanimous in his praise of his colleagues.
It must have been in many ways a tense situation for Billings, newly arrived in Philadelphia and under obligation to the University of Pennsylvania, for he had been told only three days before the banquet that he had
been selected as the Director of the New York Public Library, then newly
forming from an amalgamation of the Astor, Tilden, and Lenox libraries.
Somehow he managed to work things out with Pepper; Weir Mitchell
helped to smooth the way; and at the end of summer in 1896, after three
months in Europe to attend the Royal Society's International Conference
on Scientific Literature and study continental libraries, Billings moved to
New York, there to spend the remaining 17 years of his life.

Billings set to work. He brought the Tilden books into the Lenox building and set up some two miles of temporary wooden shelving in the Astor

---

[7] "Banquet and presentation in honor of John Shaw Billings, M.D., LL.D.," *Medical
News* (Phila) 67: 634–41 (7 Dec 1895).

building. He installed artificial lighting in both buildings. He drew up a scheme of classification of which he remarked that

"...it is not a copy of any classification used elsewhere; that it is not specially original; that it is not logical so far as the succession of different departments in relation to the operations of the human mind is concerned; that it is not recommended for any other library, and that no librarian of any other library would approve of it..."

He tried to reconcile the varying styles of cataloging, and brought in a system which was much like that of the *Index-Catalogue*, with periodical articles carded among the books. He successfully bargained with City officials and the State legislature for a building site on the land occupied by the old Croton reservoir at Fifth Avenue and Forty-Second Street. An architectural competition for the new building was held, plans were completed on the basis of rough pencil sketches which Billings had drawn up one day in Atlantic City in 1897, and the building was begun. The cornerstone was laid in 1902, and nine years later, in May 1911, the new building was opened to the public. The staff was reorganized; the collections grew from almost half a million volumes in 1901 to over a million volumes in 1913, while the 42 branch libraries which Billings established held another million volumes.

As usual, his extracurricular activities threatened to outstrip his more regular efforts. In 1902 he served as President of the American Library Association; between 1905 and 1908 he was engaged in drawing up plans for the Peter Bent Brigham Hospital in Boston, which he had the satisfaction of seeing completed in 1913; and from the founding of the Carnegie Institution of Washington in 1902 he served as a member of the Executive Committee, and from 1903 on as Chairman of the Board of Trustees.

In his last years, he had days when he preferred to keep to himself. Near the end he said to his deputy, "I no longer have any enthusiasm. I have acquired a tendency to oppose new things and new ideas." He was sometimes irascible with his colleagues in the councils of the Carnegie Institution. "Walcott," he once said, "I seem to oppose everything, don't I?" The reply was "No...but you are sometimes cross and intractable." The death of his wife in August 1912 was a severe blow. That she was a constant inspiration to him throughout his life, no one can doubt who has read his letters. The man who could be so tough and so brusque at times was also the man who could write to her in salutation: "Idle of my Sole." He was the same man who could tell stories about Daniel in the Lions' Den to a little girl on a picnic.

During his last years he was frequently unwell. He had had five operations for facial cancer between 1890 and 1892, the last performed by Dr. William S. Halsted and involving a radical neck dissection. He was troubled with renal and biliary calculi; in 1900 he was operated on by Dr. Charles McBurney, and in 1906 a cholecystectomy was performed. In 1913 he underwent another operation, pneumonia supervened, and he died on March 11, in his seventy-fifth year, one week after the inauguration of President Wilson. He was buried in Arlington National Cemetery.

In his seventy-five years, he had fought a war, had revolutionized hospital construction, had been a prime mover in public hygiene and sanitation, had played a leading role in the development of vital statistics, had challenged the medical profession to higher levels of accomplishment, had done more to advance American medical education than any other individual of his generation, had created a great national medical library and built for it bibliographical keys of comparable magnitude. He was a mover and shaker; he had organizing genius and the passion for doing. He had vision, managerial adroitness, and a dogged and relentless power of will. Once he had said to the Librarian of the Royal Society of Medicine: "I'll let you into a secret—there's nothing really difficult if you only *begin*—some people contemplate a task until it looms so big, it seems impossible, but I just begin and it gets done somehow. There would be no coral islands if the first bug sat down and began to wonder how the job was to be done." [8]

Billings was singularly fortunate in his biographers. Fielding H. Garrison, who had joined the staff of the Surgeon General's Library in 1891, brought out his remarkable memoir in 1915; Harry Miller Lydenberg, Billings' protegé and later successor as Director of the New York Public Library, prepared a shorter evaluation in 1924 to inaugurate the ALA series on American Library Pioneers. In what follows I borrow many of their words and phrases, adding some emphasis of my own.

Billings was a tall figure of powerful build and commanding appearance. He was austere and somewhat distant in manner, and did not suffer fools gladly; he was a man of imperious judgments, and much inclined to have his own way. He was fertile in ideas, straightforward in expression, and entirely wrapped up in accomplishing whatever he set out to do. (Garrison) He knew what the master word in medicine is, he knew the glory of the day's work, he had the rare gift of industry of the minute. He seized upon essentials, and sometimes left behind some baffling small details that plagued his followers. He was impatient of committees and committee work; in striking out ahead of the crowd, he sometimes lost sight of the fact that those who moved in his wake frequently gained by their efforts at standardization and cooperation, however plodding they might be. He had unshakeable confidence in his own judgment; he formed his own opinions and drew his own deductions. He was constantly drawn on into

---

[8] J. Y. W. MacAlister, *British Medical Journal* 1: 642 (1913).

new directions; rarely did he re-examine the purely technical solutions he devised so readily and well.

Through all his activities, through all periods of his life, stands out, pre-eminent and persistent, his love of books. He read wherever he was and whatever he was doing. At sea or on land, at home or away, in the city or in the country, his book and his cigar were his constant companions. (Lydenberg)

He had a strong temper, usually well under control. As reticent in praise as in reproof, the weight of either was unmistakable when he did express it. The army officer was apparent in countless ways, in what he expected as well as what he did. The medical man and the scientist appeared with equal frequency, in his attitude to life, in the way he faced the great problems of nature, in his scrupulously careful weighing of evidence, in his methods of attacking new problems. (Lydenberg)

William Welch said that John Billings was the wisest man he ever knew. He was that rare thing in modern life, an absolutely reliable man. (Garrison) Loyalty to friends and ideals, wideness of sympathy and vision, tenacity of purpose, ceaseless industry, consideration of others before himself, gentleness combined with firmness—these were the outstanding characteristics of this soldier, scholar, physician, librarian, (Lydenberg) this altogether remarkable man who dominated the American medical scene for almost half a century.

BIBLIOGRAPHICAL NOTE

The sources of information on Billings' life are pre-eminently:

Fielding H. Garrison, *John Shaw Billings, a Memoir*. New York, Putnam, 1915. 432 p. [with a genealogy of the Billings family, the military record of JSB, and a bibliography of the writings of JSB].

Harry Miller Lydenberg, *John Shaw Billings; Creator of the National Medical Library and Its Catalogue; First Director of the New York Public Library*. Chicago, American Library Association, 1924. 95 p. [American Library Pioneers, I].

National Academy of Sciences. *Biographical Memoirs*. Washington, 1917. Vol. 8. "Biographical memoir of John Shaw Billings," by S. Weir Mitchell. pp. 375–83. [Published also in *Science* 38: 827–33 (Dec. 12, 1913)].

"The scientific work of John Shaw Billings," by Fielding H. Garrison. pp. 385–416.

Fielding H. Garrison, "Billings; a Maker of American Medicine," IN *Lectures on the History of Medicine, . . . 1926–1932*. Philadelphia, W. B. Saunders Company. [Lecture given before Northwestern University Medical School, Chicago, November 8, 1928; and before the Mayo Foundation, Rochester, November 14, 1928].

"In memoriam; John Shaw Billings." *Index Medicus* March, 1913. [4 p.].

"John Shaw Billings; an appreciation." *Military Surgeon* 61: 61–4 (1927).

"Greetings from the Surgeon-General's Library." *Colorado Medicine* 13: 366–8 (1916).

Alfred A. Woodhull, "Lieut.-Col. John Shaw Billings, U. S. Army." *Journal of the Military Service Institution* 53: 328–42 (1913).

Bulletin of the New York Public Library, vol. 17, 1913.
pp. 511–30. Memorial meeting in honor of the late Dr. John Shaw Billings, April 25, 1913. [Addresses by Weir Mitchell, Wm. Osler, Wm. H. Welch, Andrew Carnegie, Richard B. Bowker, John L. Cadwalader].
pp. 531–3. Appendix [Letters from Cardinal Farley, Sir Henry Burdett, E. C. Richardson, Helen E. Haines, Cressy L. Wilbur].
pp. 534–5. Minute adopted by the American Library Association at its annual conference at Kaaterskill, New York, June 25, 1913; John Shaw Billings, April 12, 1838–March 11, 1913.
[an account of this meeting appears also in *Library Journal* 38: 334–8 (June 1913)].

Jean A. Curran, "John Shaw Billings, medical genius of the 19th century." *Bulletin of the Medical Library Association* 42: 163–71 (1954). [contains information on manuscript sources].

H. M. Hurd, "Dr. John Shaw Billings, bibliographer and librarian." *Bulletin of the Medical Library Association* 5: 35–40 (1915–16).

C. C. McCulloch, "The Surgeon-General's Library." *Bulletin of the Medical Library Association* 6: 25–39 (1916–17).

W. F. Willcox, "The past and future development of vital statistics in the United States. I. John Shaw Billings and federal vital statistics." *Journal of the American Statistical Association* 21: 257–66 (1926).

"John Shaw Billings Memorial Number," *Bulletin of the Institute of the History of Medicine*, April, 1938 (Vol. 6, No. 4).
Introduction. Henry E. Sigerist. pp. 223–4.
John Shaw Billings as an Army medical officer; a tribute on his hundredth birthday, April 12, 1938. Edgar Erskine Hume. pp. 225–70.
John Shaw Billings and the Johns Hopkins Medical School; a tribute on the one hundredth anniversary of his birth. Alan M. Chesney. pp. 271–84.
Two papers by John Shaw Billings on medical education; with a foreword by Alan M. Chesney. pp. 285–359.
John Shaw Billings and the history of medicine. Sanford V. Larkey. pp. 360–76.
John Shaw Billings and the New York Public Library. H. M. Lydenberg. pp. 377–86.

Raymond Pearl, "Some notes on the contributions of Dr. John Shaw Billings to the development of vital statistics." *Bulletin of the Institute of the History of Medicine* 6: 387–93 (1938).

"Two letters by John Shaw Billings on the history of medicine," with a foreword by Sanford V. Larkey. *Bulletin of the Institute of the History of Medicine* 6: 394–8 (1938).

Prominent among the many obituaries are:

[Sir Henry Burdett], *Hospital* (London) 53: 671–3 (March 22, 1913).
J. Y. W. MacAlister, *British Medical Journal* 1: 642 (March 22, 1913).
Sir Lauder Brunton, *British Medical Journal* 1: 642 (March 22, 1913).
        Nature 91: 62 (March 20, 1913).
Sir William Osler, *British Medical Journal* 1: 641 (March 22, 1913).
Albert Allemann, *Münchener Medizinische Wochenschrift* 60: 1096 (May 20, 1913).
Bulletin of the New York Public Library 17: 307–12 (1913).
Journal of the American Medical Association 60: 846 (1913).
J. Ewing Mears, *Transactions of the American Surgical Association* 31: xxxiv–xxxix (1913).

For general background, see the following:

John F. Fulton, *The Great Medical Bibliographers; a Study in Humanism.* Philadelphia, University of Pennsylvania Press, 1951. ["John Shaw Billings," pp. 67–75].

Estelle Brodman, *The Development of Medical Bibliography.* Medical Library Association, 1954. ["John Shaw Billings," pp. 105–27].

For history of the National Library of Medicine, see:

Dorothy M. Schullian and Frank B. Rogers, "The National Library of Medicine." *Library Quarterly* 28: 1–17, 95–121 (1958).

Dorothy M. Schullian, "Thomas Windsor, benefactor of the Army Medical Library." *Bulletin of the Medical Library Association* 38: 135–44 (1950).

Dorothy M. Schullian, "Unfolded out of the folds." *Bulletin of the Medical Library Association* 40: 135–43 (1952).

Dorothy M. Schullian, "Alfred Alexander Woodhull, John Shaw Billings, and the Johns Hopkins Hospital, 8 June 1871." *Journal of the History of Medicine and Allied Science* 13: 531–7 (1958).

Harold W. Jones, "The Army Medical Library; its history and its future obligations." *Journal of the American Medical Association* 122: 1074–9 (1943).

Richard Hood, "The Army Medical Library." *Science* 105: 422–6 (April 25, 1947).

Scott Adams, "The Army Medical Library and other medical libraries of the nation." *College and Research Libraries* 9: 126–32 (April 1948).

"Army Medical Library Number," *Medical Life,* December, 1936. (Vol. 43, No. 12).

The centenary of the Army Medical Library. H. W. Jones. pp. 533–43.

The oration commemorating the 100th anniversary of the founding of the Army Medical Library, Washington. Sir Humphrey Rolleston. pp. 543–62.

The greetings from beyond the seas. H. W. Jones. pp. 563–73.

A greenhorn's experience in the library. Percy M. Ashburn. pp. 573–9.

Dr. Billings and his work. Albert Allemann. pp. 587–90.

[The first three articles were also published in *Military Surgeon* 80: 1–31 (Jan. 1937)].

Edgar Erskine Hume, "Buildings for the Army Medical Library," *Military Surgeon* 80: 45–52 (Jan. 1937).

Frank B. Rogers and Scott Adams, "The Army Medical Library's Publication Program." *Texas Reports on Biology and Medicine* 8: 271–300 (1950).

"National Library of Medicine Anniversary Issue." *Bulletin of the Medical Library Association,* July, 1961. (Vol. 49, No. 3).

Memoir of Robert Fletcher. Estelle Brodman. pp. 251–90.

The survey and after. Janet Doe. pp. 361–8.

Reminiscences. Mary Louise Marshall. pp. 369–73.

Housing the library.

Part I. The old building. Keyes D. Metcalf. pp. 396–402.

Part II. The new building. Walter H. Kilham, Jr. pp. 403–10.

Comprehensive collecting, then and now. Leslie K. Falk and Samuel Lazerow. pp. 434–42.

Adams Jewett and John Shaw Billings, partners in acquisition. Dorothy M. Schullian. pp. 443–9.

Autobiographical Fragment

I first got a realizing sense of my own personality or individuality when, a boy about eight years old, I was at work on a hillside on the farm of Tristram Burgers, near Providence, R. I. My father was the manager of this farm, and my business that sunny afternoon was to chop up and dig out by the roots all the Canada thistles I could find in the pasture.

I had read the Bible through—verse by verse, also *Robinson Crusoe*, *Deerslayer*, *Pathfinder*, and *Pilgrim's Progress*—but I had never done any thinking that I can remember. But on this memorable afternoon, I stood on the hillside and looked over Narragansett Bay, and wondered where all the catboats and schooners with their white sails came from, and were going to. Then my thoughts took this turn: "The only person who can know that is God. He knows everything that has been, and is, and is to be. Then, hundreds and thousands of years ago, He knew that I should be here today, and that each of those boats would be just where it is, and that I should be thinking of them. Then, as His knowledge must have been perfect, it is absolutely necessary that I, just as I am, knowing just what I know, am here at this moment, looking at these ships, which also must be just where they are. Then everything must be arranged and ordered to be just as it is, and no one can prevent it. Therefore, I am not responsible for where I am nor for what I do." I was surprised at this conclusion, and thought I had made a great discovery, and resolved to tell my mother about it when she was worrying about our troubles. I did tell her about it that night, and said that there was no use in worrying any more. She looked at me in a scornful sort of way, and said, "Who's been teaching you about foreordination." "Nobody taught me," said I. "I found it out by myself—don't you see it must be so?"

My life on the Burgers' farm, from about five to ten years of age, was that of an ordinary farmer's boy. I dropped four or five grains of sweet corn in the proper place in the furrow in planting time, I helped weed the little carrots and young beets, rode the horse for horse-raking the hay crop, went to a country school for three months in the winter, made little clam-bakes along the shore with my cousins William Henry and Charles Shaw, and read everything I could lay hands on. I managed to get a dollar for subscription to a little lending library in a book shop, and the first books I

As printed on pp. 2–4 of Fielding H. Garrison's *John Shaw Billings; a memoir* (New York, Putnam, 1915). Garrison says that Billings wrote this slight sketch "at the instance of his friends a few years before his death."

took out were *Deerslayer, Pathfinder,* and *Jock o' the Mill.* I had for my own, *Robinson Crusoe, Marco Paul in the Forests of Maine, Harry and Lucy,* and Plutarch's *Lives,* and was quite sure that I did not want to be a farmer.

When I was about ten years old, my father moved to Indiana and established himself in a little crossroads village called Allensville, on the road from Rising Sun to Vevay. Here he kept a country store—was postmaster, and had a small shoemaker's shop in which one man was employed. I learned something of shoemaking—had some experiences in keeping store. I read incessantly. Came across a book—I have forgotten its title—which had a number of Latin quotations in it, asked a young clergyman (John C. Bonham) how I could learn Latin—and got a Latin grammar and reader—a copy of *Cæsar,* and a Latin dictionary, and set to work. It was difficult, but with the aid of Mr. Bonham I made good progress. Then I made an agreement with my father that if he would help me through college in the least expensive way, all of his property should go to my sister, and that I must expect nothing more. I then got some Greek books, a geometry, etc., and went on to fit myself to pass the entrance examination for the sub-freshman class at Miami University, Oxford, Ohio. I succeeded in doing this in a year—and passed the examination in the fall of 1852. For the first two years I kept bachelor's hall, living on bread, milk, potatoes, eggs, ham, etc., such things as I could cook for myself. The lessons gave me little trouble. Most of my time was spent in reading the books in the College Library. I was omnivorous, read everything in English as it came, philosophy, theology, natural science, history, travels, and fiction.

Memorandum

The Library of the Surgeon General's Office may be said to date from the late war, at the commencement of which it consisted of about 350 volumes of text-books and journals.

In October, 1865, as appears by a pamphlet catalogue of that date, the number of volumes was about 1,800, and since that time the increase by donation, exchange, and purchase has been steady and rapid; the present catalogue containing about 13,000 titles, including 13,300 volumes.

The object kept in view in the formation of the Library has been to obtain publications relating to—

1. Military hygiene, medicine, and surgery.
2. Public hygiene, medical police, and state medicine, including epidemics and quarantine.
3. Vital and medical statistics.
4. Medical and scientific journals and periodical literature.
5. Chemistry, meteorology, and physics.

As will be seen by the catalogue, a good foundation has been made for a library relating to the above subjects; but it is still very far from being complete.

That there is need in this country of a medical library of this character is sufficiently evident from the fact that, in all the public medical libraries of the United States put together, it would not be possible to verify from the original authorities the references given by standard English or German authors, such as Hennen, Reynolds, or Virchow. No complete collection of American medical literature is in existence; and the most complete, if in this country, is in private hands, and not accessible to the public; while every year adds to the difficulty of forming such a collection as the Government should possess. The books are now safely and conveniently arranged in the fire-proof building of the Army Medical Museum, and are accessible to the public under rules and regulations essentially the same as those for the Library of Congress.

It, in fact, forms a highly desirable, and, indeed, necessary supplement to the Congressional Library, and is catalogued in the same manner, the principle being to give a literal transcript of the title-page of each work, omitting titles of authors.

Prefaced to *Catalogue of the Library of the Surgeon General's Office, United States Army; with an alphabetical index of subjects.* Washington, Government Printing Office, 1872.

The alphabetical index of subjects is not intended to be complete. It includes only works readily classified, and subjects relating to which two or more works are in the Library.

Prepared and printed within six months, to meet a want which daily became more pressing, errors have been inevitable, especially those of omission. It is hoped that a corrected and much enlarged edition will be needed and can be prepared within a very few years.

Letter of Transmittal, Specimen Fasciculus

WAR DEPARTMENT, SURGEON-GENERAL'S OFFICE,
Washington, D. C., February 1, 1876.

GENERAL: I have the honor to submit the following specimen of a catalogue of what may now be properly called the National Medical Library, heretofore known as the Library of the Surgeon-General's Office.

The entire catalogue, of which this is a sample, is nearly ready for the press, and it is hoped and believed that it will be found of practical interest and value in a bibliographical point of view as well as for the immediate use of the collection to which it relates.

A few copies of this specimen have been printed in order to show the character and scope of the collection, to obtain criticisms and suggestions as to the form of catalogue which will be most acceptable and useful, and to furnish data for the decision as to whether it is desirable that such a work should be printed and distributed.

The specimen submitted is of a combined catalogue of subjects and authors, arranged in dictionary order under a single alphabet.

The first question to be decided is whether this form is preferable to two separate works, one containing the authors and the other the subjects. Having consulted some of the principal medical writers and teachers of this country, for whose use and benefit the work is intended, and after conference with some of the librarians of largest experience, the weight of opinions in favor of the single-alphabet system for this particular work has appeared sufficiently marked to warrant its employment in this specimen.

The next question is with regard to the classification adopted, which is mainly from the anatomical standpoint. By the use of numerous cross-references, it has been made certain, as far as possible, that the titles desired can be found, although not always under the heading anticipated; for in this respect it is impossible to meet the wishes of all without excessive duplication.

The references are always from the general to the more special heads; thus, under "ABDOMEN (*Tumors of*)", attention is directed to "ANEURISM (*Aortic*)", etc. An attempt has been made by the use of varieties of type to make it as easy as possible to catch the particular title desired; but there is still room for improvement in this respect, since some of the "sorts" desired were not available. If the printing of the entire work should be authorized, it is hoped that the most desirable form will be used.

Letter of transmittal, *Specimen fasciculus of a catalogue of the National Medical Library, under the direction of the Surgeon-General, United States Army.* **Washington, 1876. pp. iii–vi.**

Titles printed in the larger type, or brevier, are of books and pamphlets. Those given under authors give the collation of the book and the name of the publisher.

In the titles under subject-headings, the names of authors are in italics, to the end of the subject of "ABSCESS", after which, for purposes of comparison, they are in brevier small-capitals; the titles are as brief as possible, and collation and name of publishers are omitted. Some variations in type and mode of setting are also made, for the purpose of obtaining opinions as to the relative merit of the several styles.

In the small type, or nonpareil, are given references to articles in journals, transactions, and collections. These include the results of the examination of about 5,000 volumes of such publications. This work is still going on; and, by the time the catalogue is sent to press, it is hoped that it will be completed.

Although this is only the catalogue of a single library, and that of so recent formation as to forbid anything like completeness, an attempt has been made to prepare, as far as time and materials would allow, a work of practical usefulness for bibliographical purposes to all physicians, even if they have not access to the library itself. It makes no pretensions to being a complete medical bibliography, and should not be estimated as such; it is rather a foundation, and an outline which each must complete for his own specialty.

All medical writers know that the most valuable part of medical literature consists of the records of cases and original observations, and that, for the present century, the greater part of such records are contained in periodical publications. These are difficult to obtain and preserve, occupy a large amount of space, and, even when accessible, require much time and labor to consult. It is not very difficult, although rather expensive, for a physician who is interested in a particular subject to obtain all the really important monographs relating to it; but that which he cannot obtain, and which he must look to large public libraries to supply, are the journals and transactions containing the most valuable data for his purpose.

Special effort has therefore been made to complete the files of medical periodicals in this collection, and with very good success; although there are still some important gaps in this department, which should be filled, and the indexing completed as far as possible, before the final publication of the work.

For the information of those not already familiar with the scope and character of the library, its present condition may be briefly stated as follows:

It is the National Medical Library of this country, being essentially the Medical section of the Library of Congress; its general plan of management and of cataloguing being the same. It is at present under the direction of the Surgeon-General of the Army, in connection with the Army or National Medical Museum. For several years, the Librarian of Congress has not purchased medical books, leaving that branch of literature to be collected by this department. The library now contains about 40,000 volumes, properly so called, and about the same number of single pamphlets.

Large as this number may appear to those who are not familiar with the amount of literature on this subject, it is only about one-half what such a collection should contain in order to place the writers of this country in such a position as regards means of reference to the literature of medicine as it is desirable that they should command.

Hardly a day, and never a week, goes by that a request is not made of the librarian for some medical book which the library does not possess.

The use which is made of the collection by physicians from every section of this country, and the number of persons who consult it, either in person or by letter, is steadily, and of late rapidly, increasing; and I cannot doubt that if a sufficient number of the catalogue, of which this is a specimen, be printed, and distributed to our medical writers and teachers, so that they may at their leisure learn what aid they can obtain in their researches, no collection of the Government will be more used or be of more practical utility; that it will soon tend to elevate the standard of medical education, literature, and scholarship of the nation, and will thus indirectly be for the benefit of the whole country, since the general knowledge and skill of the medical profession become a matter of personal interest to almost every individual at some time during the course of his life.

For these reasons, and for others which will readily suggest themselves, it has appeared to me to be the duty as well as the privilege of the National Government to make this collection of the literature of medicine as complete as possible, and to provide a catalogue of it of such a kind as would be of most practical working value.

With this end in view, the following specimen is submitted, not as being a satisfactory solution of the problem, for no one knows better than myself the imperfections of the work, but as a foundation, and, in some sense, an indication, of what it is hoped the library and its catalogue may one day be made.

The complete catalogue on the present plan would make five volumes of about one thousand pages each.

Very respectfully, your obedient servant,

JOHN S. BILLINGS,
Assistant Surgeon U.S.A.

GENERAL JOSEPH K. BARNES,
Surgeon-General U.S.A.

Microscopical Memoranda

BY DR. NEWLENZ

At the close of the late war, having been brevetted lieutenant-colonel, through the untiring efforts of the member from my district, and being therefore desirous of contributing to the reputation and usefulness of some of the learned societies, I applied for admission to the Royal Microscopical Society, among others. National jealousy, probably, caused the rejection of my application, and the result was that I formed a society myself. This society has devoted itself exclusively and earnestly to histology, pathology, test-objects, the cryptogamic origin of disease, spontaneous generation, germinal matter, bacteria, and cells[1] in general.

Having constructed a one-seventieth immersion objective, on a new principle, having 191° aperture,—the immersion liquid being fluoric acid, —and, for illumination, having invented a new eccentric parallelopiped, to be used with fluorescent rays exclusively, some remarkable results have been obtained.

I take great pleasure in stating that, with regard to test-objects, all previous observers have been totally wrong in every particular, and that *Pleurosigma angulatum* is, in the first place, constructed on the plan of the Nicholson pavement, and, in the second place, that it is not a Pleurosigma at all.

The most certain test-object is the *Newlenzia difficilissima*, a very rare and remarkable diatom, in which my one-seventieth with the parallelopiped shows four kinds of beads and six sets of cross-lines, one of which sets contains 147,229,073 lines to the inch: hence, by the well-known formula of Brewster,

$$\frac{d \cdot x}{d \cdot u} = \sqrt{o \cdot x \cdot p \cdot y},$$

it is impossible that the undulations of light should pass without being previously deflagrated, and therefore no other lens can possibly show these lines, nor is it probable that this lens would with any other observer. The immense superiority of this test to Nobert's plate is apparent.

Reserving this topic for future discussion, I have a few words to say with regard to spontaneous generation and cryptogams. With regard to

---

Medical Times (Phila) 1: 200 (1 Mar 1871) [Correspondence].
[1] *Sic,*—not sells.

21

the former, the true theory was declared in 1740, in "Lucina sine Concubitu,"—a most valuable and rare work, which seems to have been overlooked by recent writers on this subject. The author, starting from the proposition of the ancient philosophers, "Non potest reperiri avesne vel ante ova generata sint, cum et ovum sine avi, et avis sine ovo gigni non possit," proceeds thus: "Je n'hésitai donc plus à regarder ce vent . . . comme le véhicule propre pour ces embrions flottans. . . . Sur ces principes, je vins à bout de fabriquer une machine,—*Cilindrico-catoptrico-rotundo-concavo-convex.* . . . Cette machine fut lutée hermétiquement d'une terre électrisée, et je le plaçai dans une position convenable vers l'Occident pour intercepter les animalcules flottans dans cette partie prolifique du ciel. . . . Je découvris clairement que ces germes étoient des petites femmes et des petits hommes exacts dans leurs membres."

It will be seen that the machine above referred to prefigured the aeroscope of Pouchet, the isolation apparatus of Hallier, and several other modern inventions. One American and one English observer seem to have entered fully into the spirit of the above-mentioned work; and I desire to offer to them the assurance of my unbounded admiration for the power of their faith and the vigor of their imagination.

The following experiments, conceived in the spirit of their method, will be found interesting:

Exp. 1.—A glass flask was filled with ditch-water, and boiled three days in a Papin's digester, under a pressure of four atmospheres. After a week it was opened, and in the first drop of the contents was found the remarkable animal shown in the accompanying sketch.[2]

Bacteria were abundant.

Exp. 2.—Some of the fluid contents of an ovarian tumor (a remarkable case, removed by myself through the perineum, of which I shall give a full account in my report to the American Medical Association on Perineotomy) was examined by fluorescent light. It was full of spontaneously-generated corpuscles, starch-fibres, and cotton granules, with many invisible germs.

Exp. 3.—Two ounces of water, containing, among other things, *Gemiasma, Euglena, Podura nivalis, Micrococcus, Cryptococcus, Arthrococcus,* and an entirely new and original coccus,—viz., *Newlenziacoccus,*—were drunk, by mistake, by a friend of the author. For twenty-four hours he was afflicted with a conglomerated epidemic which presented nearly every symptom described in Da Costa's Manual. Cryptogamismus is the only appropriate term for his condition.

My most remarkable discoveries, however, have been in the blood. Space

---

[2] The sketch is necessarily omitted. It looks remarkably like *Pediculus capitis.*—ED.

is wanting to enumerate here the many forms of Coccus, Algæ, and Rhizopods that I have found in the blood, *when the proper conditions of observation were afforded.*

I can only say here, in conclusion, to the numerous persons who have written to me on this subject, that a minute investigation with the one-seventieth and the parallelopiped requires much labor. I always give at least an hour to each specimen; and, as I have had to examine over twenty thousand specimens within the last year, I am compelled to state that, in future, unless fifty dollars are sent with the drop of blood on which I am to furnish diagnosis and treatment, I shall not notice it.

IMMERSION HALL, February 2, 1870.

A Century of American Medicine
1776-1876

Literature and Institutions.

"Wherefore, by their fruits ye shall know them."

Besides his duties to his patients, the physician is under certain obligations to contribute, by way of interest, his quota to the common stock of medical knowledge from which he has drawn so freely. The skilful diagnosis, judicious medication, or bold and successful operation, if not properly recorded, benefit the individual only, not being available for those comparisons and higher generalizations which alone can make medicine a science. By the manner in which this duty, of preserving and transmitting the results of its labour and experience, has been performed, the medical profession of a country, as well as the individual physician, must to a great degree be judged, and the question now presented is, to what extent and in what manner have the physicians in the United States fulfilled this part of their professional obligations during the century just passed.

In the retrospective reviews, historical sketches, and centennial addresses which have, during the past year, been devoted to American medicine, our most important contributions to the healing art have been duly pointed out, and for the most part sufficiently eulogized. That the United States has a medical literature, has been cumulatively demonstrated, even to the extent of raising a suspicion of the existence of a doubt upon this point; and that this literature contains many valuable original contributions to the art, if not to the science, of medicine may be considered as unanimously affirmed and admitted.

If the defects of which all are more or less aware, have been but slightly referred to, it is because the purpose of the writers has been rather eulogistic than critical. In this final article of the present series, the object is not to select for praise the best of the work, nor the reverse, but to endeavour to give an idea of the quantity and value of the whole of it. So far as individual writers are concerned, an attempt will be made to supplement the information given in previous papers, but these have

---

American Journal of the Medical Sciences 72: 439–80 (1876). [The fourth and final article of a series which appeared under the general title "A Century of American Medicine, 1776–1876;" earlier articles were by E. H. Clarke (Practical Medicine), H. J. Bigelow (Anesthesia), and T. G. Thomas (Obstetrics and Gynecology).]

been so complete as regards that which is worthy of notice, that little need be said of single books and articles.

We will first endeavour to give some account of the quantity of medical literature produced in the United States during the last hundred years; making use for the purpose of some statistics obtained from a nearly complete list of the medical books published in this country from 1776 to the present time, and from which it may be considered certain that no important work has been omitted.

In these statistics we do not include works intended for the non-medical public, those relating to "ics" or "pathies," nor the great mass of what are called pamphlets in the technical sense of the word, that is, books of less than one hundred pages. The great majority of these pamphlets are either reprints from periodicals, addresses inaugural or valedictory, a few of which contain historical data of interest, or controversial and personal disquisitions which are best forgotten. While it is true that there is no necessary connection between the size of a work and its practical or scientific value, it will be found that with a very few exceptions, which have been pointed out in the preceding articles of this series, nothing of interest or importance is omitted by this division. The books to be counted may be classified as follows:—

    I. Systematic treatises and monographs by physicians residing in this country, including reports of hospitals, corporations, and government departments.

    II. Reprints and translations of foreign medical books.

    III. Medical journals.

    IV. Transactions of medical societies.

The first, third and fourth classes include what is ordinarily meant by the phrase "American Medical Literature." From them are excluded books written by American authors, but printed abroad, as, for instance, those of Dr. Wm. Charles Wells; while on the other hand, they include books written by physicians born and educated abroad, but who may be said to have become citizens of this country, such as Tytler, Pascalis, Busche, Dunglison, Jacobi, and Knapp.

The statistics of the four classes above given, include not only the medical literature of the United States for the century, but nearly all which the country has produced since the first settlement. At the commencement of the Revolutionary War, we had one medical book by an American author, three reprints, and about twenty pamphlets. The book referred to is the "Plain, Precise, Practical Remarks on the Treatment of Wounds and Fractures," by Dr. John Jones, New York, 1775. It is simply a compilation from Ranby, Pott, and others, and contains but one original observation, viz., a case of trephining followed by hernia cerebri.

The libraries of our physicians were composed, according to Bartlett,[1] of the works of Boerhaave, with the Commentaries of Van Swieten, the Physiology of Haller, the Anatomy of Cowper, Keil, Douglass, Cheselden, Monroe, and Winslow; the Surgery of Heister, Sharp, Le Dran, and Pott; the Midwifery of Smellie; the Materia Medica of Lewis; and the works of Sydenham, Whytt, Mead, Brookes, and Huxham. The works of Cullen were just beginning to be known. The only public medical library was that of the Pennsylvania Hospital, which contained, perhaps, two hundred and fifty volumes. There were probably not two hundred graduates of medicine in the country, and not over three hundred and fifty practitioners of medicine who had received a liberal education. Two medical schools had just begun, but had accomplished little previous to the war which closed them, there were no medical journals, and but one State Medical Society, that of New Jersey, had been organized. From this unpromising condition of things, have been developed the literary results, of which we now present a summary.

It will be seen from Table I, that the medical literature of the United States really commences with the present century, and this is still more apparent, if the character of the works issued prior to 1800, be considered.

The first literary contributions of our physicians, after the close of the war, are contained in the memoirs of the American Academy of Arts and Sciences, Boston, 1785, and in the Transactions of the American Philosophical Society at Philadelphia, 1786. The first original separate work was the "Cases and Observations by the Medical Society of New Haven County, in the State of Connecticut," New Haven, 86 pp. 8vo., 1788. This is a collection of twenty-six articles, including several cases and autopsies of interest, and a paper on the production of dysentery among troops by overcrowding and foul air, in which the connection of cause and effect is clearly demonstrated.

The majority of the succeeding publications, to the end of the century, related to the yellow fever, which was then epidemic along the whole Atlantic coast. The most prominent author of this period is Benjamin Rush, noteworthy also as an orator and politician. His writings excel in manner rather than matter, and the undoubted influence which he exerted over the earliest stages of American medicine, was probably due to his lectures rather than his published works. The best of his essays, and indeed the only one to-day worth consulting, is that on diseases of the mind, which contains some original observations of interest. One of his eulogists, Dr. Ramsay,[2] says: "On the correctness of this opinion [viz., his fondness for

---

[1] A Dissertation on the Progress of Medical Science in the Commonwealth of Massachusetts, Boston, 8vo., 1810.

[2] Eulogium upon Benjamin Rush, by David Ramsay, Philadelphia, 1813, 8vo., pp. 79.

TABLE I

TABLE SHOWING NUMBER OF MEDICAL BOOKS PRINTED IN THE UNITED STATES
FROM JANUARY 1, 1776, TO JANUARY 1, 1876

	1775 to 1799	1800 to 1809	1810 to 1819	1820 to 1829	1830 to 1839	1840 to 1849	1850 to 1859	1860 to 1869	1870 to 1875	Total
Class I. American Medical Books										
No. 1st edition	39	24	51	48	83	96	101	157	130	729
No. later editions	9	4	14	17	34	49	80	85	44	336
No. Vols. Total	51	31	77	86	136	162	197	256	180	1176
Class II. Reprints and Translations										
No. 1st edition	28	39	64	72	145	135	99	104	81	767
No. later editions	11	23	28	33	36	67	76	64	50	388
No. Vols Total	49	76	111	135	192	214	184	160	137	1274
Class III. Medical Journals										
No. Journs. com'ced	1	5	6	17	18	26	52	38	32	195
" " discont'd	—	3	5	10	18	14	31	36	20	137
"A." Original										
No. Vols. com'nced	2	21	27	85	104	173	376	292	296	1376
No. Vols. compl'ted	2	20	27	79	98	166	366	271	283	1312
"B." Reprints										
No. Journals	—	—	1	4	—	5	1	3	3	17
No. Volumes	—	—	9	29	20	46	71	51	32	258
Class IV. Transactions Med. Societies										
No. Volumes	7	3	2	5	17	27	76	88	111	336

the use of the lancet] his fame as an improver of medicine in a great degree must eventually rest." And to the correctness of this judgment we entirely assent.

The work of James Tytler[3] is a good compilation, and contains, among other data not to be found elsewhere, an interesting letter by Dr. John Warren, of Boston. Tytler was born in Scotland in 1747, came to this country about 1796, and was drowned in 1804; he possessed extensive and varied learning, and wrote much, but for the most part on non-medical subjects.

The works of Noah Webster,[4] though mainly historical, are still of interest, and worth preservation.

Another writer of this period is Dr. William Curry, a native of Pennsylvania, 1755–1829. At first educated for the church, he acquired an

[3] A Treatise on the Plague and Yellow Fever, with an Appendix. 8vo., 1799.

[4] A Collection of Papers on the subject of Bilious Fevers, prevalent in the United States for a few years past. 246 pp. 8vo. New York, 1796. A Brief History of Epidemic and Pestilential Diseases; with the principal Phenomena of the Physical World which precede and accompany them, and Observations deduced from the facts stated. 2 vols., 8vo., Hartford, 1799.

excellent knowledge of Latin and Greek, and studied medicine under Dr. Kearsley, of Philadelphia. During the Revolutionary War he served as surgeon in the American army, being attached to the military hospital on Long Island, in 1776. After the war, he at first settled at Chester, but removed to Philadelphia about 1791. He was one of the original fellows of the College of Physicians of Philadelphia, and for many years a member of the Board of Health. His principal works in addition to his numerous pamphlets and articles on yellow fever, are his "Historical Account of the Climates and Diseases of the United States," 1792; and his "View of the Diseases most Prevalent in the United States," Philadelphia, 1811.

Towards the close of the century, and for a few years thereafter, there were published in Boston, New York, and Philadelphia, a number of medical theses, which, being classed as pamphlets, are not taken into account in our statistics, and are noticed here for the sake of saying a word with regard to this class of medical literature. A medical dissertation prepared, not for the press, but simply as a formality necessary for the obtaining of a diploma, as is the case with nearly all those which have been presented at our medical schools for the last fifty years, fairly merits the denunciation of Professor Gross, "that not one in fifty affords the slightest evidence of competency, proficiency, or ability, in the candidate for graduation."

Such was not the case, however, with regard to the theses above referred to, nor can it be justly said with regard to any series of printed theses of the European schools. It would seem, therefore, that when prepared as they should be, with reference to the probable criticisms, not merely of a single professor, but of the press and the public, there is the strongest inducement to refrain from plagiarism, and to produce the best work of which the candidate is capable; and it is well known to those who have had frequent occasion to consult them, that collections of printed medical theses are valuable, as historical documents, presenting a reflex of the teachings of the school, and as containing accounts of cases and original investigations, or particular doctrines of the student's preceptor, which cannot be found elsewhere. The proportion of copied matter, vague speculations, and other rubbish, does not, upon the whole, appear to be so much greater in this than in some other classes of medical literature, as to warrant their wholesale condemnation; and the remedy for the present unsatisfactory character of the theses of our medical students, appears not to be their abolition, but the requiring that they shall be printed, and considered as an important and real test of the merit of the candidate. They should of course be written in the vernacular. The influence which a teacher has in directing the thoughts of his pupils, is very well shown in the theses of the Philadelphia school, a considerable number of which related to medical botany, under the stimulus given by Dr. Barton to that branch of study.

During this period, and prior to the establishment of any medical journal, or regular publication of the transactions of any medical society, a number of communications from American physicians were sent to societies in Europe, and appear in their transactions. Perhaps the most notable paper of this kind was "An Experimental Inquiry into the Properties of Opium," by John Leigh of Virginia, which obtained the Harveian prize for 1785, and was printed at Edinburgh in the following year. It is worth consultation, not only for the facts which it records, but for the method of investigation pursued, which was unusual in that day of theories.[5]

From the year 1800 to the present time, the above table shows that there has been a steady increase in the amount of our indigenous medical literature, corresponding in the main to our increase in population and wealth. To obtain some notion of the quality and value of this production, a more detailed analysis is necessary.

The greater part of these books are compends relating to the treatment of diseases and injuries. Those which have been most popular, and are the best known, are the text-books and systematic treatises. These are for the most part compilations, but their importance is by no means to be underestimated, for the practice of the majority of the physicians of this country to-day, is based on the text-books of the teachers in the New York and Philadelphia schools. Also we must remember that "there are compilations and compilations." The preparation of such systematic treatises as those of Flint, Gross, Stillé, and Wood, does not require less labour or thought, or give less scope for display of genius, than the so-called original monographs.

Writers of this class bring into their proper relations the isolated facts and observations scattered through many books, give them the mint stamp of value, and put them into general circulation.

For reasons already stated, and for want of space, but few books can here be noticed, even by title, and in connection with these will be given some very brief biographical data relating to a few authors. Of living writers and their works, as little as possible will be said.

In Anatomy our principal systematic works have been produced by Wistar, Horner, Morton, Richardson, Agnew, Hodges, Leidy, and Smith. None of them are now of interest. Dr. Caspar Wistar, 1761–1818, was of German descent, and a native of Philadelphia. Having obtained a good classical education, he studied medicine under Dr. John Redman, and took the degree of Bachelor of Medicine, in 1782. He continued his studies at Edinburgh, where he graduated M.D. in 1786. Returning to Philadelphia,

---

[5] In this connection also may be mentioned a rare and little known work, being the oration delivered at the University of Virginia in 1782, by J. F. Coste, the Medical Director of the French Forces. Its subject is "Antiqua novum orbem decet medico philosophia;" it is dedicated to Washington, of whom the author was a personal friend, and makes a volume of 103 pages, 8vo.; printed at Leyden, in 1783.

he became Adjunct Professor of Anatomy in 1791, and continued to lecture until his death. His System of Anatomy was issued in parts, 1811–1814, making two volumes, and was a popular text-book for a long time. The first work issued by Dr. Horner was a Dissector's Manual, in 1823. This was followed by his treatise on General and Special Anatomy in 1826, his Anatomical Atlas, and treatise on General and Special Histology. A good original work has yet to be written on this last subject, in this country. In surgical anatomy, Drs. Anderson and Darrach have produced partial treatises, the first on the groin, pelvis, and perineum, New York, 1822; the second on the anatomy of the groin, Philadelphia, 1830.

Drs. N. R. Smith, Goddard, and Neill, have each issued a work on the Surgical Anatomy of the Arteries. Among the few original works in this department, should be mentioned those of Dr. John D. Godman, a native of Annapolis, Md., 1794–1830. Poor and almost friendless, but urged on by an unquenchable thirst for knowledge, he persisted in obtaining an education in spite of the greatest difficulties and discouragements, and at last took the degree of M.D. at the University of Maryland in 1818.

In 1821 he went to Cincinnati to accept a chair in the Medical College of Ohio, but dissensions in the faculty induced his speedy resignation. He then established a medical journal hereafter to be alluded to, but in 1822 went to Philadelphia and began a course of private lectures in anatomy. In 1826 he accepted the chair of Anatomy in Rutgers College in New York, but failing health soon compelled him to cease teaching, although he continued to use his pen until just before his death. Dr. Godman was an anatomist by nature, and though the necessities of bread-winning prevented him from accomplishing any great work, his treatise on the fascia[6] and his contributions to physiological and pathological anatomy[7] are really original and valuable productions.

The papers of Dr. John Dean on the "Microscopic Anatomy of the Lumbar Enlargement of the Spinal Cord," Cambridge, 1861, and on "The Gray Substance of the Medulla Oblongata," published by the Smithsonian Institution in 1864, are the results of careful work, and are noteworthy for the use made of photo-lithography from micro-photographs to obtain the illustrations.

The craniological works of Drs. Morton and J. A. Meigs should be referred to here. Dr. Samuel George Morton, 1799–1851, was a native of Philadelphia, and graduated in medicine at the University of Pennsylvania in 1820, after which he continued his studies for three years at Edinburgh,

----

[6] Anatomical Investigations, comprising Descriptions of Various Fasciae of the Human Body, 8vo., Philadelphia, 1824.

[7] Contributions to Physiological and Pathological Anatomy, 8vo., Philadelphia, 1825.

obtaining his degree in 1823. From 1839 to 1843 he was Professor of Anatomy in the Pennsylvania Medical College. His fame rests upon his "Crania Americana," Philadelphia, 1839, and his "Crania Egyptiaca," ibid., 1844; works which have a world-wide reputation, and whose value is permanent. His labours in this direction have been continued by Dr. J. Aitken Meigs, whose "Catalogue of Crania," Philadelphia, 1857, is well known to all who are interested in this subject.

In physiology, our text-books have been the works of Dunglison, Draper, Dalton, and Flint, all too well known to require more than a mere reference. The work of Professor Draper, published in 1853, was the first in this country in which micro-photographs were used to obtain illustrations. To these may be added the works of Reese, Oliver, Goadby, and Paine. Of special treatises and essays, the most important are Beaumont's Experiments on Digestion, Plattsburgh, 1833; Draper "On the Forces which produce the Organization of Plants," New York, 1844; Joseph Jones' "Investigations," published by the Smithsonian in 1856; S. W. Mitchell's "Researches upon the Venom of the Rattlesnake," idem, 1860; and Hammond's "Physiological Memoirs," Philadelphia, 1863. In this department Brown-Séquard may be claimed as an American author; some of his researches having been made, and the results first published in this country. Those who are familiar with the literature of thirty years ago will remember with a smile, the treatise of Emma Willard on the circulation of the blood, and the controversies to which it gave rise. The "Essays on the Secretory and the Excito-Secretory System of Nerves," by Dr. H. F. Campbell of Georgia, Philadelphia, 1857, should be remembered in this connection, as also the pamphlets of Dr. Dowler of New Orleans.

In the department of Materia Medica and Therapeutics, we have made a good record. In Medical Botany, the works of B. S. Barton and Jacob Bigelow deserve especial mention as works of permanent value. The "Illustrations of Medical Botany," edited by Dr. Carson, Philadelphia, 1847, containing one hundred plates, in folio, is a rare and costly work, a considerable part of the edition having been destroyed by fire.

The first systematic treatise on Materia Medica and Therapeutics, produced in this country, was that of Dr. Chapman, Philadelphia, 1817. This was followed by the works of Eberle, J. B. Beck, Dunglison, Harrison, G. B. Wood, T. D. Mitchell, Biddle, Stillé, Riley, and H. C. Wood, all of which have been, or are popular text-books in the schools.

The majority of these authors will be referred to under other sections, but of three, a few words may here be said. Dr. John P. Harrison was born in Louisville in 1796; studied under Dr. Chapman, and graduated in medicine in 1819. He was Professor of Materia Medica in the Cincinnati College from 1836 to 1839. In 1841 he accepted the same chair in the Medical

College of Ohio, in 1847 was transferred to that of Theory and Practice, and died of cholera in 1849. He was one of the editors of the Western Journal of Medicine, and of the Western Lancet; published a collection of his essays in 1835, and his "Elements of Materia Medica and Therapeutics" in 1846.

The principal work on Materia Medica is the "United States Dispensatory" of Wood and Bache. Dr. Franklin Bache was born in Philadelphia in 1792, and died in 1864. Graduating as Bachelor of Arts in 1810, he studied under Dr. Rush, and obtained his medical degree in 1814. His tastes led him to the special study of chemistry, of which branch he was appointed professor in the Franklin Institute, in 1826. In 1841 he accepted the same chair in the Jefferson School. His principal work was in connection with the United States Pharmacopœia and the Dispensatory, which have made his name familiar to every physician in the United States. The first proposal to form a Pharmacopœia in this country was made to the College of Physicians of Philadelphia, in 1787, with the result of the appointment of a committee, which seems to have continued about ten years, but effected nothing. In 1808 a Pharmacopœia was published by the Massachusetts Medical Society, and in 1816 another was issued by the New York Hospital. Our present national Pharmacopœia originated in a plan submitted to the New York County Medical Society, in 1817, by Dr. Lyman Spalding. A leading part in the formation of the first edition, by the convention which met in Washington in 1820 for that purpose, was taken by the College of Physicians of Philadelphia, through its delegates, and more especially by Dr. Thomas T. Hewson; and in the subsequent revisions, Drs. Hewson, Bache, and Wood were the principal workers. The first revision, adopted in 1830, was entirely the production of these gentlemen, and was substantially a new work. The Dispensatory was projected by Drs. Wood and Bache as an exposition of the Pharmacopœia, and a means of making it more popular.

The exposition has, so far as our physicians are concerned, entirely overshadowed the text, and in a financial point of view, the Dispensatory is the most successful medical book ever published in this country.

Among writers on Materia Medica, distinguished in their day, may be mentioned Dr. William Tully, 1785–1859, who graduated at Yale in 1806, and attended medical lectures at Dartmouth College in 1808–9. He received the honorary degree of M.D. from Yale in 1819. In 1824, he was appointed Professor of Theory and Practice in the Castleton School, and in 1826 removed to Albany, forming a partnership with Dr. Alden March. In 1829, he accepted the chair of Materia Medica and Therapeutics at Yale, and removed to New Haven, but continued his lectures in Castleton until 1838. He ceased teaching in 1841. His principal works were the "Essays on Fevers," published with those of Dr. Miner, 1823, a work which gave rise to much controversy, and was, upon the whole, not favourably received; a prize essay upon Sanguinaria, published in the American Medical Recorder in 1828; some papers in the Boston Medical Journal; and finally, his treatise entitled "Materia Medica, or Pharmacology and Therapeutics," Springfield, 1857–58, in two large volumes 8vo. This was published in numbers, was not a popular work, nor calculated for the use of a student, but shows great industry and learning in every page. Complete copies of it are not now easily obtained, although it cannot be said to be rare. His style is discursive, diffuse, and polysyllabic, and a decided effort is necessary to peruse his writings; but his knowledge of facts was minute and exact, and his last work is a mine of information, which is even now worth exploring by the curious.

In surgery, our indigenous text-books have been produced by Dorsey, Gibson, S. D. Gross, Ashhurst, and Hamilton. On Operative Surgery we have the treatises of Pancoast, Piper, H. H. Smith, Stephen Smith, and Packard. The posthumous work of McClellan is not a systematic treatise, but a series of essays and cases, in which the description of Shock is especially noteworthy as being true to life. Of monographs, the most valuable are those by Professor Gross, on Wounds of the Intestines, 1838; on Diseases of the Bladder, 1851–55; on Foreign Bodies in the Air-passages, 1854 and 1862; and Diseases of the Bones and Joints, 1830; F. H. Hamilton on Fractures and Dislocations, 1860, fifth edition, 1875; Durkee and Bumstead on Venereal; Van Buren and Keyes, and Gouley on the Urinary Organs; Bushe on Diseases of the Rectum; Carnochan on Congenital Dislocations of the Head of the Femur; H. J. Bigelow on the Mechanism of Dislocation and Fracture of the Hip; Ashhurst on Injuries of the Spine; Markoe on Diseases of the Bones; and Garretson's Oral Surgery. Specially valuable collections of cases, are the works of John C. Warren, on Tumors, Boston, 1837; and of J. Mason Warren; the pamphlets of Sayre on Orthopædic Surgery; N. R. Smith on Fractures of the Lower Extremity; and J. C. Nott, "Contributions to Bone and Nerve Surgery." As an example of careful statistical work, the treatise of R. M. Hodges on "The Excision of Joints," Boston, 1861, is to be specially commended.

The treatise of Dr. Gross, on Wounds of the Intestines, above referred to, first appeared in the "Western Journal of Medicine;" it contains the results of numerous experiments and observations, and is of much practical value and interest. It is a rare book, and a copy of it may properly be considered a prize by the collector.

In Military Medicine and Surgery nothing of value was produced by the revolutionary war, the war of 1812, or the war with Mexico. This deficiency has been, to a great extent, made up by the number and value of works resulting from our late war.

The Medical and Surgical History of the War will be, when completed, the largest medical work ever produced in this country. The publications of the Sanitary Commission, including the works of Flint, Gould, and Lidell, contain valuable data. The manuals of military surgery have been written by Gross, Hamilton, Tripler, Blackman, Chisholm, and Warren. Other works which should be remembered in this connection are, Woodward on Camp Diseases, the statistical reports and circulars issued from the Surgeon General's Office, and the medical statistics of the Provost-Marshal General's Office, compiled by Dr. Baxter, making two handsome quarto volumes, which are a most valuable addition to our knowldge of anthropometry and medical topography.

In the departments of Theory and Practice of Medicine, we have produced a fair amount of monographs and text-books, the most important of the latter class being those of Chapman, Eberle, G. B. Wood, and Flint. The following is a brief outline of the lives of a few who were our principal writers and teachers in this branch of medicine, but who now rest from their labours. Among them, there are few, who, in their day, had a more extended reputation, or were more popular than Dr. Nathaniel Chapman.

Born in Virginia in 1780, he received an excellent general education, became a pupil of Dr. Rush, with whom he was a favourite, graduated at the University in 1800, then spent three years in Europe, one as a pupil of Abernethy, and two at Edinburgh, and in 1813 was elected to the chair of Materia Medica in his Alma Mater, to be exchanged in 1816 for that of the Theory and Practice of Medicine, which he held until 1850, when he resigned. He died in 1853. His "Therapeutics and Materia Medica," published in 1817, was the best work of the kind in English at that date. He was the first President of the American Medical Association after its permanent organization; President of the American Philosophical Society, a popular lecturer, a genial companion, and in his prime probably the most distinguished physician in the United States. He edited, for seven years, the Philadelphia Journal of the Medical and Physical Sciences. Many of his lectures were published in the "Medical Examiner," in 1838–40. Two volumes of these lectures were published in 1844, and a compendium of his course on theory and practice was issued in 1846.

Contemporary with Dr. Chapman, and for twenty-five years associated with him as a teacher, was Dr. Samuel Jackson, 1787–1872, a native of Philadelphia, and educated in the University of Pennsylvania, having graduated in medicine in 1808. From 1825 to 1863, he was Professor of the Institutes of Medicine in his Alma Mater. His "Principles of Medicine" (Philadelphia, 1832, 8vo.) was a treatise on pathology, founded on the doctrines of Broussais, and received high praise in its day. It was also the subject of a long and acrimonious critical review by Dr. Caldwell. The popular story that Dr. Jackson recalled all the copies of this work that he could is incorrect; the entire edition was sold in the usual manner, and the publishers desired to issue another, but the author refused, on the ground that the science was undergoing such rapid and great changes that he would feel it necessary to re-write the entire work, a labour which his health and the demands of his private practice would not allow him to undertake. His most important writings are contained in the American Journal of the Medical Sciences, the last being a paper on a rare disease of the joints, in the July Number for 1870.

Dr. John Eberle, 1788–1838, was of German descent, and a native of Pennsylvania. After graduating in medicine in 1809, he went into politics, edited a newspaper, acquired intemperate habits, and became a bankrupt. Commencing life again, in 1825 he took the chair of Theory and Practice in the Jefferson School, which he held until 1831, when he removed to Cincinnati, and became connected with the Faculty of the Medical College of Ohio. In 1837, he removed to Lexington, Ky., to accept a chair in the Transylvania School, but could not lecture, and soon died. His treatise on the Practice of Medicine, first published in 1829, was, in its day, a very popular work, in part at least because of the formulæ which it contained, but is now forgotten.

Dr. Elisha Bartlett, born in Rhode Island in 1804, died 1855, graduated in medicine at Brown University in 1826, after which he spent a year in Paris. He held Professorships at Woodstock, Vt., Pittsfield, Mass., Dartmouth, Baltimore, Lexington, Louisville, and finally, in 1850, in the University of the City of New York. Of the numerous productions of his pen, the most noteworthy are the "Inquiry into the Degree of Certainty in Medicine," etc., Philadelphia, 1848; "The History, Diagnosis, and Treatment of Typhoid and Typhus Fever," Philadelphia, 1842; and, "The History, Diagnosis, and Treatment of the Fevers of the United States," Philadelphia, 1847; of which, three subsequent editions were issued. To these may be added his essay on the Philosophy of Medical Science, in which the importance of facts and observations is insisted on, and all theorizing is denounced, in accordance with the teachings of Louis.

Dr. David Hosack, 1769–1835, a native of New York, graduated as Bachelor of Arts at Princeton in 1789, and as Doctor of Medicine in the University of Pennsylvania in 1791. After practising a year at Alexandria, Va., he spent two years in Edinburgh and London. Returning to New York, he entered into partnership with Dr. Samuel Bard, was appointed Professor of Botany in Columbia College in 1795, to which was added the chair of Materia Medica, in 1797. In 1807, he was chosen Professor of Surgery and Midwifery in the newly-formed College of Physicians and Surgeons of the State of New York, and in 1813, took the chair of Theory and Practice. In 1826, he resigned, with others, and went into the Rutgers Medical

College. His writings appear in the philosophical transactions, in the "Medical and Philosophical Register," of which he was the founder, and as occasional lectures and pamphlets. They were collected and published as "Essays on various subjects in Medical Science," in three volumes, New York, 1824–1830. His "System of Nosology" reached two editions; his "Lectures on Theory and Practice" were edited by Dr. Ducachet, and published at Philadelphia in 1838. His most important paper was his "Observations on Febrile Contagion," and on the means of improving the Medical Police of the City of New York, N. Y., 1820. As a lecturer, editor, and writer, he exercised much influence on the profession, and his literary and scholarly tastes were imparted to his pupils, and especially to Dr. John W. Francis, who, after his graduation in 1810, became associated with him in practice. Dr. Francis was the son of a German grocer, born in New York, 1789, died 1861. He was for thirteen years Professor in the College of Physicians and Surgeons, and followed Dr. Hosack to Rutgers, the close of which ended his career as a teacher.

Dr. Joseph Mather Smith, 1789–1866, graduated at the College of Physicians and Surgeons in 1815, and was Professor of Theory and Practice of Physic, same school, 1826 to 1855, when he took the chair of Materia Medica. He contributed largely to literature through the medical journals; presented some interesting reports to the American Medical Association, and published "Elements of Etiology," a "Philosophy of Epidemics," New York, 223 pages, 8vo.

For beauty of style as a writer and lecturer, Dr. Samuel Henry Dickson is pre-eminent. Born in Charleston in 1798, he graduated at Yale in 1814, and in Medicine at the University of Pennsylvania in 1819; was Professor in the Charleston Medical School from 1824 to 1831, 1833–34, 1850–7; in the New York University, 1847–50; and in the Jefferson School, 1858; he died March 31, 1872. His systematic works were not very successful, or worthy of special remark, but his journal contributions, and especially his volumes of essays, are among the most attractive literature of medicine.

John K. Mitchell, born in Virginia, 1793, took his academical degrees at the University of Edinburgh, commenced his medical studies under Dr. Chapman in 1816, and graduated in medicine at the University of Pennsylvania in 1819. After three voyages to India and China, for the sake of his health, he returned to Philadelphia, and in 1822, began to deliver lectures on Medical Chemistry in the Summer School. In 1841, he was elected to the chair of the Practice of Medicine in the Jefferson Medical College, which he filled to the date of his death in 1858. As an original investigator, and clear logical reasoner, his name stands among the highest, and is probably destined to a higher relative position in the future, than it enjoys even now. His papers on Endosmosis, Mesmerism, Ligature of Limbs for Spasm, and Cryptogamous Origin of Fevers, will be consulted, not only for the original facts which they set forth, but as models of suggestiveness, if the phrase may be permitted.

Dr. Charles Frick, born at Baltimore August 8, 1823, received the degree of Doctor of Medicine from the University of Maryland in 1845. In 1856, he was chosen to the chair of Materia Medica in the Maryland College of Pharmacy, and in 1858, he became Professor of Materia Medica and Therapeutics in the University of Maryland. His most valuable contributions to literature are his "Analysis of the Blood," American Journal of the Medical Sciences, January, 1848; "Treatise on Renal Diseases," 1850; "On Diabetes," American Journal of the Medical Sciences, 1852; "On Urinary Calculi," American Medical Monthly, April, 1858. He died March 25, 1860, of Diphtheria, contracted from a patient upon whom he had performed the operation of Tracheotomy five days previous. All his papers are careful, conscientious reports of original observations, with the least possible amount of theory, and with direct reference to practice.

Among the diseases which have received the greatest amount of attention in this country may be mentioned yellow and malarial fevers, and diseases of the chest. Our literature on yellow fever includes over one hundred books and pamphlets, besides more than six hundred journal articles. It was the epidemic of this disease along the North Atlantic coast which gave the first impetus to medical authorship in this country, and produced a mass of controversial writings which, although of little value in a scientific point of view, were useful, as giving their authors the habit of writing for the press. The earlier books have already been referred to, but mention should be made of the writings of Felix Pascalis *Ouviere*, generally known under the name of Pascalis. Dr. Pascalis was a native of Provence, France, and was born about 1750. Having graduated in medicine at Montpellier, he went to St. Domingo, and there practised his profession until driven out by the Revolution of 1793, when he came to Philadelphia, and subsequently settled in New York, where he died in 1833. Besides his works on Yellow Fever, he wrote a treatise on Syphilis, New York, 1812, and contributed papers to journals. He was one of the editors of the Medical Repository.

Another writer on Yellow Fever who seems to be little known except in the South is Dr. J. L. E. W. Shecut, a native of South Carolina, born in Beaufort, 1770; died in Charleston, 1836. He studied under Dr. Ramsay, of Charleston, graduated M.D. at Philadelphia in 1791, and at once commenced practice in Charleston.[8] His most important essays were collected and published in one volume, Charleston, 1819, under the title of "Shecut's

---

[8] For these data I am indebted to Dr. Robert Lebby, Charleston.

Medical and Philosophical Essays." This book, which is quite rare, contains his account of the yellow fever of 1817, first published in that year, and also his "Essays on Contagions and Infections," first published in 1818, and should be consulted by those who wish to trace the history of opinions in the South relating to this disease.

The principal work on Yellow Fever, which includes the information of all others of a prior date, is that of Dr. Réne la Roche, published in 1855. Dr. La Roche was of French descent, born in Philadelphia, in 1795, his father being an emigrant from St. Domingo. Unlike the majority of prominent American physicians, he was not connected with a large medical school, and his justly deserved reputation rests entirely upon his writings, and especially on his treatise on Yellow Fever, which is a model of research, and is remarkable, not only for the number, but the accuracy of its references, and the impartiality with which opposing statements are given.

The most valuable recent articles on this disease are in the New Orleans and the Charleston Medical Journals, but the great majority of them are historical and controversial.

During the course of an epidemic, physicians are too busy to make observations which require much time or care, or to make more than brief notes. The papers of Drs. Faget,[9] Logan,[10] and Sternberg,[11] giving temperature observations, make an advance in the right direction, but we lack data as to the pathological chemistry of the disease, and as to its relations with the malarial fevers. With regard to this last class of diseases, our literature is even more extensive than that of the preceding, and occupies much space in the journals of the West and South.

Our most valuable contribution to the natural history of malarial disease is the treatise of Dr. Daniel Drake, on the principal diseases of the Interior Valley of North America. This work is the "Magnum Opus," and results of the life-long labour, including extensive personal observations, literary research, and matured reflection, of a man whose fame, as compared with that of his contemporaries, will probably be greater a century hence than it is to-day, and whose name, even now, should be among the first on the list of the illustrious dead of the medical profession of the United States. The son of an illiterate Kentucky pioneer, brought up in a log cabin, attending a country school in the winter, and using the remainder of the year working on a farm, he surmounted the obstacles thus placed in his way, and by unceasing labour, joined to a sound common

---

[9] New Orleans Med. and Surg. Journal, 1873, i., N. S., p. 145.
[10] New Orleans Med. and Surg. Journal, 1874, ii. p. 779.
[11] Amer. Jour. Medical Sciences, 1875, lxx. p. 99.

sense, which rose to the level of genius, took a leading position as author, editor, practitioner, and teacher. Commencing the study of medicine at the age of sixteen, he attended his first course of lectures in 1805, and his second in the University of Pennsylvania, in 1815, at the end of which he graduated. He was Professor successively in the Transylvania School, the Medical College of Ohio; a second time in the Transylvania; the Jefferson School; the Medical Department of Cincinnati College; the University at Louisville; and again in the Medical College of Ohio. He died November 6, 1852. His first publication was a pamphlet on the climate and diseases of Cincinnati, published in 1810, and reissued as "The Natural and Statistical View or Picture of Cincinnati and the Miami Country," published in 1815. This work is quite rare, and is interesting as being the germ from which sprung his great work above referred to.

He founded the "Western Journal of the Medical and Physical Sciences," which would be of much value, if for no other reason, on account of a series of essays on Medical Education, by Dr. Drake, which were published in it. These essays were issued in a separate volume, in 1832, and form, upon the whole, the most satisfactory contribution to this vexed question which this country has ever produced. He commenced the preparation of his work on the diseases of the Mississippi Valley in 1822, and the second volume was not issued until after his death. Very few of the younger physicians of this country are familiar with his writings. Of his essays on Medical Education and Diseases of North America, no second editions have been published; but if there are any books to which the hackneyed phrase of the reviewer, "No physician's library is complete without it," apply, it is to these works of Dr. Drake, as far as American physicians are concerned, and they are most distinctively and peculiarly American books, in subject, mode of treatment, and style of composition.

The dissertation of Dr. J. K. Mitchell "On the Cryptogamous Origin of Malarious and Epidemic Fevers," is an ingenious piece of reasoning, and presents a summary of all the à priori arguments in favor of this theory which can be advanced. The papers of Dr. Salisbury on the same subject are without value.

Upon the subject of diseases of the chest the most noteworthy monographs have been the works of Morton, McDowell, Lawson, and Flint on Consumption; of Horace Green on the Diseases of the Air-Passages; La Roche on Pneumonia, and of Gerhard and Flint on Diagnosis of Diseases of the Chest. The treatise on Phthisis, by Dr. L. M. Lawson, adds another to the numerous examples of careful studies by physicians of diseases with which they are themselves afflicted. Dr. Lawson was a native of Kentucky; born 1812, died 1864. His early education was defective. At the age of twenty he was licensed to practise, but it was not until 1838 that he obtained his diploma from the Transylvania School. In 1844 he was elected to a Professorship at Lexington; from 1847 to 1853 he filled the chair of Materia Medica in the Medical College of Ohio, and then became Professor of Principles and Practice of Medicine. During the winter of 1859–60, he lectured on Clinical Medicine in the University of New Orleans. He founded, and for a long time conducted, the "Western Lancet," in which many of his lectures were published.

Dr. W. W. Gerhard, 1809–72, was a native of Philadelphia, and a graduate of the University of Pennsylvania. After taking his degree he spent two years in Paris, and became thoroughly indoctrinated with the teachings of Louis. On his return to Philadelphia he was appointed lecturer at the Medical Institute, and Assistant Clinical Lecturer to Professor Jackson. For twenty-five years he was the senior Physician to the Pennsylvania Hospital. Some of his clinical lectures appeared in the "Medical Examiner," of which he was one of the editors. His principle work was his "Treatise on Diagnosis of Diseases of the Chest," Philadelphia, 1842; second edition, 1846.

Dr. Horace Green, 1802–1866, was a native of Vermont, and a graduate of Castleton Medical College in 1824. From 1840 to 1843 he was Professor of Theory and Practice in the same school; and in 1850 took the same chair in the New York Medical College, of which he was one of the founders, continuing to lecture until 1860. In connection with this school he established, with his colleagues, the "American Medical Monthly." He was the first in this country to devote himself to a specialty, and his works on the local treatment of diseases of the air-passages attracted much attention, although they are not of a character to add permanently to his fame.

In medical jurisprudence, the systematic works of Beck, and Wharton and Stillé, and the treatise of Dr. Wormley on Poisons, are the most important, and each of them compares most favourably with any similar works in existence.

There are probably not to be found in the annals of medicine so large and valuable contributions to its literature by three brothers, as were made by the Beck family of New York.

John B. Beck, 1794–1851, graduated in Columbian College in 1813, became a pupil of Dr. Hosack, and graduated in Medicine at the College of Physicians and Surgeons in 1817, presenting, as a thesis, a paper on Infanticide, which was published, and is still a standard work on this subject. In 1822 he assisted in establishing the "New York Medical and Physical Journal," with which he was connected for the next seven years, and in which he published numerous articles. In 1826 he became Professor of Materia Medica in the College of Physicians and Surgeons, just newly organized. His principal works, in addition to those already alluded to, were his "Essays on Infant Therapeutics," New York, 1849; second edition, 1855; and his Historical Sketch of the State of Medicine in the American Colonies; "Lectures on Materia Medica," and a collection entitled, "Researches in Medicine and Medical Jurisprudence."

Theodoric Romeyn Beck, 1791–1855, graduated at Union College, Schenectady, studied under Dr. Hosack, and graduated as M.D. at the College of Physicians and Surgeons, in 1811. He was appointed Professor of the Institutes of Medicine and Medical Jurisprudence in the College at Fairfield, in 1815. In 1817 he became Principal in the Albany Academy, and gave up the practice of medicine. In 1840 he took the chair of Materia Medica in the Albany Medical College, which he held until 1854. His great work was his treatise on Medical Jurisprudence, which appeared in 1823, in two volumes, and of which, including four English editions, ten editions were issued during the author's life.

Dr. Lewis C. Beck, 1798–1853, the younger brother of the preceding, studied medicine under Dr. Dunlop, and was admitted to practice in 1818. In 1826 he was elected Professor of Botany and Chemistry in the Vermont Academy of Medicine. This position he resigned in 1832. In 1836 he was appointed Mineralogist to the Geological Survey of the State of New York, and in 1840 was elected Professor of Chemistry and Pharmacy in Albany Medical College. His contributions to medical literature, to chemistry, meteorology, and mineralogy, were numerous. His principal medical work was his Report on Cholera, made to the Governor of New York in 1832.

The literature of obstetrics has been so fully given by Dr. Thomas, in a preceding article of this series, that further reference to it is superfluous. We will add only, with regard to Dr. Hugh L. Hodge, that he was a graduate of Princeton, a pupil of Dr. Wistar, and that his early taste was for surgery rather than obstetrics. He was induced to change his specialty by Dr. Dewees. He was afflicted with defective vision, which increased with age, and his great work on Obstetrics was produced entirely by dictation. He commenced as a lecturer in the Medical Institute, and was elected Professor of Obstetrics in the University of Pennsylvania in 1835, the rival candidate being Dr. Charles D. Meigs, a lecturer in the Philadelphia Association for Medical Instruction, who six years later obtained the chair of Obstetrics in the Jefferson School. The literary works of Dr. Meigs compare very unfavourably with those of his rival as to scientific value and exactness, but they are much more attractive to students and those who read for pleasure rather than instruction.

We have three names of American medical writers whose works should be mentioned here, viz., Coxe, Watson, and Dunglison.

Dr. John Redman Coxe, 1773–1864, was a type of the medical scholar,

who loves books for their own sake, and who takes more pleasure in discovering a forgotten sentence in a folio of the fifteenth century than in
original investigations in the light of the present day. Born in Trenton,
New Jersey, he completed his classical education at Edinburgh, studied
medicine under Dr. Rush, and took his degree of M.D. at the University
of Pennsylvania in 1794, after which he continued his medical studies in
London, Edinburgh, and Paris for about two years. He was elected Professor of Chemistry in the University of Pennsylvania in 1809, and of
Materia Medica and Pharmacy in 1818. He filled the latter chair until 1835,
at which date he retired, and was but little known thereafter. His Dispensatory[12] and Medical Dictionary[13] were useful compilations, and met an
existing want. His Observations on Vaccination[14] was his best original contribution to medicine. His Inquiry on the Discovery of the Circulation of
the Blood was a paradoxical attempt to disprove the claims of Harvey.
His last work, and the one most in accordance with his tastes, was "The
Writings of Hippocrates and Galen," Philadelphia, 1846. He founded the
first medical journal published at Philadelphia, preceding that published
by Dr. Benj. Smith Barton by two months, and his library was, in its day,
the best collection of ancient authors on medicine in this country.

Dr. John Watson, of New York, has been alluded to in the article on
surgery. His literary tastes led him to historical studies and the collection
of a valuable library, and his historical sketch of ancient medicine[15] shows
that he consulted and enjoyed consulting the original works of the fathers
in medicine.

Dr. Robley Dunglison, a native of Keswick, England, born in 1798, was
one of the most prolific of medical authors. He obtained his medical education at Edinburgh, Paris, and London; settled in the latter city, where he
wrote a treatise on the diseases of children [1824], and was one of the
editors of the London Medical Repository in 1823–24. In 1824 he accepted
the invitation of Thomas Jefferson to fill the chair of Anatomy, Physiology, Materia Medica, and Pharmacy, in the University of Virginia. At
this place he published in 1827 a syllabus of his course on Medical Jurisprudence and prepared his Medical Dictionary. In 1833 he took the chairs
of Materia Medica, Therapeutics, Hygiene, and Medical Jurisprudence
in the University of Maryland, and from 1836 to 1868 was Professor of the
Institutes of Medicine in the Jefferson School. He died April 1, 1869. His
Systems of Physiology (first edition 1832), Hygiene (first edition 1835),
Therapeutics (1836), Practice (1842), and Materia Medica (1843), were

[12] The American Dispensatory. Phila., 1806, 4th ed. 1818.
[13] The Philadelphia Medical Dictionary. Phila., 1808, 2d ed. 1817.
[14] Practical Observations on Vaccination. Phila., 1802.
[15] The Medical Profession in Ancient Times. 8vo., N. Y., 1856.

popular in their day, nearly all of them passing through several editions. The work by which he will be remembered is his Medical Dictionary. The first edition of this was published at Boston in 1833, in two volumes. A peculiarity of this edition is that it contains brief biographical sketches of physicians, omitted in subsequent issues. The last edition, Philadelphia, 1874, edited by his son, is the most convenient work of the kind in existence.

Our literature on insanity and the pathology of mental disease is insignificant in comparison with the importance of the subject and the opportunities existing for its study, the only monograph of permanent value being the "Contributions to Mental Pathology," by Dr. Isaac Ray, 8vo., Boston, 1873. Considering the number and size of the asylums for the insane in this country, and the amount of money which has been spent upon them, it is rather curious that the medical officers connected with them should have contributed so little to the diagnosis, pathology, or therapeutics of diseases of the nervous system. An examination of the works relating to this subject, and more especially of the American Journal of Insanity, which is the most important, and which contains the transactions of the Association of American Superintendents of Hospitals for the Insane, will show that the thoughts of these specialists have been mainly directed to the subjects of construction and management of asylums and to the jurisprudence of insanity. This last subject is one of great and increasing importance; but our contributions to its literature consist rather of opinions and ontological speculations than of scientific observations. The annual reports of our insane asylums consist, for the most part, of business and financial statistics, and are intended for the use of appropriation committees rather than of physicians. There are some signs, however, that more attention will hereafter be given to recording of the physical phenomena of mental disease, and it is to be hoped that we may soon have some published results from the pathological department of the Utica Asylum, which will stimulate other institutions to undertake similar work. No more promising field to-day exists in medical science for valuable discoveries than in the wards and laboratory of a large, well-appointed hospital for the insane.

Upon the subject of hygiene no systematic work has yet been produced in this country, with exception of the treatise on Military Hygiene, by Dr. Hammond. One of the principal writers in this department was Dr. John Bell, a native of Ireland, 1796–1875. He came to this country with his parents, who settled in Virginia in 1810, and graduated in medicine in the University of Pennsylvania, after which he lectured for some years in the Philadelphia Medical Institute, and for two years in the Medical College of Ohio. His treatise on Baths and Mineral Waters is the only comprehensive and respectable treatise on this subject published in this country. The most important contributions to the literature of hygiene which we have produced are the reports of the various State and municipal boards of health, most of which, however, are of comparatively recent origin, and it is to be hoped are only just fairly commencing their career of usefulness.

The subject of hospital construction and hospital hygiene has been much discussed in this country, the latest production being a large and handsomely illustrated work published by the trustees of the Johns Hopkins Hospital of Baltimore.

The publications of our municipal, State, and national governments, relating to vital and medical statistics, are among our most valuable contributions to medical literature. The reports of city and State boards of health show each year evidences of more careful investigation into the probable causes of disease and the means of removing or diminishing them, and the necessity and economic value of such work is slowly but steadily becoming apparent to the educated classes of the community by means of the publications referred to.

The circulars and reports of the Medical Department of the Army are sufficiently well known, and within the last few years a series of reports have been commenced by the Medical Department of the Navy and by the Marine Hospital Service of the Treasury Department, which it is to be hoped will become important additions to our medical literature, not only in regard to statistics, but in the departments of hygiene, pathology, and therapeutics. It should not be forgotten by the physicians of the United States that they are, to a certain extent, responsible for the condition of the medical departments of the government, since the sympathy and opinions, expressed or implied, of the medical profession at large as to the work which these departments have done, or are trying to do, furnish the encouragement and stimulus which are necessary to the continuous production of good results, and also influence to a considerable extent the action of our legislators with regard to the officers of these departments.

The reports of the Surgeon-Generals of the Army, the Navy, and the Marine Hospital Service, while ostensibly presented to the Secretaries of War, the Navy, and the Treasury, are really, in a sense, made to the physicians of the country, who are the only competent judges as to whether the work is satisfactory, and commensurate with the means which have been allowed for its performance.

Of encyclopedic works, the result of the combined labour of many authors, like the great French dictionaries, but one specimen has been attempted in this country. This was the American Cyclopædia of Practical Medicine and Surgery, edited by Dr. Isaac Hays, of which two volumes, completing the letter "A" were published at Philadelphia in 1834–36, and reissued with a new title, "Medical and Surgical Essays," in 1841. The time is perhaps not far distant when a first-class publication of this character will be sufficiently in request in this country to warrant an attempt at its production.

Reprints and Translations.—The second class of medical works referred to in our statistics, includes the reprints and translations, which cannot be overlooked in an account for our medical literature, since they have formed an important part of the libraries of American physicians, even if quantity only be considered.

Prior to the Declaration of Independence, the largest and most important medical book printed in this country was the "Lectures on Materia Medica," of Cullen, issued at Philadelphia in 1775, in 4to., and advertised as "The very cream of physic," and as "absolutely necessary for all American physicians who wish to arrive at the top of their profession." [16]

In 1776 was published, at Philadelphia, the treatise of Van Swieten on the Diseases Incident to Armies, with Ranby on Gunshot Wounds, and Northcote on Naval Surgery, forming a small volume of 164 pages, which is usually found bound with the second edition of John Jones' "Practical Remarks," etc., of the same date, and was probably the principal guide of the army surgeons during the Revolutionary War. Cullen's "First Lines of the Practice of Physic" was reprinted from a smuggled copy, in 1781, at Philadelphia, in two volumes, 8vo., and five later American editions, the last edited, with a great flourish of trumpets, by Dr. Caldwell, in 1822, attest its popularity.

For thirty years after the Declaration of Independence, the majority of the reprints were works of English and Scotch writers, and especially of the Edinburgh school, the favourite authors being Cullen, Brown, John Hunter, Benjamin Bell, Denman, Smellie, Hamilton, Beddoes, and Robert Jackson. The largest edition sold was probably of the "Edinburgh New Dispensatory." The only translations of French or German medical works issued in this country prior to 1800 were, Swediaur on Venereal, New York, 1788, and Blumenbach's "Elements of Physiology," Philadelphia, 1795. The first medical book printed in Louisiana was "Médicaments et précis de la Methode de M. Masdevall," a pamphlet of 48 pages, relating to the yellow fever, issued in 1796.

The beginning of the influence of the French schools, which for the next fifty years was so powerful in the United States, especially in surgery, is marked by the editions of Boyer and Desault, Philadelphia, 1805, to which rapidly succeeded the works of Alibert, Richerand, and Bichat. In this connection may be permitted a reference to two works which are omitted

---

[16] A copy of this work was purchased by the Library of the Pennsylvania Hospital 1780, for £135 5s. currency, equal to £1 15s. specie.

from our statistics, since they were intended for non-professional use, but which had an extensive sale, and indirectly exerted a very considerable influence, viz., Buchan's Domestic Medicine, of which several editions were issued, the most important being that of Philadelphia, 1795, revised by Dr. S. P. Griffitts, and the "Primitive Physic," of John Wesley, of which there are several American editions of the last century.

Many foreign medical works have been issued in this country in connection with periodicals, such as the "Register and Library of Medical and Chirurgical Science," published at Washington, D. C., 1833–36, in which were issued "Bell on the Nerves," "Lawrence on the Eye," Velpeau's Surgery, etc.; The Select Medical Library, edited by John Bell; the American Medical Library, published under the supervision of Dr. Dunglison; and the "Medical News and Library," in which some valuable books have been issued.

The number of translations of French medical works which have been published in this country is one hundred and forty-eight (148). One hundred and one of these were issued prior to 1842, and only eight have appeared within the last ten (10) years.

The number of translations of German works issued has been sixty-four (64), of which but fourteen (14) were issued prior to 1842, and twenty-eight (28) within the last ten years.

The number of reprints of English medical books has been five hundred and eighty-four (584), thirty (30) of these were issued prior to 1800; two hundred and seventeen (217) during the next forty years, and three hundred and thirty-seven (337) since 1840, the production gradually increasing.

It is largely to French and German sources that we owe our works on pathology, pathological anatomy, pathological chemistry, and physiology.

The best systematic treatise on the practice of medicine from the German, published in this country, was that of Niemeyer, in 1869, the name of the author having been made somewhat familiar to the American public by a translation of his lectures on Phthisis, published the year previous. The works of Billroth on General Surgical Pathology, New York, 1871, Rindfleisch, a Text-book of Pathological Histology, Philadelphia, 1872, are the books which are to-day directing the work of the younger professional men of the country. The Cyclopædia of the Practice of Medicine, edited by Ziemssen, now in course of publication, is the most extensive medical work, native or foreign, which has ever been issued in the United States, and is probably destined to exercise great influence upon our investigation of diseases, whatever it may do for the practice.

Of the translations from the French, the most important have been those relating to anatomy, physiology, and surgery. The favourite authors have been Bichat, D. J. Larrey, Boyer, Orfila, Magendie, Laennec, Cazenave,

Baudelocque, Louis, Velpeau, Broussais, Cazeaux, Colombat, Ricord, Vidal, and Malgaigne.

It would be useless to give lists of the titles of these; it is sufficient to say that they include nearly every important monograph or text-book produced by English writers: from Cullen, Brown, and Darwin, to Bennett, Watson, and Aitken; from John Hunter, Benjamin, John and Charles Bell, Pott, Hey, and the Coopers, to Erichsen, Paget, and Holmes; and from Hamilton and Smellie to Simpson, Barnes, and Duncan. The works of nearly all the great English teachers have been quickly reproduced on this side of the water, and their modes of treatment are those followed by the majority of our practitioners.

A few medical books have been printed in Spanish at Philadelphia, for the Mexican trade, including the "Compendio de la Medecina," by J. M. Venegas, 1827. The number of reprints in this country has been largely due to the want of an international copyright law, for which reason publishers found it much cheaper to take the work of an English author gratis, than to pay an American writer for his MS. Sometimes the name of an American physician is given as editor of the reprint, but in most cases, this means little more than he approves the book, the so-called editing being imperceptible. To this remark a few honourable exceptions should be made, such as the additions by John Bell to the lectures of Stokes, of Gerhard to Graves; the reprints of Copland's Dictionary, in which the bibliographical additions, made by Dr. Charles A. Lee, are numerous and valuable, the editions of Velpeau's Surgery by Mott and Blackman, and the editions of Aitken's Practice by Dr. Clymer, who has added much to the completeness of the work.

This so-called editing was the subject of some caustic criticism, and has of late years almost entirely disappeared. With regard to the merits of the International Copyright question, there has been much discussion. On the one side, it is truly said that the desire for books increases by the supply, and that the sale of the cheap reprints produces a market for indigenous productions. On the other side, it is affirmed with equal truth, that it deprives our own writers, to a great extent, of pecuniary inducements to labor. The question is one to be decided, however, by the laws of morality rather than expediency, and the majority of educated non-interested parties agree that the passage of an international copyright law would be an act in accordance with the dictates of common honesty and justice.

Undoubtedly, the cheapness and abundance of these republications have done much to diffuse knowledge among our practitioners, and the libraries of many physicians have been mainly composed of the "pepper and salt sheepskin covered Philadelphia reprints." Of late years there has been a marked improvement in the quality of paper and typography of our medical books, while the stout bindings of sheep and calf of fifty years ago, have been largely superseded by the more showy, but, at the same time, more flimsy cloth bindings now in vogue. The German fashion of publication in parts has been almost unknown, except as connected with periodicals, and it is to be hoped that it may be long before the annoyance and confusion which attends the Lieferung and Hefte may be connected with our medical publications. "The American Clinical Lectures," edited by E. C. Seguin, and published by G. P. Putnam & Sons, look in this direction most unpromisingly, and the publication of such totally unconnected papers, in a series of continuous paging, even if special paging is added, must be unhesitatingly condemned by all who have occasion to either make or to verify bibliographical references to them.

It may be of interest to refer to some statistics of the locality of publication of these works. Of class one we find that three hundred and seventy-three (373) first editions were published in Philadelphia, one hundred and seventy-three (173) in New York, eighty-one (81) in Boston, twenty-four (24) in Cincinnati, sixteen (16) in New Orleans, and fifteen (15) in Baltimore, leaving ninety-six (96) published elsewhere. If each edition be reckoned as a separate work, we find that six hundred and thirteen (613) have appeared in Philadelphia, two hundred and twenty-six (226) in New York, ninety-six (96) in Boston, and eighteen (18) in Baltimore. Of the reprints and translations, six hundred and eighteen (618) books, or seven hundred and fifty-three (753) editions have been issued from Philadelphia, one hundred and seventy-seven (177) books, or two hundred and nineteen (219) editions from New York, eighty (80) from Boston, and ninety-four (94) elsewhere. It appears then that more than one-half of our medical books have been published in Philadelphia, and about one-fifth in New York. The firm of Carey, Lea & Carey, now H. C. Lea, has published nearly six hundred editions of medical works; and those of Lindsay & Blakiston, and Lippincott, each between one and two hundred. In New York, the principal publishing house is that of S. S. & W. Wood, now Wm. Wood & Co., which has issued about one hundred and fifty (150) editions.[17]

Medical Journals.—It is not in text-books or systematic treatises on special subjects that the greater part of the original contributions to the literature of medicine have been first made public during the last century, either in this or other countries. Since the year 1800 medical journalism has become the principal means of recording and communicating the observations and ideas of those engaged in the practice of medicine, and

---

[17] The figures of this distribution among publishers are only an approximation, and are probably too small, since the publishers' names are not stated in many of the lists of books from which titles have been derived.

has exercised a strong influence for the advancement of medical science and education.

To this class of literature this country has contributed a noteworthy share. Excluding those devoted to dentistry, pharmacy, popular hygiene, and "isms" of various kinds, we find that one hundred and ninety-five medical journals have been commenced in this country, including reprints of foreign journals, making in all one thousand six hundred and thirty-seven volumes, or a greater bulk than the text-books and monographs.

Prior to the establishment of medical periodicals, there was little or no encouragement or opportunity for a physician to record his observations. The professor in a medical school might, in an introductory notice to the thesis of one of the students—the so-called programma or propempticon inaugurale—make a statement, not to exceed sixteen pages upon any subject, whether connected with that treated of in the thesis or not, and sometimes such a paper was continued through the programmata of twenty or thirty different dissertations, making it very difficult at the present day to secure the entire work.

But if the country doctor had a communication to make to his brethren, he must either do it by a pamphlet printed at his own expense, or must forward it to some one connected with a medical school or scientific association, and trust to him that it should be made known and recorded. The professors themselves, as was natural, gave the greater part of their thought and labour to their systems, theories, and commentaries.

It was the day of large books, and unless one could produce a volume, he received little encouragement to write. At the present day, the demand for brief papers and reports of single cases, exceeds the supply.

The weekly and monthly periodicals are omnivorous and insatiable in their requests for contributions. Through the medical journals have been given to the world nearly all the discoveries which the science and art of medicine owes to American physicians. They furnish the original data which are the foundations of monographs and text-books, and their files remain interesting and vauable when the latter have become obsolete and are forgotten.

Medical journalism in the United States presents some peculiarities, although not nearly so many as is commonly supposed, and has been the subject of severe, and, to some extent, merited criticism; but while it includes some of the worst, it also contains the best of our medical literature, and some details as to its rise, progress, and character, may therefore be of interest.

The first medical journal printed in this country was a selection and translation from the "Journal de Médicine Militaire," issued in Paris from 1782 to 1788. This translation was published in New York about 1790, forming a volume of one hundred and twenty pages 8vo., which is quite rare.[18] The original journal from which this is made up is one that is valuable to the army surgeon; and the reprint is here referred to as being the first medical journal printed in the United States; and because the fact of its existence is probably known to very few.

The first American medical journal was a quarterly, "The Medical Repository," edited by S. L. Mitchell, Edward Miller, and E. H. Smith, and published at New York, from 1797 to 1824. That this met an existing want is shown by the fact that the demand for the earlier volumes was sufficient to warrant the issue of a second edition of the first and second volumes in 1800, and a third edition of the same volumes in 1804–5.

Dr. Elihu H. Smith, the projector of this journal, was born in Connecticut in 1771, graduated at Yale in 1786, and died in 1798. Although so young, he had edited several works, and contributed largely to literary periodicals, as well as to his own medical journal.

Dr. Samuel L. Mitchell, 1764–1831, studied under Dr. Bard, and graduated in medicine at Edinburgh, in 1786. As Professor of Chemistry and Natural History in Columbia College, and from 1820 to 1826 of Materia Medica and Botany, chief editor of the "Medical Repository," representative in Congress in 1801–4, and 1810–13, and United States Senator, 1804–9, he lectured and wrote upon almost all subjects, and his papers are scattered through various periodicals at home and abroad. He was rather a naturalist than a physician, and has very properly been called a "Chaos of Knowledge."

Dr. Edward Miller, 1760–1812, was a native of Delaware, and a graduate of the Medical Department of the University of Pennsylvania in 1789. In 1807 he accepted the chair of the Practice of Physic in the College of Physicians and Surgeons, and in 1809 was appointed one of the Physicians to the New York Hospital. His writings were collected and published in one volume in 1814, the most important being his papers on Yellow Fever.

The idea of the publication of the "Medical Repository" was probably taken from the "Annals of Medicine" of Duncan, a continuation of the "Medical and Philosophical Commentaries of Edinburgh," and of which the "Edinburgh Medical Journal" of the present day is the successor. Although, owing to the tastes of Dr. Mitchell, it contains many dissertations which are now obsolete, the entire set of twenty-three volumes is even today well worthy of a place in the physician's library. At its close its sub-

---

[18] "A Journal of the Practice of Medicine, and Surgery and Pharmacy in the Military Hospitals of France. Published by order of the King. Reviewed and digested by M. De Horne, under the inspection of the Royal Society. Annotated from the French by Joseph Brown. No. I., vol. i., New York: J. McLean & Co."

scribers passed to the "New York Medical and Physical Journal," and from that time, New York city has never been without a medical periodical. Thirty-one medical journals have been commenced in that city, besides nine devoted to specialties, and six reprints of foreign journals. The most important of these, in addition to those already named, are the "American Medical and Philosophical Register," edited by Drs. Hosack and Francis, 1810–14; the "New York Medical Magazine," edited by Mott and Onderdonk, the "New York Journal of Medicine and Surgery," 1839–41, one of the best journals in this country, edited by Drs. Watson and Swett, the "New York Journal of Medicine," edited by Forry, Lee, Stephen Smith, and others, continued as the "American Medical Times," of which the "Medical Record" of to-day may be considered as the representative; the "New York Medical Journal," edited successively by Drs. Hammond, Dunster, and Hunter, 1865–76, and the "Archives of Scientific and Practical Medicine," edited by Brown-Séquard, 1873, which unfortunately ceased with its fifth number. The "Buffalo Medical Journal," edited by Dr. Austin Flint, 1845–60, and then merged in the "American Medical Monthly," is also a valuable series.

The second medical journal published in this country was the "Philadelphia Medical Museum," edited by Dr. Coxe, 1804–1811, followed almost immediately by the "Philadelphia Medical and Physical Journal," edited by B. S. Barton, and published at irregular intervals, 1804–1809. This journal, as was to be expected from the tastes of its editor, contains a large proportion of articles on natural history. Other well-known journals published in Philadelphia are the "American Medical Recorder," a quarterly, 1818–29, whose subscription list passed to the "American Journal of the Medical Sciences;" the "North American Medical and Surgical Journal," 1826–31; the "Medical Examiner," 1838–56, which united with the "Louisville Review," forming the "North American Medico-Chirurgical Review," 1857–61; the "Medical and Surgical Reporter," 1856–76; the "Photographic Review of Medicine and Surgery," 1870–72; and the "Philadelphia Medical Times," 1870–76.

The most important journal on our list is the "American Journal of the Medical Sciences." This began as the "Philadelphia Journal of the Medical and Physical Sciences," in 1820, under the editorship of Dr. N. Chapman, who is said to have undertaken it under the stimulus of the phrase of Sidney Smith, so often quoted during the past year: "Who reads an American book?" In 1825 a new series began, edited by N. Chapman, W. P. Dewees, and J. D. Godman. This continued until 1827, when Dr. Isaac Hays, who had been associate editor in the last volume—number five of the new, or fourteen of the whole series—took charge of the Journal and gave it its present name. The ninety-seven volumes of this Journal need no eulogy.

They contain many original papers of the highest value; nearly all the real criticisms and reviews which we possess; and such carefully prepared summaries of the progress of medical science, and abstracts and notices of foreign works, that from this file alone, were all other productions of the press for the last fifty years destroyed, it would be possible to reproduce the great majority of the real contributions of the world to medical science during that period. It is evident that its editor has exercised a careful supervision over every part, but his personality is nowhere apparent, there being no editorial articles, and very few papers appearing over his signature.

Baltimore produced the third of our medical journals, the "Baltimore Medical and Physical Recorder," edited by Dr. Tobias Watkins, 1808–9. This only reached number one (1) of the second volume, and it is somewhat curious that of the ten medical journals and one reprint which have been commenced in that city, the duration of each has been comparatively brief. One little known may be referred to, "The Baltimore Philosophical Journal and Review," edited by Dr. J. B. Davidge, of which one number was published in 1823. It contains "a memoir on fractures of the thighbone," and "a case of extirpation of the parotid," each by the editor.

The first medical periodical published in Boston was of a popular character, "The Medical and Agricultural Register," 1806–7. The "New England Journal of Medicine and Surgery" began as a quarterly in 1812, and in 1828 was consolidated with the "Boston Medical Intelligencer," and became a weekly, forming "The Boston Medical and Surgical Journal," which has continued to the present time. The original quarterly was well edited, and contains some valuable papers. Under the editorship of Dr. J. V. C. Smith, which lasted for over fifty volumes, it would seem that no articles were ever refused admission to the weekly. As stated by Dr. Hunt,[19] "John C. Warren and X. Chabert were received with equal courtesy. In its department of reviews it was most complacent. From Rokitansky to Mrs. Joel Shew all were erudite. On its editorial pages nothing was attacked, everything was conciliated. Legitimate medicine was right to be sure, but the community would apreciate it better if it were not quite so right. Contributors of merit dropped off, and the journal became the receptacle of more 'remarkable cases' than any other was ever blessed with." From the date of this criticism there has been great improvement, and it is to-day one of the best.

The first medical journal west of the Alleghanies was the "Western Quarterly Reporter of Medical, Surgical, and Natural Science," edited by John D. Godman, Cincinnati, 1822–23, which reached number two of the

---

[19] Buffalo Medical Journal, 1856, xii. p. 312.

second volume. This was followed by the "Ohio Medical Repository," edited by Guy W. Wright, issued semi-monthly, Cincinnati 1826–27. This has become one of the rarest of American medical journals. The only articles of interest which it contains are a series of papers by Dr. John Locke, on the Medical Botany of the West, and a few reports of cases and contributions to pathological anatomy, by Dr. John P. Harrison. (This journal must not be confounded with another of the same name, published at the same place, in 1835–36.) It was merged into the "Western Medical and Physical Journal," edited by Drs. Daniel Drake and Wright. At the end of the first volume, in 1828, the editors agreed to disagree, and Dr. Wright published one number of a second volume, but the real continuation was issued by Dr. Drake, under the title of the "Western Journal of the Medical and Physical Sciences." This contained some of Dr. Drake's best and most characteristic writings, and forms a valuable and interesting series.

Two attempts were made by Dr. Eberle to establish a journal at Cincinnati; the first, the "Western Medical Gazette," after one or two suspensions, ceased with the second volume, in 1835; the second, the "Western Quarterly Journal of Practical Medicine," 1837, did not get beyond the first number. "The Western Lancet," edited by L. M. Lawson, continued from 1842 to 1857, when it took the name of "The Cincinnati Lancet and Observer," which is still flourishing. Several medical journals were started at Columbus, only one of which, "The Ohio Medical and Surgical Journal," 1848–64, was successful. A rare medical periodical and curiosity in its way is "The Belmont Medical Journal," published at Bridgeport, Ohio, under the auspices of the Belmont County Medical Society, 1858–60. With this belong the transactions of the same society from 1847 to 1857, forming in all, three small volumes in 12mo. These publications are unique in their way, and illustrate what can be done by a county medical society, composed entirely of country practitioners. They contain some amusing flights of rhetoric, and some well-recorded cases, and many of the papers are interesting because it is evident that they were written precisely as the authors talked.

The first medical journal of Kentucky was the "Transylvania Journal of Medicine," a quarterly, published at Lexington, from 1828 to 1839, forming a series of twelve volumes, of which complete sets are rare and valuable. In 1840 commenced "The Western Journal of Medicine and Surgery," Louisville, 1840–55, which may be considered as a continuation of Dr. Drake's "Western Journal," above referred to, combined with the "Louisville Journal of Medicine and Surgery," edited by Drs. Yandell, Miller, and Bell, in 1838, and of which but two numbers were published.

"The Richmond and Louisville Medical Journal," now in course of publication, edited by Dr. E. S. Gaillard, 1868–76, is a continuation of the

"Richmond Medical Journal," published at Richmond, Va., 1866–68. "The American Practitioner," edited by Drs. D. W. Yandell and T. Parvin, 1870–76, is a continuation of the "Cincinnati Journal of Medicine," commenced in Cincinnati in 1867.

"The Illinois Medical and Surgical Journal" commenced at Chicago in 1844, and has continued to the present time under various names, being now known as "The Chicago Medical Journal and Examiner."

The first journal published west of the Mississippi was "The St. Louis Medical and Surgical Journal," founded by Dr. M. L. Linton, in 1843, which is still in existence.

In the South the first medical periodical was the "Journal de la Société Médicale de la Nouvelle Orleans," a quarterly, published in 1831. A monthly journal of the same name appeared in 1859–61. The most important is the "New Orleans Medical and Surgical Journal," which, with two suspensions, has continued from 1844 to the present time. "The Southern Medical and Surgical Journal," edited by Anthony Eve and others, published at Augusta, forms a series of twenty-one volumes, which contain many valuable cases, papers, and reports. "The Charleston Medical Journal and Review," 1846–60, and 1873–76, is the principal medical periodical of South Carolina.

In Tennessee, "The Nashville Journal of Medicine and Surgery," 1851–61, and 1866–76, and "The Southern Journal of the Medical and Physical Sciences," 1853–57, are worthy of note.

The principal medical journal in Virginia was "The Virginia Medical and Surgical Journal," edited by G. A. Otis and others, Richmond, 1853–61. In the same city was published, during the war, "The Confederate States Medical and Surgical Journal," 1864–65, a quarto sheet containing much valuable data in military surgery. Complete files of this are very rare.

On the Pacific coast eight medical journals, in all, have been commenced, two of which did not get beyond the first number. The oldest one now in existence is "The Pacific Medical and Surgical Journal," which began in 1858.

Five medical journals have been commenced in Michigan, two of which are now in existence.

Connecticut, Iowa, Maine, Minnesota, New Hampshire, New Jersey, Oregon, Vermont, and West Virginia have each had one journal, all of which are now extinct except "The West Virginia Medical Student." Perhaps two may be claimed from Maine, counting "The Journal of the Medical Society of Maine," one number of which was issued at Hallowell in 1834.

Of journals devoted to dentistry there have been about twenty, making one hundred and thirty volumes in all.

The earliest one was the "American Journal of Dental Science," which commenced in New York, in 1839, was suspended from 1860 to 1867, and is still in existence.

In 1876 there are four dental journals in existence in this country, while England has but one, France two, and Germany one.

Of journals devoted to pharmacy, there have been six worth mentioning; the oldest being the present "American Journal of Pharmacy," which began in 1825, as the "Journal of the Philadelphia College of Pharmacy." This journal is by far the most valuable of this class in this country, and is furthermore noteworthy, and to be specially commended for having done what no medical journal in this country has accomplished, namely, the publishing of a complete index for its series, which was done in 1873, and which doubles the practical value of the set. The total number of volumes published of this class is ninety-four.

Besides the regular encyclopedic medical journals, there have been about as many more devoted to "isms" and "pathies," and to popular and family medicine and hygiene, many of these last being merely advertisements.

With the recent development of specialties in medicine, several journals devoted to particular subjects have appeared, and an increase in the number of these may be expected.

In this connection may be mentioned, as a curiosity in literature, a periodical publication devoted to the abuse of an individual physician, namely, the "Rush Light," published in New York in 1800, by William Cobbett, under the pseudonym of Peter Porcupine, for the vilification of Dr. Benjamin Rush. Seven numbers were issued, of which only the first two bore the imprint of place of publication, the last two were printed in London, and a complete set is very rare.

A most powerful agent for the diffusion in this country of the knowledge of the labours and writings of European physicians, has been the republication of the principal English Quarterly Reviews, of "Braithwaite's Retrospect," and of "Ranking's Abstract." To this should be added, perhaps, the so-called "American Edition of the London Lancet," which is a selection rather than a reprint, and the subscription list of which was at one time very large.

Of journals printed in foreign languages, there have been commenced, three in German, three French, and one Spanish. The French journals were all issued at New Orleans; two of the German journals appeared in the State of New York, and one in Philadelphia.

The Spanish journal was intended mainly for circulation in Cuba.[20] Its issue ceased with the third number.

---

[20] "Revista Medico-Quirurgica y Dentistica." Quarterly. New York and Havana, 1868.

Our medical journals vary so much in character, style, and purpose, that it is hardly possible to make any assertion with regard to the mass which shall be at the same time broad and true. They may be divided into three classes: first, those not connected with any medical school, and which draw their contributions from a wide field, including such as the "American Journal," "The New York Journal," "The Medical Record," "The Medical Times," and "The Boston Medical and Surgical Journal;" second, those which rely for contributions and material mainly on the professors of a medical school and the hospital clinics connected with it, but which are not specially devoted to its interests; third, those which are mainly devoted to advocating the interests of a school, and the attacking rival institutions, and which are, to use Carlyle's phrase, "Windmills put out to catch or take advantage of the wind of popular favour." These journals sometimes contain valuable reports of cases obtained from the college clinics, but the personal editorial element in them is usually in excess, and they are of interest to but a small local circle. To them applies the untranslatable French criticism, "Il y a trop de tintamarre la dedans, trop de brouillamini."

Of the first class, some compare favourably with the best of the journals of other countries: of the last class, some are as bad as, but not worse than, the worst. Comparatively few persons are acquainted with the poorer class of foreign medical journals, published in the smaller towns of the provinces, which have most of the defects which are so strongly condemned in some of our own publications as if they were unique.

The reports to the American Medical Association, by its committees on American Medical Literature, devote much space to periodicals, and contain many judicious criticisms upon their defects and errors. A common complaint is that there are too many. The reply to this is usually that of Dr. Drake, that it is desirable that the country practitioners be induced to write, and that one means of doing this is the diffused localization of journals. This is due to the fact that inexperienced and modest men will furnish an article or report to a journal in their immediate neighbourhood, with whose editor they are personally acquainted, while they would not do so to one at a distance.

The number of subscribers to the greater number of our journals is small, the issue being, for many, less than a thousand, and, for some, hardly five hundred copies.

The motive for the existence of the minor journals is not for direct profit, but as an indirect advertisement for certain individuals, or—and this is more common—the desire to have a place in which the editor can speak his mind and attack his adversaries without restraint. The defects in the medical journals are, to a certain extent, the characteristic ones in our medical literature, and are chargeable mainly to the lack of general education and mental culture in the majority of readers whose tastes are to be accommodated. An urgent want of many of the subscribers is a sort of continuation of the course of education given in the schools. We find, for instance, in the pages of some medical journals, articles which make no pretensions to originality, but are simply didactic lectures to a class *in absentia*. The defects in the so-called original contributions are, for the most part, due to imperfect education in the writers, and betray, not merely an ignorance of facts previously ascertained and recorded, but defective mental training and an inability to comprehend the relations of the facts which are known, the result of which is the stringing out of a series of irrelevant and tedious details, and, in the attempts at deduction, the production either of vague and valueless generalizations, or conclusions which do not follow from the premises. As an illustration, take the majority of the artilces which have appeared on a disease which would seem to be peculiar to this country, viz., the so called "milk-sickness" or "trembles."

Since the first notice on this affection in Dr. Drake's Notices of Cincinnati, in 1809, there have been printed four pamphlets and one hundred and ten (110) articles in journals and transactions, on this subject. Yet it cannot be said to-day, that we have any definite knowledge as to the pathology or causes of this affection, or that, so far as man is concerned, we are absolutely certain that there is any special disease which should be thus named, as being caused by the milk, or flesh of cattle affected with the "trembles." It has been said to be caused by certain plants, yet no scientific experiments have been made on the effects of these plants. No attempt has been made to produce the disease in an animal remote from infested localities, by the use of the suspected plants, or better, by the use of an extract containing their active principles; no chemical or microscopical examinations have been made, in short, we have nothing but an account of symptoms, and much of that is from hearsay.

Many articles intended to be practical, are very far from being such, although the authors would probably be surprised and indignant to hear them termed otherwise. They profess to give the results of the writer's personal experience with a certain disease, but this disease is only named, not described, and the gross results only are given, that is to say, we are told how many recovered. The object of such writers, to use their own words, is to tell us "what is good for biliousness, or low fever, or pneumonia." Their productions read curiously, like the literature of the last century, and are to be classed with old women's advice; amusing generally; practically suggestive sometimes; clear, scientific, and conclusive, never.

The so-called clinical lectures, and reports of cases and operations, are of two kinds. When properly prepared they are most useful and valuable, and are the best contributions to a journal which the majority of physicians can make, although by no means the highest class of medical literature. But a large number of such articles as are published, are simply padding, worse than useless, since their titles become a part of the bibliography of medicine, compelling each succeeding inquirer to refer to them, or risk the loss of some really valuable reference.

We have reached that stage of development, when it is in no way desirable that we should be informed that one dislocated shoulder was reduced, one leg amputated, and two hare-lips operated upon, not even if the usual text-book explanations are added, so as to make up the five or six pages of the report of a college clinic. We have had enough reports of specimens of "Aneurism of the Aorta," or "Medullary Sarcoma," or "Tumour of the Breast," in which little or no information is given with regard to the symptoms during life, and the principal fact stated is the size or weight of the specimen.

It is a useless case of labour which lingers through three or four pages, to terminate in the usual manner with the stale old moral about "meddlesome midwifery," and it is at once amusing, exasperating and pathetic, to glance over the "contributions from the clinic" of the young specialist who has set to work to write himself into notice, not in a journal devoted to his specialty, but in one of the encyclopedic periodicals, having been instructed that this is "legitimate advertising."

"Medical journalism is not a profession in this country. With one or two exceptions, our medical editors are engaged in practice and lecturing, and their labour in connection with the journals is not directly remunerative, nor is it the main object of their thoughts." The result of this appears in that large section of almost every journal which is devoted to reviews, abstracts, news items, etc. Nevertheless, as we have before stated, our medical journals are the most important and valuable part of our medical literature, and it is mainly in and by them that improvement may be hoped for and effected.

At the beginning of 1876, there were in course of publication throughout the world about 280 regular medical journals. Of this number, Germany and Austria had 57; France 52; Great Britain, not including her Colonies 29; the United States 46; Italy 31; Belgium 8; Mexico 8; Canada 7; Holland 6; Spain 6. As to the form of publication, the United States has the largest proportion of monthlies, and France and Germany of weeklies and bi-weeklies.

The proportion of periodical to other forms of medical literature is in excess in this country, as will be clearly seen if we compare the number of medical books published in the several countries. Taking the "Bibliotheca Medico-Chirurgica," of Ruprecht, for the years 1874–75, and counting the publications noted in it, excluding journals, pamphlets, and popular and irregular works, we find that the United States is credited with 55 volumes; England 179; France 409; Germany 419; Italy 120; Spain and Portugal 104. If we count only first editions of original works, we find that the United States has published during these two years 36; England 92; France 314; Germany 288; Italy 88; and Spain and Portugal 30.

These figures are, of course, not exact, but the proportions shown are probably nearly correct. Taking the number of volumes of medical publications of all nations, excluding journals, for these two years, the United States has published about six per cent. of the whole, certainly not the quantity which should have been produced if everything was as it should be.

Medical Societies.—An important influence upon the progress of medicine, and the relations of physicians to each other, and to the public, has been exerted by our medical societies, some of which date from the last century, and which are found almost everywhere. The first State medical societies, such as those of New Jersey, Massachusetts, Delaware, New York, etc., were charged with the duty of licensing persons to practise medicine, to which license an examination was a necessary preliminary. In this way these societies were the principal agents in fixing the standard of medical education, and although after the establishment of medical schools the diploma of one in good repute was accepted in lieu of an examination, this was by courtesy rather than law, and made it necessary that the standard of the schools should at least be equal to that prescribed by the society. For convenience of reference, we give a list of the most important medical societies of the United States, arranged in alphabetical order by States:—

	Organized	First Publication	No. of Vols. of Publications
American Medical Association	1847	1848	27
American Ophthalmological Society	1864	1865	7
American Otological Society	1868	1869	1
American Pharmaceutical Association	1852	1852	24
American Public Health Association	1872	1875	1
National Quarantine and Sanitary Convention	1857	1857	4
Medical Association of the State of Alabama	1847	1848	19
State Medical Association of Arkansas	1870	1871	5
Medical Society of the State of California	1870	1870	5
Territorial Medical Society of Colorado	1871	1872	5
Connecticut State Medical Society	1792	1844	20
Medical Society of Delaware	1789	—	—
Medical Society of the District of Columbia	1833	1874	2
Clinico-Pathological Society of Washington	1865	—	—
Florida Medical Association	1874	1875	1

	Organized	First Publi- cation	No. of Vols. of Publica- tions
Georgia Medical Association	1849	1850	20
Georgia Medical Society of Savannah	1804	—	—
Illinois State Medical Society	1851	1851	23
Drake Academy of Medicine	1872	1874	1
Indiana State Medical Society	1849	1849	27
Iowa State Medical Society	1850	1850	10
Medical Society of the State of Kansas	1858	1867	2
McDowell Medical Society	1874	1875	1
Kentucky State Medical Society	1851	1851	19
Société Médicale de la Nouvelle Orleans	1812	1831	3
Medical Society of the State of Maine	1834	1834	1
Maine Medical Association	1853	1853	6
Medical and Chirurgical Faculty of Maryland	1789	1853	4
Boston Society for Medical Improvement	1828	1853	5
Boston Society for Medical Observation	1846	—	—
Boylston Medical Society	1811		{70 prize essays published in journals.
Gynaecological Society of Boston	1869	1869	5
Massachusetts Medical Society	1781	1790	41
Michigan State Medical Society	1819	1850	15
Minnesota State Medical Society	1855	1870	6
Medical Association of the State of Mississippi	1856	1870	1
Medical Society of the State of Missouri	1850	1850	12
Nebraska State Medical Society	1868	1869	6
New Hampshire Medical Society	1791	1854	21
New Jersey State Medical Society	1766	1859	17
Medical Association of Southern Central New York	1847	1848	11
Medical Society of the County of Albany	1806	1864	2
Medical Society of the County of Kings	1822	1858	2
Medical Society of the County of New York	1806	—	—
Medical Society of the State of New York	1807	1808	34
Medico-Legal Society of New York	1867	1874	1
New York Academy of Medicine	1847	1851	8
New York Medical Journal Association	1864	—	—
Pathological Society of New York	1844	—	—
Physico-Medical Society of New York	1815	1817	1
Medical Society of the State of North Carolina	1850	1850	22
Academy of Medicine of Cincinnati	1857	—	—
General Medical Society of Ohio	1827	1829	2
Medical Convention of Ohio	1835	1835	13
Ohio State Medical Society	1846	1850	26
Belmont Medical Society	1847	1848	8
Medical Society of the State of Oregon	1874	—	—
College of Physicians of Philadelphia	1787	1793	11
Medical Society of the State of Pennsylvania	1848	1851	18
Pathological Society of Philadelphia	1857	1869	4

	Organized	First Publi- cation	No. of Vols. of Publica- tions
Philadelphia County Medical Society	1849	—	—
Philadelphia Obstetrical Society	1868	1873	3
Rhode Island Medical Society	1812	1859	1
Medical Society of South Carolina	1789	—	—
South Carolina Medical Association	1848	1849	16
Tennessee State Medical Society	1830	—	—
Medical Association State of Texas	1869	1869	4
Medical Society of the State of Vermont	1814	1864	4
Medical Society of Virginia	1821	1871	5
Medical Society of Washington Territory	1873	1873	3
Medical Society of the State of West Virginia	1867	1868	8
Wisconsin State Medical Society	1842	1856	9

The formation of the American Medical Association was due to a wide spread and loudly expressed dissatisfaction on the part of the leading physicians of the country, with the low standard of medical education, and to a general conviction that the remedy for this lay neither with the schools nor the State medical societies. It was hoped that by forming an association which should represent all parties interested, a sufficient pressure of opinion might be brought to bear upon physicians and upon the schools, to secure the return to the requirements for graduation of the earlier medical colleges. After one or two futile attempts, the New York State Medical Society set on foot a movement which resulted in a meeting of a convention in the city of New York, in the year 1847, in which were present representatives of medical societies and colleges from sixteen States. A similar convention met the following year in Philadelphia, at which the title, by which it is now known, was assumed. The series of its annual volumes of transactions contains some reports and papers of much value and interest, mingled with much that is unworthy of publication under the auspices of our National Medical Society, or indeed of any other. Many of the reports of the chairmen of the several committees are of permanent historical value. Its most valuable contribution to our literature, has been the publication of a code of ethics, which is, theoretically at least, accepted as authoritative throughout the United States, and which, although some of its provisions have been objected to, is, as a whole, the most satisfactory exposition in existence of the proper relations of physicians to each other, and to the public.

Of late years, the original purpose of this association has been to some extent departed from.

It was not primarily intended to promote literature or scientific research, or to afford a means of publication for writers. Our national and State medical societies have been mainly useful as social gatherings, promoting acquaintance, and the feeling of professional brotherhood and *ésprit de corps* among their numbers, and as giving the means for agreement, and the expression of opinion, upon questions relating to education, ethics, etc.; by that large body of physicians engaged in general practice, who do not write or lecture, but simply vote. As sources of addition to the science and literature of medicine, they do not play a conspicuous part, nor is it easy to see how it can be otherwise; the real discovery, the carefully prepared paper, the description of a new symptom, pathological appearance or remedy are not usually communicated to such societies. No effectual supervision as to quality of papers which may be read or printed can, or at least will be exercised by committees, and a communication which a first class medical journal has "declined with thanks," may be taken to the State, and even to the National Society with a reasonable certainty that it can be made to appear in the transactions. The discussions on papers in such associations seldom have any scientific value, from want of special preparation on the part of the speakers, although they are sometimes amusing, and, to use an expressive word, "spicy," from the use of personalities. Whether this state of things can be improved is doubtful, though attempts to do so are of course commendable.[21]

The journals have to a great extent superseded the necessity of using societies as a means of publication, and the best work of such associations seems to consist in bringing the leaders into personal relation with the mass of the profession, and in serving as courts of arbitration and appeal, where local difficulties can be adjusted, and whose decisions will command the assent of the majority of their members.

The Transactions of the New York State Medical Society were, for a number of years, published by the State, which proved, upon the whole, to be not a desirable mode of issue, and the last volume, published by the society itself, is a great improvement upon its predecessors. What such societies might do is shown by the paper of Dr. Thomas C. Brinsmade, giving an accurate record of his practice for twenty-one years. This makes 300 pages of the volume of the Transactions of the New York State Medi-

---

[21] The best suggestion to this end for the American Medical Association which I have heard is that each section should elect its own officers and members, and should be managed by a special committee who shall designate the subject for discussion, and the leaders in debate. If the members of the committee each year are selected from a single city, it would have an additional advantage. For instance, let the managing committee of the surgical section be, this year, all residents in New York city, while Boston takes obstetrics, Philadelphia practice, etc. The next year New York can take practice, Chicago surgery, etc. In other words, transfer all the responsibility for scientific work to the sections, and let these sections be organized and managed systematically to that end alone.

cal Society for 1858, and contains carefully analyzed statistics of 37,872 cases. This had been preceded in 1851 by an elaborate account of the medical topography of the city of Troy, his place of residence. Taken together, these papers are very valuable, and set an example of a mode of adding to the store of medical knowledge, which is within the power of every practitioner.

An interesting experiment is now in course of trial in Alabama, where the State Medical Society has been made the State Board of Health, and the official adviser of the Legislature in all matters pertaining to public hygiene.

The American Public Health Association, organized in 1872, may now be considered as fairly established. The operations of this society have special interest to the medical profession, since it may become an important means of educating the public, and enabling it to distinguish between the scientific physician and the ignorant pretender.

We have another class of medical societies which require an abundance of clinical and pathological material; members actually engaged in original investigations, and frequent meetings, as conditions for usefulness and success. As a rule, these can only exist in large cities, where they exert a powerful influence and stimulus to exertion on their individual members. It must be admitted that our societies of this kind seldom bring out the best work of their members, and that such discussions as occur in similar societies in London and Paris, continued week after week, and even month after month, for which elaborate preparation is made by the speakers, and in which the results of clinical observation and extensive literary research are rendered attractive and striking, by splendor of diction and perfection of style, are very rare.

The most important of these societies are the College of Physicians of Philadelphia, the New York Academy of Medicine, the pathological societies of Philadelphia and New York, the Boston Society for Medical Improvement, and certain societies devolted mainly to specialties. Among these should be mentioned the Medico-Legal Society of New York, organized in 1867. In 1874 it published a volume of papers relating to medical jurisprudence, which will be followed by others. It is also forming a valuable library in its own department, and has been the means of bringing the members of the medical and legal professions of New York to better acquaintance with each other. It is but justice to say that much of its good work and prosperity is due to the energy of its late president, a prominent lawyer, Mr. Clark Bell.

The majority of our physicians are, and must be, content to leave to a few special workers the labour and pleasure of sifting and selecting from the original sources of medical literature, having neither the wish nor the power to examine for themselves the works of the great leaders and teachers of times past, or the mass of books and pamphlets which are daily streaming from the press; but there is nevertheless among them a fair amount of appreciation of the value and necessity of such work, and of the usefulness and desirability of collections of the records of their science. During the last ten years, the writer has had occasion to examine many private libraries of physicians in all parts of the country, in country villages as well as the large cities, and it has been a matter of surprise and pleasure to find so much interest taken in subjects relating to the history and bibliography of medicine by men remote from large libraries, and without the stimulus of companionship in, and sympathy with such tastes. And it will usually be found that the physician who has on his shelves half a dozen old folios and quartos, including perhaps copies of Sydenham, Morgagni, and Van Swieten, is a man of more culture and broader views than the one who has only the modern manuals, or rather those which were modern when he attended lectures.

Until recently few of our writers have made much use of bibliographical research. We now have public medical libraries in this country, which afford to the student and scholar good facilities for research, and which bid fair, at no distant day, to rival in magnitude and practical working value, if not in manuscripts and incunabulæ, the best in the old world.

Philadelphia has several libraries of much interest and value to the medical bibliographer and scholar. The oldest medical library in this country is that of the Pennsylvania Hospital, founded in 1762, and now containing about 13,000 volumes, many of which were selected for the hospital by Doctors Lettsom, in London, and Louis, in Paris. Its classed catalogue, issued in 1857, is a valuable work of reference.

The Library of the College of Physicians, of Philadelphia, which dates from 1788, now contains about 19,000 volumes well selected, receives about eighty current journals, and, next to the library at Washington, is the most valuable collection of the kind in this country. Much of its prosperity and excellence is due to Doctor Samuel Lewis, whose donations, amounting to several thousand volumes of choice books, are kept in a room by themselves, and known as the "Lewis Library." The great want of this library is a good printed catalogue, which would double its value and usefulness. The medical part of the Loganian Section in the Philadelphia Library contains about 1800 volumes, mostly old and rare. These three libraries supplement each other to a great extent, there being probably not less than 26,000 volumes between them, which are not duplicates. The fourth library is at the University of Pennsylvania, in West Philadelphia, and contains about 3000 volumes, the gift of Dr. Alfred Stillé. It may be noted here that almost all attempts to establish medical libraries in connection with medical schools have been failures. Commenced with enthusiasm, they soon become antiquated, are rarely consulted, except by one or two species of beetles, are never properly catalogued or cared for, and dust and mould reign in them supreme. Students and teachers want the newest books and journals only. Libraries are used by the scholar and author, and for such are the true universities.

In New York, the library of the New York Hospital is the largest of its class, containing about 10,000 volumes. An excellent foundation for a library has been acquired by the Academy of Medicine, by the gift from Dr. Purple of a complete file of regular American medical journals and of a large number of rare pamphlets. The collections of journals of the Medical Journal Association of New York, and the German Dispensary are valuable sources of information to the student.

The Boston Public Library has at present the best collection of medical books in that city, numbering about 11,000 volumes, for the most part standard works and periodicals. Its usefulness is much diminished from the want of a good printed catalogue of this section. The library of Harvard College contains between 5000 and 6000 volumes on medicine; and the Treadwell Library, at the Massachusetts General Hospital, has about 5000 volumes. The medical library of most promise in Boston is that of the Medical Library Association, which, though only a year old, has about 3000 volumes, and will probably rapidly increase.

In Cincinnati the City Hospital has a fair collection. The Mussey Medical and Scientific Library, at present, is a special deposit in the Cincinnati Public Library, and contains about 4000 volumes and 2000 pamphlets.

The National Medical Library at Washington, under the direction of the Surgeon-General of the Army, contains 40,000 volumes, and about the same number of pamphlets. It has been formed within the last twelve years, and the use that is made of it by physicians from all parts of the country, and the general and strong interest that is felt in its progress affords satisfactory evidence, if such were needed, that it meets a want of the profession. Its subject catalogue is nearly ready for the press.

Besides these public libraries, there are several valuable private collections of medical works in this country, some of which have been already given to public use, such as those of Drs. Purple, Stillé, and Mussey, already referred to. Two others are worthy of special mention, the first being that of Dr. G. J. Fisher, of Sing Sing, which is rich in the classics of medicine; and the second, that of Dr. J. M. Toner, of Washington, which is especially devoted to American medical literature, and contains many rare pamphlets, besides a nearly complete file of American medical journals. In connection with this last, there is nearly ready for the press a complete index. Besides these, there are a number of valuable private medical libraries in this country, ranging from 1000 to 8000 volumes, and the number of foreign works imported, and the taste for original editions is steadily increasing. It is now possible to verify in this country the majority of the references made by European medical authors, and it is no longer necessary to make costly importations, or to visit Europe to obtain literary data.

With the libraries should be classed the *medical museums*, of which several of much interest and importance have been formed in the United States, for the most part in connection with medical societies and hospitals. The catalogues of these collections, when properly prepared, are very useful books of reference, and some excellent work of this kind has been accomplished, such as the Catalogues of the Warren Anatomical Museum of Harvard, and of the Museum of the Boston Society for Medical Improvement, each by Dr. J. B. S. Jackson; of the Pathological Museum of the Pennsylvania Hospital, by Dr. Wm. Pepper; of the Pathological Cabinet of the New York Hospital, by Dr. Ray; and of the Army Medical Museum at Washington, by Drs. Woodhull, Curtis, and Woodward.

The College of Physicians of Philadelphia has a valuable collection, including the Mütter Museum, and a series of unique preparations by Hyrtl.

The practical value of large special museums in connection with good libraries devoted to the same specialties is great, but they are useful rather to the educated physician than to the student; and the numerous small collections which are scattered over the country, in hospitals and private cabinets, are simply so much wasted and unused material, in a scientific point of view, and, though gratifying to the owner as trophies or mementoes, are of little more real use than the strings of teeth which the barbers of old hung out as signs of their skill.

The value of a single specimen of any lesion is usually very small; it is only when they can be brought together by scores and compared that useful and reliable results can be hoped for. As we get older and wiser, we shall probably have fewer journals, medical schools, museums, and libraries than we now possess, for all these means of culture, to have the best effect, require concentration.

Although the permanent importance of oral teaching has, to some extent, been diminished by the diffusion of periodical literature, since the latest discovery or theory can now be promptly made known to those remote from the great centres of learning, the increased use made of clinical instruction, and the necessity for practical demonstration of instrumental methods of diagnosis, have in a great degree compensated for this.

The medical history of a country cannot be considered complete without some account of its *medical schools*, but we have space for little more than a list of those which have flourished in the United States.

The following table gives a list of the regular chartered medical schools of this country, which have had the power of conferring the degree of doctor of medicine, with the date of first graduating class, date of cessation, and number of graduates to the spring of 1876, so far as it has been possible to obtain the data:—

It is possible that a few minor schools of short duration have been overlooked, but such must have been of small importance. No note is made in the list of the various changes of name which some of the schools have assumed. The number of graduates has been obtained by collation of all the catalogues that could be obtained, and by correspondence. From these data an estimate has been made for the missing years, and the limit of error in the total does not probably exceed one-half of one per cent. It should be observed that little reliance can be placed upon many of the catalogues as to the number of students in attendance, and there are some discrepancies even as to graduates.

Name	Year of First Graduation	Date of Cessation	Total No. of Graduates
Alabama			
Medical College of Alabama [Mobile]	1860	—	203
California			
Medical College of the Pacific, Med. Dept. of University (City) College [San Francisco]	1859	—	90
University of California, Med. Dept. of (Toland Hall) [San Francisco]	1865	—	86
Connecticut			
Yale College, Med. Dept. of [New Haven]	1814	—	899
District of Columbia			
National Medical College, Med. Dept. of Columbian University [Washington]	1826	—	427
Georgetown University, Med. Dept. of [Washington]	1852	—	387
Howard University, Med. Dept. of [Washington]	1871	—	37
Georgia			
Medical College of Georgia [Augusta]	1833	—	1278
Savannah Medical College [Savannah]	1854	—	140
Atlanta Medical College [Atlanta]	1855	—	560
Oglethorpe Medical College [Savannah]	1856	1861	86
Illinois			
Rush Medical College, Med. Dept. of University of Chicago [Chicago]	1844	—	1786
Illinois College, Med. Dept. of [Jacksonville]	1848	1848	39
Rock Island Medical School [Rock Island]	1849	1849	19
Chicago Medical College, Med. Dept. of Northwestern University [Chicago]	1860	—	481
Indiana			
Indiana Medical College, Med. Depart. of Laporte University [Laporte]	1842	1851	136
Medical College of Evansville [Evansville]	1850	—	74

Name	Year of First Graduation	Date of Cessation	Total No. of Graduates
Indiana Central Medical College [Indianapolis]	1850	1852	39
Indiana Medical College [Indianapolis]	1870	—	251
Indiana College of Physicians and Surgeons [Indianapolis]	1875	—	—
Iowa			
College of Physicians and Surgeons [Keokuk]	1850	—	777
Iowa State University, Med. Dept. of [Iowa City]	1871	—	111
Kentucky			
Transylvania University, Med. Dept. of [Lexington]	1818	1859	1860
University of Louisville, Med. Dept. of [Louisville]	1838	—	2395
Kentucky School of Medicine [Louisville]	1851	—	520
Louisville Medical College [Louisville]	1870	—	402
Hospital College of Medicine, Med. Dept. of Central University [Louisville]	1875	—	91
Louisiana			
University of Louisiana, Med. Dept. of [New Orleans]	1835	—	1703
New Orleans School of Medicine [New Orleans]	1857	1870	397
Charity Hospital Medical College of N. O. [New Orleans]	1876	—	10
Maine			
Bowdoin College and Med. School of Maine [Brunswick]	1821	—	1137
Maryland			
University of Maryland, Med. Dept. of [Baltimore]	1811	—	3104
Washington University, School of Medicine [Baltimore]	1828	—	680
College of Physicians and Surgeons [Baltimore]	1873	—	118
Massachusetts			
Harvard University, Med. Dept. of [Boston]	1785	—	2206
Berkshire Medical College, [Pittsfield]	1823	1867	1136
Michigan			
University of Michigan, Med. Dept. of [Ann Arbor]	1851	—	1405
Detroit Medical College [Detroit]	1869	—	204
Missouri			
Missouri Medical College [St. Louis]	1841	—	921
St. Louis Medical College [St. Louis]	1843	—	1293
Humboldt Medical College [St. Louis]	1867	1869	16
Kansas City College of Physicians and Surgeons	1870	—	46
St. Louis College of Physicians and Surgeons [St. Louis]	1870	1870	8
New Hampshire			
Dartmouth College, Medical School of [Hanover]	1798	—	1283
New York			
College of Physicians and Surgeons of the City of New York, Med. Dept. of Columbia College [N. Y. City]	1769	—	3179
College of Physicians and Surgeons of the Western District of New York [Fairfield]	1816	1840	585
Geneva College (Rutgers Med. Faculty) [N. Y. City]	1827	1830	104
Geneva Medical College [Geneva]	1835	1872	849
Albany Medical College [Albany]	1839	—	1287
University of the City of New York, Medical Dept. of [N. Y. City]	1842	—	3393
University of Buffalo, Med. Dept. of [Buffalo]	1847	—	848

Name	Year of First Graduation	Date of Cessation	Total No. of Graduates
New York Medical College and Charity Hospital [N. Y. City]	1851	1864	310
Long Island College Hospital [Brooklyn]	1860	—	531
Bellevue Hospital Medical College [N. Y. City]	1862	—	1908
College of Medicine of Syracuse University [Syracuse]	1873	—	26
Ohio			
Medical College of Ohio [Cincinnati]	1821	—	2170
Cincinnati College, Med. Dept. of [Cincinnati]	1836	1839	95
Starling Medical College [Columbus]	1836	—	887
Cleveland Medical College, Med. Dept. of Western Reserve College at Hudson [Cleveland]	1844	—	1162
Cincinnati College of Med. and Surgery [Cincinnati]	1852	—	760
Miami Medical College [Cincinnati]	1853	—	578
University of Wooster, Med. Dept. of [Cleveland]	1865	—	328
Oregon			
Willamette University, Med. Dept. of [Salem]	1867	—	63
Pennsylvania			
University of Pennsylvania, Med. Dept. of [Philadelphia]	1768	—	8845
College of Philadelphia [Philadelphia]	1790	1791	10
Jefferson Medical College [Philadelphia]	1826	—	6668
Pennsylvania College at Gettysburg, Med. Dept. of [Philadelphia]	1840	1861	769
Franklin Med. College of Philadelphia [Philadelphia]	1847	1849	25
Philadelphia College of Medicine [Philadelphia]	1847	1859	502
Rhode Island			
Brown University, Medical School of [Providence]	1814	1826	68
South Carolina			
Medical School of the State of South Carolina [Charleston]	1825	—	2439
University of South Carolina, Med. Dept. of [Columbia]	1868	—	26
Tennessee			
Memphis Medical College [Memphis]	1847	1873	231
University of Nashville, Med. Dept. of [Nashville]	1852	—	1741
Shelby Medical College [Nashville]	1859	1861	30
Vanderbilt University, Med. Dept. of [Nashville]	1875	—	75
Texas			
Galveston Medical College [Galveston]	1866	—	123
Texas Medical College and Hospital [Galveston]	1874	—	38
Vermont			
Castleton Medical College [Castleton]	1820	1861	1449
University of Vermont and State Agricultural College, Med. Dept. of [Burlington]	1823	—	573
Vermont Medical College [Woodstock]	1830	1860	575
Virginia			
University of Virginia, Med. Dept. of [Charlottesville]	1828	—	533
Medical College of Virginia [Richmond]	1839	—	947
Winchester Medical College [Winchester]	1846	1862	75
Total			73,588

If we take the number of graduates by decades of years during the present century, the result is as follows:—

Years	Graduates No. of	Years	Graduates No. of
1769–1799	221	1840–1849	11,828
1800–1809	343	1850–1859	17,213
1810–1819	1,375	1860–1869	16,717
1820–1829	4,338	1870–1876	14,704
1830–1839	6,849		

The first medical school in this country was established by Drs. John Morgan and William Shippen at Philadelphia in 1765, and is now known as the Medical Department of the University of Pennsylvania. From its halls have graduated the majority of the distinguished medical writers, teachers, and practitioners of the United States, and the names of its professors have become household words.

Organized upon the plan of the Edinburgh Medical School, of which its founders were graduates, it has been the model and pattern by which all our medical colleges have been shaped. Its largest graduating class was in 1849, numbering 191. In the following year Professor Chapman resigned, and for the next ten years the Jefferson School graduated the greater number, reaching its maximum of 269 in 1854. The Jefferson Medical College was founded in 1824, under the charter of Jefferson College in Canonsburg, Pennsylvania. The first course of lectures was delivered in 1825–26, the Faculty being Drs. Eberle, McClellan, Rhees, Green, and Beattie. Numerous changes were made in professors, and its classes varied much in size until 1841, when all the chairs were vacated and refilled by Drs. Dunglison, J. K. Mitchell, Pancoast, R. M. Huston, Mütter, Meigs, and Bache. This Faculty continued until 1856, when Professor S. D. Gross succeeded Dr. Mütter. In 1857 Dr. T. B. Mitchell took the place of Dr. Huston, and in 1858 Dr. Dickson that of Dr. J. K. Mitchell.

The second medical school founded in this country was at New York, under the charter of King's College, in 1767. This school has had many vicissitudes, but is now in a flourishing condition, and known as the College of Physicians and Surgeons of the City of New York, being the Medical Department of Columbia College. Its largest graduating class was 110 in 1875.

The Medical Department of Harvard University was founded by Dr. John Warren in 1782. Its maximum class of graduates was 99 in 1866. Recently it has led the way in elevating the standard of medical education, by extending its curriculum to three years, establishing a graded course, and by having decided to institute a real examination into the preliminary education of its students. This has of course diminished its classes somewhat, but no one can doubt that the decision to aim at quality instead of quantity is a wise one, and will in the fulness of time receive its due reward.

The first medical school in the West was established in Lexington, Ky. So early as 1799 a Medical Department was added to Transylvania University, Dr. Samuel Brown being appointed the first professor. Various appointments in the Medical Faculty were made, and a few partial courses of lectures were delivered, but the first full course was not given until 1817, and the degree of M.D. was first conferred in 1818. The founders of the school were Drs. Dudley and Caldwell. Its period of greatest prosperity was from 1830 to 1837, at which last date a disruption took place, and a part of the Faculty removed to Louisville.

The Medical Department of the University of Louisville began as the Medical Institute, chartered in 1833. Nothing was accomplished, however, until the quarrel in the Transylvania School above referred to took place, when Dr. Caldwell enlisted in the cause of the Louisville School, and in 1837 succeeded in obtaining for it a grant of a square of ground, and money for buildings and apparatus. Lectures began the same year, the Faculty consisting of Drs. Caldwell, Cooke, and Yandell, from the Lexington School, and of Drs. Cobb, Henry Miller, and J. B. Flint. In 1839 Dr. Drake joined the School, and in the following year Dr. S. D. Gross took the place of Dr. Flint. In 1846, the School was transferred to the University, and in 1874 it had 123 graduates, its largest class.

In connection with these schools a special reference is due to Dr. Charles Caldwell, their principal promoter. He was of Irish descent, born in North Carolina in 1772; died 1853. After obtaining the best education which his native State could afford, he went to Philadelphia in 1792, and continued the study of medicine under Dr. Rush, passing his examination in 1794, and taking his diploma in 1796. During the next twenty years his pen was constantly busy with lectures, addresses, and controversial articles, many of which related to yellow fever. In 1819 he accepted an invitation to the Transylvania School, and from this time he gave his best energies to this institution, and subsequently to the Louisville School. He was one of the most voluminous writers which this country has produced, but he contributed little or nothing of permanent or scientific value to the literature of his profession, and the only work of his which is worth perusal to-day is his autobiography. His critical reviews, being dictated almost exclusively by personal prejudices, are in almost all cases samples of special pleading rather than true criticism, and characterized by their "smartness" rather than their justice.

In the South the Medical College of South Carolina, chartered in 1823, leads the way. The Medical College of Louisiana was incorporated in 1835,

and in 1845 became the Medical Department of the University of Louisiana. This school is remarkable as having received State aid to the amount
of $121,000.

In connection with the medical schools, notice should be taken of the
Medical Institute of Philadelphia, otherwise known as the Summer School,
which, in addition to furnishing instruction to students and supplementing
the winter course, was of very great value as a training school for Professors.
It was founded in 1817 by Dr. Chapman, and with it were connnected, from
time to time, Drs. Chapman, Horner, Dewees, Samuel Jackson, J. K.
Mitchell, John Bell, Hodge, Neill, Gibson, Gerhard, Norris, and Pepper.

The total number of graduates from our medical schools during the five
years ending July 1, 1875, was about 10,250, that is, a little over 2000 per
year; the number in 1875 being about 400 more than in 1871.

Dr. J. M. Toner estimated the average age of beginning practice to be
24½ years, of death 58 years, making an average of about 34 years practice
to each.[22]

Dr. S. E. Chaillé estimates that there are about 47,000 regular physicians
in the United States, being about one to every 700 of the population.[23]

Space is wanting for further details with regard to our medical schools.
That there are too many of them is a general complaint, the answer to
which is the same as that given above with regard to the like objection with
regard to medical journals, and which answer is of about the same value
in each case.

In attempting to estimate the quantity and value of the additions made
by the medical profession of this country to the world's stock of knowledge
of the laws of healthy and diseased action, and the means of modifying
these actions, it is very difficult to make generalizations which shall be at
once clear, comprehensive, and correct. This difficulty becomes an impossibility, if we are to speak of the education, mental characteristics, and
professional qualifications of the whole body of physicians of this, or any
other country, since only the most vague and indefinite statements will
hold good. We have had, and still have, a very few men who love science
for its own sake, whose chief pleasure is in original investigations, and to
whom the practice of their profession is mainly, or only, of interest as furnishing material for observation and comparison. Such men are to be
found for the most part only in large cities where libraries, hospitals, and
laboratories are available for their needs, although some of them have preferred the smaller towns and villages as fields of labour. The work of our

---

[22] Statistical Sketch, etc. Indiana Journ. of Med., 1873, vol. iv. p. 1.
[23] The Medical Colleges, etc. New Orleans Med. and Surg. Journ., 1874, vol. i. N. S.
p. 818.

physicians of this class has been for the most part fragmentary, and is found in scattered papers and essays which have been pointed out in preceding essays; but buds and flowers, rather than ripened fruit, are what we have to offer. Of the highest grade of this class we have thus far produced no specimens; the John Hunter, or Virchow, of the United States, has not yet given any sign of existence.

We have in our cities, great and small, a much larger class of physicians whose principal object is to obtain money, or rather the social position, pleasures, and power, which money only can bestow. They are clear-headed, shrewd, practical men, well educated, because "it pays," and for the same reason they take good care to be supplied with the best instruments, and the latest literature. Many of them take up specialties because the work is easier, and the hours of labour are more under their control than in general practice. They strive to become connected with hospitals and medical schools, not for the love of mental exertion, or of science for its own sake, but as a respectable means of advertising, and of obtaining consultations. They write and lecture to keep their names before the public, and they must do both well, or fall behind in the race. They have the greater part of the valuable practice, and their writings, which constitute the greater part of our medical literature, are respectable in quality, and eminently useful.

They are the patrons of medical literature, the active working members of municipal medical societies, the men who are usually accepted as the representatives of the profession, not only here, but in all civilized countries; they may be famous physicians and great surgeons in the usual sense of the words, and as such, and only as such, should they receive the honour which is justly their due. They work for the present, and they have their reward in their own generation.

There is another large class, whose defects in general culture and in knowledge of the latest improvements in medicine, have been much dwelt upon by those disposed to take gloomy views of the condition of medical education in this country. The preliminary education of these physicians was defective, in some cases from lack of desire for it, but in the great majority from lack of opportunity, and their work in the medical school was confined to so much memorizing of text-books as was necessary to secure a diploma. In the course of practice they gradually obtain from personal experience, sometimes of a disagreeable kind, a knowledge of therapeutics, which enables them to treat the majority of their cases as successfully, perhaps, as their brethren more learned in theory. Occasionally they contribute a paper to a journal, or a report to a medical society; but they would rather talk than write, and find it very difficult to explain how or why they have succeeded, being like many excellent cooks in this respect. They are honest, conscientious, hard-working men, who are inclined to place great weight on their experience, and to be rather contemptuous of what they call "book learning and theories." To them our medical literature is indebted for a few interesting observations, and valuable suggestions in therapeutics, but for the most part, their experience, being unrecorded, has but a local usefulness.

These three classes have been referred to simply for the purpose of calling attention to the fact that, in speaking of "the physicians of the United States," it is necessary to be careful. There are many other classes, and they shade into each other and into empiricism in many ways. In discussions upon this subject, it seems to be often assumed that all physicians should possess the same qualifications, and be educated to the same standard, which, in one respect, is like saying that they should all be six feet high, and in another, is like the army regulations, which prescribe the same ration and allowance of clothing for Maine and Florida, Alaska and Oregon. A young and energetic man who has spent six years in obtaining a University education, and four more in the study of medicine as it ought to be studied, that is to say, in preparing himself to study and investigate for the rest of his life, will not settle in certain districts. He has invested ten years' labour, and from five to ten thousand dollars, and a locality which will give him a maximum income of, perhaps, fifteen hundred dollars per annum will not be satisfactory, in part because the capital should bring a better interest, in part because he will have acquired tastes which will make his life unpleasant in such places. Yet these places must have physicians of some sort, and it is not clear as to how they are to be supplied, if some of the universal and extensive reforms in medical education which have been proposed were to be enforced.

Certainly the standard for admission and for graduation at almost all our medical schools is too low, and one-half, at least, of these schools have no sufficient reason for existence; but it is not probable that it would improve matters much to establish a uniform, which must, of course, be a minimum, standard.

Of the material aids and instruments required for the advancement of medical science, such as hospitals, libraries, and museums, we have obtained as much as could be expected. With the proper use of those we now possess will come the demand for, and the supply of, still better facilities for the work of the scholar and observer.

The defects in American medicine are much the same as those observed in other branches of science in this country, and to a great extent are due to the same causes.

Culture, to flourish, requires appreciation and sympathy, to such an extent, at least, that its utterances shall not seem to its audience as if in an unknown tongue.

We have no reason to boast, or to be ashamed of what we have thus far accomplished; it has been but a little while since we have been furnished with the means of investigation needed to give our observations that accuracy and precision which alone can entitle medicine to a place among the sciences properly so called; and we may begin the new century in the hope and belief that to us applies the bright side of the maxim of Cousin, "It is better to have a future than a past."

Medical Libraries in the United States

EXTENT OF MEDICAL LITERATURE—SEVERAL IMPORTANT COLLECTIONS—
CATALOGUING AND INDEXING—MEDICAL PERIODICAL LITERATURE—THESES
AND INAUGURAL ADDRESSES—FORMING A MEDICAL LIBRARY—ARRANGEMENT
OF PAMPHLETS—NECESSARY WORKS OF REFERENCE

It is proposed in the following sketch to give some account of the resources available to the medical scholar and writer in the United States in
the way of libraries which have been formed with reference to his special
wants, and to make some remarks on the formation and care of such collections.

Comparatively few persons have any idea of the amount of medical
literature in existence, or of its proper use and true value, and the result
is that the same ground is traversed over and over again. Cases are reported as unique and inexplicable which, when compared with accounts
of others buried in obscure periodicals or collections of observations, fall
into their proper place and both receive and give explanation. Old theories
and hypotheses, evolved from the depths of the inner consciousness of men
too zealous or too indolent to undergo the labor of examining the works
of their predecessors, re-appear, and are re-exploded with the regular pe-
riodicity of organic life; and even when literary research is attempted, it
is too often either for controversial purposes, to serve the ends of prejudiced
criticism, or to support a charge of plagiarism, or else for the purpose of
obtaining a goodly array of foot-notes, which shall imply that the subject
is exhausted, and give a flavor of erudition to the work. This state of things
is by no means peculiar to medicine, but its literature is certainly an excellent illustration of the maxim "The thing which has been is that which
shall be, and there is no new thing under the sun."

The record of the researches, experiences, and speculations relating to
medical science during the last four hundred years is contained in between two and three hundred thousand volumes and pamphlets; and while
the immense majority of these have little or nothing of what we call
"practical value," yet there is no one of them which would not be called
for by some inquirer if he knew of its existence.

Hence, it is desirable, in this branch of literature, as in others, that in
each country there should be at least one collection embracing everything

---

Chapter VI, *Public libraries in the United States of America; their history, condition,
and management.* (U.S. Department of the Interior. Bureau of Education.) Washington,
1876. Part I. pp. 171–82.

that is too costly, too ephemeral, or of too little interest to be obtained and preserved in private libraries.

When the great work of Mr. Caxton, the History of Human Error, is written, the medical section will be among the most instructive and important, and also that for which it will be most difficult to obtain the data.

There are a number of valuable private medical libraries in this country of from four to ten thousand volumes each. Having been collected for the most part with reference to some special subject or department, they are the more valuable on that account. The majority of the medical schools also have libraries of greater or less value to the student.[1]

The collections relating to medicine and the cognate sciences, which are available to the public and are of sufficient interest to require notice in this connection, are those of Boston, Philadelphia, New York, Cincinnati, and Washington. No one of these indeed approaches completeness, but each supplements the other to such an extent that it seldom happens that bibliographical inquiries cannot be answered by referring to them in succession.

MEDICAL LIBRARIES IN BOSTON

The principal medical collection in Boston is that of the Boston Public Library, which now comprises about 11,000 volumes, for the most part standard works and periodicals, the latter containing files of the principal American and foreign publications. There is no separate printed catalogue of the medical section nor of any of the medical libraries of Boston, which fact much impairs their practical usefulness.

The Boston Athenæum has about 5,000 volumes of medical works. The Boston Society for Medical Improvement has 1,000 volumes of bound periodicals. The Treadwell Medical Library at the Massachusetts General Hospital contains about 3,542 volumes. Harvard University Library, including the library of the medical school, has between 5,000 and 6,000 volumes of medicine, including some of much rarity and value.

A collection which gives promise of much usefulness is that of the Boston Medical Library Association, which, although only about a year old, already contains about 3,000 volumes and receives the most important medical periodicals.

If the resources of Boston and vicinity in the way of medical literature available to the student could be shown by a good catalogue indicating where each of the several works may be found, the practical working value of the collections would be greatly enhanced. The difficulties in the way of

---

[1] For statistics of the principal libraries of medical schools and societies, see table at the end of this article.—EDITORS.

accomplishing such a desirable result, although great, do not appear to be at all insuperable, and might be readily overcome by the conjoint action of the medical societies and of the libraries interested. The same remark will apply to the medical collections of New York and Philadelphia.

MEDICAL LIBRARIES IN NEW YORK

The library of the New York Hospital is the oldest and largest collection in the city, and now contains about 10,000 volumes. It is well housed in a building which although not fire proof is comparatively so. The books are conveniently arranged, and there is room for twice the present number. It receives about 100 current periodicals, but with this exception does not contain much recent literature. An alphabetical catalogue of authors was published in 1845; three supplementary catalogues have since been printed, and a fourth is now in the press. The one published in 1865 is a list of the donation of Dr. John Watson, consisting of 481 volumes of rare and valuable books. This library is for consultation and reference only, as no books are loaned, and is open daily, except Sunday, from 9 a. m. to 10 p. m.

The collection of the New York Medical Library and Journal Association now contains about 3,500 volumes, and is mainly valuable for its collection of periodical literature. It receives about 95 current journals. No catalogue of this collection has been printed.

The Mott Memorial Library is free and numbers 4,700 volumes.[2]

The Academy of Medicine of New York City has recently taken steps to purchase a building, with the intention of forming a library which shall meet the requirements of so important a medical centre as New York, and valuable aid to this end from private collections is promised, notably from the library of Dr. S. S. Purple, which is remarkably complete in American medical periodicals and in early American medical literature. A large, well appointed, and well sustained medical library is much needed in the city of New York, and it is to be hoped that the effort referred to will be crowned with success. The library at present numbers 3,000 volumes.[3]

---

[2] This library was founded by the widow of the eminent surgeon, Valentine Mott, M.D., and is free for consultation and study to medical students and members of the profession. Additions to the collection are made annually by Mrs. Mott and her son; the latter manages its affairs. It has no permanent fund for its increase.—EDITORS.

[3] The Medico-Legal Society of New York, organized in November, 1872, began in 1873 the formation of a special library. The following is taken from a circular published by the president of the society in October, 1875:

"The Medico-Legal Society of New York has voluntarily assumed the labor of organizing and maintaining a complete library of all accessible works upon medical jurisprudence—especially in the English, French, and German tongues.

"There is not at the present time any notable collection of such works in the United

MEDICAL LIBRARIES IN PHILADELPHIA

The medical libraries of Philadelphia are large and valuable, and an interesting account of their history and condition is given by Dr. Richard Dunglison.[4]

The library of the College of Physicians has received large additions within the last few years, and is now the most valuable working collection in the country, with the exception of that in Washington. It numbers more than 19,000 volumes, receives about 80 current journals, and is rich in the early medical literature of this country. It is a reference and consultation library to the public, and loans books to the members of the college. It is much to be regretted that it has no printed catalogue nor a catalogue of subjects in any form. It has about 5,000 volumes of medical journals.

The Library of the Pennsylvania Hospital, numbering 12,500 volumes, is the oldest medical collection in this country, having been begun in 1763. The last printed catalogue, issued in 1857, is a classed catalogue with an index of authors, on the plan of the catalogue of the Library of the Medical Society of Edinburgh, and is a valuable work for reference, which should be in every public medical library. A supplement to it was issued in 1867.

According to Dr. Dunglison, there is a remarkable absence of duplication between this collection and that of the College of Physicians, and together they well represent the early medical literature of this country, especially of Philadelphia imprints.

States. The great law libraries in the city and State of New York, and indeed in the United States, have only a few standard works of this character, and there is no reason to suppose any change is likely to occur presently in this regard. The medical libraries of the nation are nearly as poor as are the law libraries in works upon medical jurisprudence.

"The society, by a general resolution unanimously adopted, voluntarily assumed the obligation on the part of each of its members, of contributing one volume per annum to this library. A membership, which has grown from a small list to upwards of four hundred in three years, and which bids fair to be the strongest, numerically, of any of the kindred societies, makes this means alone likely, in time, to furnish a collection of great value. Liberal contributions of money have also been made by individual members, which have been invested in volumes, obtained by correspondence with all the dealers and most of the librarians of such works throughout the world.

"A catalogue of the names of all works ever published on these subjects is in course of preparation by members of the society, and is now far advanced towards completion."

The annual reports of the society show that up to November, 1875, the contributions to the library had been 390 bound volumes, 121 pamphlets, besides $198 for the purchase of books.—EDITORS.

⁴ Philadelphia Medical Times. Reprinted, 46 pp. 8°. Philadelphia: J. B. Lippincott & Co., 1871.

Since the Medical Department of the University of Pennsylvania has occupied its new buildings in West Philadelphia, a valuable foundation for a medical library, consisting of about 3,000 volumes, has been presented to it by Dr. Alfred Stillé, provost of the university.[5]

MEDICAL LIBRARIES IN CINCINNATI

In Cincinnati there is a small but valuable collection of medical books at the City Hospital. The Mussey Medical and Scientific Library contains about 4,000 volumes and 2,000 pamphlets, and is at present a special deposit in the Cincinnati Public Library.

MEDICAL LIBRARY IN WASHINGTON

The Library of the Surgeon-General's Office is deposited in the Army Medical Museum at Washington, but may be considered as the medical section of the Congressional, or National Library, and is managed and catalogued in substantially the same manner as that collection. It now numbers about 40,000 volumes and 40,000 pamphlets, or, to state it in another form, about 70,000 titles. The library is intended to cover the entire field of medical and surgical literature, and is now an excellent foundation for a national medical library that shall be worthy of the name, and put the writers and teachers of this country on an equality with those of Europe so far as accessibility to the literature of the subject is concerned.

It has been formed within the last twelve years, and is of course too young to contain many of the incunabula or the books noted as rare and very rare, which are the delight of the bibliomaniac; nor, indeed, has any special effort been made to obtain such. Yet there are few of the ancient authors whose works it does not possess, although not always in the most desirable editions. It is comparatively full in American, English, French, and German medical literature of the present century, and in works relating to surgery, pathological anatomy, and hygiene. Of the early medical literature of this country, that is, prior to 1800, it has but little. It possesses a few valuable manuscripts, the oldest of which is a fine copy of the Lilium Medicinæ of Bernard de Gordon, dated 1349.[6]

---

[5] This library is thus characterized by the generous donor: "The collection comprises upwards of 3,000 volumes, including a considerable number of pamphlets. The bulk of the library consists of American, English, French, and German periodicals. The other works are in English, French, and German, and are chiefly medical as distinguished from surgical."—EDITORS.

[6] There are libraries belonging to several schools in which the Eclectic and Homeopathic theories of medicine are taught, the only one of the former reported being that of Bennett Medical College at Chicago, containing 500 volumes; and the largest of the latter class that of the Hahnemann Medical College at Philadelphia, which numbers 2,000 volumes. The American periodical literature of neither of these schools is exten-

CATALOGUING AND INDEXING

For the benefit of those who are not familiar with the practical workings of a large library, and who, therefore, do not appreciate the amount of time and labor involved, the following account is given. It will give no information to the skilled librarian, who will see at once many defects in the mode of recording—due in this case to the lack of clerical force.

The working catalogue of this library is a card catalogue of the usual form; that is, each separate work, whether it be a pamphlet of two leaves or a cyclopædia of fifty volumes, is catalogued on a slip of stout paper about 7 by 5 inches, giving under the name of the author the exact title of the work, the place and date of publication and the collation, that is, the number of pages or leaves, the size or form of the book, and the number of plates or tables. These cards are arranged in drawers, according to names of authors in dictionary order, anonymous works forming a separate class.

---

sive. The following statement is from the pen of the dean of the faculty of the Eclectic Medical Institute at Cincinnati, also editor of the Eclectic Medical Journal. He thus sketches the history of the library of the institute:

"Beginning in 1845, it was deemed an important object to secure a good medical library of books, both new and old, and as a nucleus of such, a private library was purchased, at a cost of $1,500. It was a singular collection of books, both old and rare, and yet, with a few exceptions, it was wholly worthless for the uses of the medical student. The antiquary who desired to unearth old theories and crude methods of treatment would have been delighted with it. To this were added, from time to time, works of the present generation until, in 1853, some 3,000 volumes had been collected, when, the library room being required for enlargement of the college halls, the books were stored in a small room, and the college was without a library for five years. In 1858 changes in the building were again made, and the books were dusted, some of them rebound, numbered, and catalogued, and made ready for use. But still the students were not inclined to use them, even with the aid of a nicely carpeted, lighted, and heated reading room, and, after two winters of disuse, the dust was allowed to accumulate on the books, and they rested in peace until the fire of 1870, when they were fortunately consumed.

"While thus somewhat unfortunate in our general library, we have to record marked benefit from a collection of books of a different character. In a medical college there are often spare moments between lectures that students might improve, if books were at hand; and quite frequently study would be much facilitated if reference could be made to a standard authority, even for a moment. Often some important fact will have escaped the learner's mind, which, could he recall it, would make an entire subject plain and enable him to meet a coming examination. A moment's reference to an authority between lectures is sufficient, while without it there might be complete failure. Frequently an entire train of thought is arrested by the want of a single fact which is an initial point; the struggle of the mind to recall this fact is frequently sufficient to incapacitate it for the day.

"A reading room furnished with several sets of the latest text books for reference was provided, and with most satisfactory results. The books were in constant use.

"I believe that these working libraries are to be commended in all higher schools."— Editors.

From these cards was printed the catalogue of authors, which was completed in 1873, and makes two volumes, royal octavo, of about 1,200 pages each, with a supplementary volume containing the anonymous works, reports, periodicals, and transactions. The cards from which this was printed were then distributed according to subjects, the subjects being arranged in dictionary order. This forms the subject catalogue. As new books were added a second card catalogue was carried on for them, which is known as the supplementary catalogue.

The subject catalogue above referred to has been very greatly extended by a process of indexing original papers in medical periodicals and transactions. The preparation of this index was begun January 1, 1874, since which date every number of current foreign medical journals and transactions has been indexed as soon as received. When a number of the London Lancet, for instance, is received, the librarian indicates in it by a slight pencil check the articles which should be indexed. The journal is then handed to a clerk who indexes each article checked upon one of the catalogue cards. The top line is left blank for the subject. Next is given the name of the author, the title of the article, literally transcribed, or if there be no title, one is made for it, and finally the abbreviated title of the journal, the year, the number of the volume, and the pagination. This mode of indexing is on the plan pursued in the Catalogue of Scientific Papers, 1800–1863, compiled and published in six quarto volumes by the Royal Society of London. The number of the journal, with the cards thus prepared, is returned to the librarian, who indicates in pencil the subject under which each card should be distributed, and the cards go to the subject catalogue. The journal receives a red stamp showing that it has been indexed, is checked off on the register of periodicals received, and goes to the files.

At first only foreign journals were thus indexed, it being known that Dr. J. M. Toner, of Washington, was preparing an index of American journals, which it is his intention to make complete to the year 1876. Upon inquiry, however, the work of Dr. Toner was found to be on a very different plan, as it includes all articles, whether original or copied, while on the other hand the titles of articles are much abbreviated.

It has therefore been thought best to index all journals, American and foreign, beginning with January 1, 1875. At the same time as much as possible is being done to index preceding volumes of important journals and transactions, of which about 1,000 volumes were indexed during the past year. This work will be continued as rapidly as possible. The statistics shown in Table I are the total number of what may be called regular medical journals which have been established since the first, namely, Les Nouvelles Découvertes sur toutes les parties de la Médecine, Paris, 1679,

TABLE I

	Number Begun	Number of Volumes Published	Number That Did Not Get Beyond the First Volume	Number Represented in the Library	Volumes Represented in the Library	Current Number January 1, 1875
British America	19	50	6	18	49	6
United States	214	1,320	66	209	1,259	53
Mexico	6	11	—	2	10	1
West Indies and South America	10	56	—	7	19	1
Belgium	29	343	4	10	309	5
France and Algeria	193	2,684	11	91	1,846	58
Germany and Austria	386	3,280	95	208	2,504	47
Great Britain	112	1,327	14	80	1,129	23
Greece	2	13	—	—	—	—
Holland	30	200	5	11	97	2
Italy	65	671	9	31	527	41
Japan	—	—	—	—	—	1
Russia	12	168	2	8	87	2
Spain and Portugal	31	191	1	8	15	6
Sweden, Norway, and Denmark	20	289	3	19	260	6
Switzerland	16	114	2	10	84	1
Syria	1	1	—	1	1	—
Turkey	1	18	—	1	18	1
Total	1,147	10,736	218	714	8,214	254

as well as the time and labor which the making of such an index will require.

From this table it will be seen that the library now contains about 75 per cent. of all that has been published in medical journals. It would not probably be desirable to extend an index of these farther back than 1800, as the works of Ploucquet and Reuss fairly cover all medical periodical literature of any importance prior to that date. A few of the journals will be very difficult, if not impossible, to obtain; but these will be for the most part of little practical importance. Several medical officers of the Army, whose stations made it possible to send sets of journals to them without too much inconvenience, have assisted in the work, and if this aid can be continued, it is hoped that the index will be completed in about two years. There is little doubt that it will then be printed, and it will form a valuable contribution to medical bibliography.

Such an index is proposed in the preface to the Catalogue Raisonné of the Medical Society of Edinburgh, published in 1836, but Professor Maclagan states that nothing has been done in this direction.[7]

The important part of a medical library, that which will give it character and value, and for deficiency in which nothing can compensate, is its file of medical journals and transactions. The difficulty of obtaining and preserving these is in proportion to the importance of the matter. The majority of them are essentially ephemeral in character; small editions are published; they are rarely preserved with care, and even when attempts are made to preserve them by binding, it is often, and indeed usually, without sufficient attention to the collation, so that in examining files of old journals it will be found that at least one-half lack a leaf, a signature, or a number. This fact causes much trouble and disappointment to the librarian, and must always be kept in view in the collection of this class of literature. In the attempt to make a complete collection of American medical journals for this library, it has been repeatedly found that what purported to be the volume or number wanting to complete a file was defective. It is probable that there is not a complete collection in existence at any one point, although there are two public and at least three private collections in this country which are very full, those of the library of the Surgeon General's Office; of the College of Physicians, of Philadelphia; of Dr. Toner, of Washington; of Dr. Hays, of Philadelphia, and of Dr. Purple, of New York.

The rarest American medical journals are probably some of those printed in the West and South; for instance, the Ohio Medical Repository (1826–'27) and the Confederate States Medical and Surgical Journal (1864–'65).

Another class of medical literature which is important to the librarian, and the value of which is usually underestimated, consists of medical theses and inaugural dissertations. To obtain complete series of these is even more difficult than to get journals, for the reason that they are more ephemeral, and because it is scarcely possible to ascertain what have been published, or when the series may be considered complete. For a few schools, lists have been published of the theses presented by their graduates, such as Paris and Edinburgh, but even for Edinburgh, the only catalogue of the theses which the writer has been able to obtain, does not show when the regular printing of all theses ceased. Callisen has been led into error in this way in his otherwise very complete Bibliographical Lexicon, in which he gives the titles of many theses which were never printed, notably of the Universities of Pennsylvania and Transylvania. The value of these theses is fourfold. As material for the history of medicine they may be taken to represent the theories and teaching of the school; they often contain re-

---

[7] Edinburgh Medical Journal, January, 1873, p. 585.

ports of cases, or accounts of investigations made by the student under the direction of a professor, which are of much value, and they are necessary to medical biography, the more so as in most of the German universities a sketch of the life of the candidate is appended to the thesis. In addition to this, prior to the era of medical journalism, it was the custom for the president or one of the professors to add an introduction of ten or twelve pages to the dissertation, treating on some subject usually having no direct relation to the thesis, and forming the sort of paper which would now be sent to a medical journal. The number of these theses in existence is very great; there are in the Library of the Surgeon-General's Office about 40,000.

A few words of advice to those who may be desirous of forming a public medical library in connection with a medical school may be of some use; at all events, they are the result of practical experience. The first thing is to obtain works of medical bibliography, and a list of a few which will be found the most useful is appended. In addition to these it will be necessary to make arrangements to obtain regularly as published the catalogues of medical books issued or furnished by the following booksellers:

In Boston, Schœnhof & Mœller, James Campbell; in New York City, Wm. Wood & Co., L. W. Schmidt, B. Westermann & Co., E. Steiger, Stechert & Wolff, F. W. Christern; in Philadelphia, H. C. Lea, Lindsay & Blakiston.

The next thing is to take steps to obtain the current medical periodicals as completely as possible, and also the current ephemeral pamphlets, such as reports of hospitals and asylums, boards of health and health officers, transactions of medical societies, addresses, etc. These things, as a rule, cannot be purchased, and while they may usually be had for the asking at the time of their publication, it will be found very difficult, if not impossible, to get them after a few years, or it may be only a few months, have elapsed.

With regard to the purchase of books, so much depends on the amount of funds available that no general advice can be given. The majority of large works, of which there is little danger that the supply will be exhausted for several years, should not as a rule be purchased at the time of their publication, unless they are wanted for immediate use. In a year or two they can be obtained at a much reduced price. It will often be good economy to buy a lot of books in bulk, even although a number of duplicates be thus obtained, and this is especially the case at the commencement of the formation of a collection. On a small scale the same rule applies to the purchase of bound volumes of pamphlets. All duplicates should be preserved for purposes of exchange. It may seem hardly worth the trouble to preserve what most physicians would throw at once into the waste-basket, but unless this is done the library will never be a success. There need be no special haste about the disposal of duplicates, as they increase in value with age.

PAMPHLETS

The pamphlets in the Library of the Surgeon-General's Office have been disposed of in three ways: First, there are 760 volumes of bound pamphlets, mostly purchased in that condition, which are for the most part classified according to subjects; these volumes are numbered consecutively. Second, about 2,000 pamphlets are bound in separate volumes. These are numbered as single volumes, and include those which are considered rare or especially valuable. The remainder of the pamphlets, including the majority of the inaugural dissertations of the German universities, are kept in file-boxes. These boxes are made of walnut, and the pamphlets stand in them with their title-pages looking toward the back of the shelf, the boxes being of widths suitable for octavos, quartos, etc. The box has no top, and the rear end slides in and out, and can be fixed at any point. Each box will hold about 100 pamphlets.

The boxes are arranged on shelves suited to their height, thus preventing the admission of dust. The front of the box has a ring, by which it can be pulled out, and presents an ample surface for labeling its contents. By loosening the rear end, which can be done by a touch, and withdrawing it, the title of the work is before the examiner, and a pamphlet can be added or withdrawn without disturbing the others. When a pamphlet is required for use it is bound temporarily in stout covers, the backs of which are pressed together by a strong spring. These covers have an enameled card on the side, on which is written in pencil the title of the pamphlet within. This can be readily erased to make room for the next.

The theses of the schools of Paris, Montpellier, and Strasbourg are bound in volumes, following the usual arrangement for those schools.

With regard to binding, it is believed that the advice of the Librarian of Congress is the best that can be given: "Bind in half turkey, and in most cases let the color be a bright red." Binding in calf should not be used, except to match what has already been so bound. The binding in of covers and advertisements is an important point, and gives increased value to a volume so bound; indeed, it is sometimes impossible to collate serial publications without the assistance of the covers.

Following is a list of works which will be found especially useful for reference in medical bibliographical work, and which should be in every medical library. For additional titles consult Pauly, *infra*, pp. 1 to 15.

Allibone, S. A. A critical dictionary of English literature and British and American authors. 3 v. Roy. 8°. Phila., 1863–'71.
Atkinson, J. Medical bibliography. 8°. London, 1834.

Brunet, J. C. Manuel du libraire et de l'amateur de livres. 5me éd. 6 v. Roy. 8°. Paris, 1860–'65.

Callisen, A. C. P. Medicinisches Schriftsteller Lexicon der jetzt lebenden Ärzte, Wundärzte, Geburtshelfer, Apotheker, und Naturforscher aller gebildeten Völker. 33 v. 8°. Copenhagen, 1830–'45.

Haller, A. v. Bibliotheca anatomica. 2 v. 4°. Tiguri, 1774–'77.

—Bibliotheca chirurgica. 2 v. 4°. Bernæ, 1774–'75.

—Bibliotheca medicinæ practicæ. 4 v. 4°. Basiliæ et Bernæ, 1776–'88.

Pauly, A. Bibliographie des sciences médicales. 8°. Paris, 1872–'74.

Ploucquet, W. G. Literatura medica digesta; sive, Repertorium medicinæ practicæ, chirurgiæ atque rei obstetricæ. 4 v. 4°. Tubingæ, 1808–9.

Roy, C. H. à. Catalogus bibliothecæ medicæ. 5 v. 8°. Amst., 1830.

Watt, R. Bibliotheca Britannica; or a general index to British and foreign literature. 4 v. 4°. Edinburgh, 1824.

Catalogue raisonné of the Medical Library of the Pennsylvania Hospital, by Emil. Fischer. xxvi, 750 pp. 8°. Philadelphia, 1857.

Catalogue of the library of the New York Hospital, arranged alphabetically and analytically. 194 pp. 8°. New York, 1845. [With supplements to the same published in 1861, 1865, and 1867.]

Catalogue of the library of the Surgeon-General's Office, United States Army, with an alphabetical index of subjects. 2 p. l., 454 pp. Roy. 8°. Washington, D.C., 1872.

Catalogue of the library of the Surgeon-General's Office, United States Army. 3 v. Roy. 8°. Washington, 1873–'74.

Classed catalogue of the library of the Royal College of Surgeons of London. lxii, 1171 pp. 8°. London, 1843.

Catalogue of the Royal Medical and Chirurgical Society of London. vii, 762 pp. 8°. London, 1856.

Index to the above. vii, 293 pp. 8°. London, 1860.

Bibliothèque impériale, départment des imprimés. Catalogue des sciences médicales. Vols. 1 and 2. iii, 794 pp., 1 l.; 778 pp., 1 l. Imp. 4°. Paris, 1857 and 1873.

Rozier, Victor. Essai d'une bibliographie universelle de la médecine, de la chirurgie, et de la pharmacie militaires. 234 pp. 8°. Paris, 1862.

Dictionnaire des sciences médicales; biographie médicale. [Par A. J. L. Joardan.] 7 v. 8°. Paris, C. L. F. Panckoucke, 1820–'25.

Reuss, J. D. Repertorium commentationum a societatibus litterariis editarum. Tomes X–XV. Scientia et ars medica et chirurgica. 6 v. 4°. Gottingæ, 1813–'20.

Englemann, Wm. Bibliotheca medico chirurgica et anatomico-physiologica. Alphabetisches Verzeichniss der medicinischen. . . . Bücher welche vom Jahre 1750 bis 1847 in Deutschland erschienen sind. 734 pp. 8°. Supplement Heft 1848–'67. 350 pp. 8°. Leipzig, 1848–'68.

Catalogue of scientific papers, (1800–1863.) Compiled and published by the Royal Society of London. 6 v. 4°. London, 1867–'72.

TABLE OF THE PRINCIPAL MEDICAL LIBRARIES IN THE UNITED STATES

[For further information respecting the following and other medical libraries in the United States see general table of statistics elsewhere in this report.]

Place	Name	Date of Origin	Number of Volumes
Connecticut			
New Haven	Medical Institution of Yale College	1812	2,200
Dist. of Columbia			
Washington	Surgeon-General's Office, United States Army	1865	40,000ᵃ
Georgia			
Augusta	Medical College of Georgia	1831	5,000
Savannah	Savannah Medical College	1853	4,000
Illinois			
Chicago	Chicago College of Pharmacy	1859	2,500
Kentucky			
Lexington	Transylvania Medical College of Kentucky University	—	5,383
Louisville	University of Louisville, Medical Department	1837	4,000
Louisiana			
New Orleans	University of Louisiana, Medical Department	1834	2,000
Maine			
Brunswick	Medical School of Maine	1820	4,000
Massachusetts			
Boston	Harvard University Medical School	1782	3,530
Boston	Medical Library Association of Boston	1875	2,500
Boston	Treadwell Library, Massachusetts General Hospital	1857	3,542
Salem	Essex South District Medical Society	1805	2,000
Worcester	Worcester District Medical Society	1798	4,000
New York			
Albany	Albany Medical College	1839	4,800
New York	Academy of Medicine	1846	3,000
New York	Medical Library and Journal Association	1864	3,500
New York	Mott Memorial Free Medical and Surgical Library	1867	4,700
New York	New York Hospital	1796	10,000
Syracuse	College of Physicians and Surgeons	1872	2,000
Utica	New York State Lunatic Asylum	1814	4,358
Ohio			
Cincinnati	Cincinnati Hospital	1870	2,119
Cincinnati	Medical College of Ohio	1819	5,000
Cleveland	Cleveland Medical College	1843	2,000

TABLE OF THE PRINCIPAL MEDICAL LIBRARIES IN THE UNITED STATES—*Continued*

Place	Name	Date of Origin	Number of Volumes
Pennsylvania			
Philadelphia	College of Physicians	1789	18,753
Philadelphia	Hahnemann Medical College	1867	2,000
Philadelphia	Pennsylvania Hospital	1763	12,500
Philadelphia	Philadelphia College of Pharmacy	1821	2,350
Philadelphia	University of Pennsylvania, Medical Department	1765	3,000
Rhode Island			
Providence	Rhode Island Hospital	1868	2,000

 a The library contains in addition to the bound volumes, a collection of 40,000 pamphlets relating to medicine and surgery.

The Medical Journals of the United States

The Boston Medical and Surgical Journal has now been issued for fifty years, and it is thought that some account of the medical journals which have appeared in this country to the present time will form a fitting and useful introduction to what it is hoped will prove to be the second half century of its existence.

The first number of this journal is dated February 19, 1828, and formed the continuation and consolidation of the *New England Journal of Medicine and Surgery* and the *Boston Medical Intelligencer,* the particulars with regard to which will be found in the list to be given at the end of these remarks.

The first editors of this journal were Drs. J. C. Warren, W. Channing, and John Ware. After these came Dr. Chandler Robbins and Dr. James Wilson, and in Vol. XI., 1835, the name of Dr. J. V. C. Smith appears on the title-page (Ms. note of Dr. B. E. Cotting), the publication of the journal at the same time passing into the hands of Mr. D. Clapp as publisher.

At the time of its commencement there were in existence in the United States eight medical journals, namely: in Philadelphia, *The American Journal of the Medical Sciences, The American Medical Recorder, The Monthly Journal of Foreign Medicine, The North American Medical and Surgical Journal,* and *The Philadelphia Monthly Journal of Medicine and Surgery* (which ceased February 28, 1828); in New York, *The New York Medical and Physical Journal;* in Cincinnati, *The Western Medical and Physical Journal;* and in Lexington, Ky., the *Transylvania Journal of Medicine and the Associate Sciences.*

Prior to this time thirty-one medical journals had been commenced in the United States, twenty-three of which had suspended or merged in other journals.

Table 1 shows by quinquennial periods the number of medical journals which have commenced and ceased in this country, excluding those devoted to pharmacy and dentistry.

The mortality statistics of our medical journals as shown in Table 2 will be found interesting.

Tables 1 and 2, if examined in connection with the following list

Boston Medical and Surgical Journal 100: 1–14 (January 2, 1879) An errata note, published in the same journal, issue of January 16, 1879 (v. 100, p. 108), has here been incorporated.

TABLE 1

Years, Both Inclusive	Regular		Homoeopathic		Botanic		Eclectic	
	Begun	Closed	Begun	Closed	Begun	Closed	Begun	Closed
1797–1802	2							
1803–1807	2							
1808–1812	6	5						
1813–1817	1							
1818–1822	7	2						
1823–1827	13	14						
1828–1832	11	14			1			
1833–1837	12	10			7	2	1	
1838–1842	12	14	3	2	6	5		
1843–1847	17	5	3	1	3	6	4	2
1848–1852	21	7	10	5	1	2	4	4
1853–1857	21	27	4	10	1	3	5	8
1858–1862	32	35	5	5		1	5	4
1863–1867	18	15	13	4			5	3
1868–1872	31	22	6	7			6	6
1873–1877	30	24	8	9			11	7
1878	13	2	1				1	1
Total	250	196	53	43	19	19	42	35

TABLE 2

	No. of Titles Commenced	No. of Vols. Commenced	Only One No. Issued	Vol. I Not Completed	No. That Did Not Go Beyond Vol. I	Not Beyond Vol. II	Current, November, 1878
Regular...............	247	1630	10	21	61	39	53
Homoeopathic.........	53	214	3	8	22	5	9
Botanic, etc...........	21	91		4	5	9	
Eclectic...............	41	169	6	6	17	5	7
Popular...............	124	431	20	22	71	12	8
Pharmaceutical........	25	167		3	9		8
Dental................	33	187	1	6	10	4	7
Reprints..............	13	198	1	1	4		2

of our medical journals as arranged by States, afford abundant material for comment and reflection, but it is believed that the limited space available can be more usefully employed in giving the list referred to than in pointing out the errors of those who are responsible for the existence of such a list. It is as useless to advise a man not to start a new journal as it is to advise him not to commit suicide.

As I have elsewhere remarked, the motive for the existence of the minor journals is not for direct profit, but as an indirect advertisement, or—and this is more common—the desire to have a place in which the editor can speak his mind and attack his enemies without restraint. How shall the would-be journalist be persuaded that no one except his personal acquaintances will care anything about his opinions, his praise, or his blame?

It will be found interesting to compare the geographical distribution of this class of publications, and to inquire why, for instance, Baltimore medical journals are so short-lived, why New England has produced so few in comparison with Ohio and Kentucky, etc., etc.

LIST OF MEDICAL JOURNALS OF THE UNITED STATES ARRANGED BY STATES

ARKANSAS.

The Arkansas Medical Record. Monthly. Conducted by J. I. Hale. Little Rock. Nos. 1–4, Vol. I. January to April, 1878. 8vo.

CALIFORNIA

The San Francisco Medical Journal. W. H. Miller, Editor. San Francisco. No. 1, Vol. I. January, 1856. 8vo.

The California State Medical Journal. Quarterly. J. F. Morse, Editor. Sacramento. Vol. I. July, 1856, to April, 1857. 8vo.

The Marysville Medical and Surgical Reporter. Quarterly. L. Hubbard and H. W. Teed, Editors. San Francisco. No. 1, Vol. I. November, 1858. 8vo.

The Pacific Medical and Surgical Journal. Monthly. Edited by J. B. Trask and others. San Francisco. Vols. I.–IX. 1858–67. New Series, Vols. I.–XI. 1867–78. 8vo. Current. In 1865 absorbed the following, and added the words "and Press" to its title.

The San Francisco Medical Press. Quarterly. Edited by E. S. Cowper. San Francisco. Vols. I.–IV. 1860–65. 8vo. Consolidated with the preceding.

The California Medical Gazette. Monthly. Edited by T. Bennett and others. San Francisco. Vols. I.–II. July, 1868, to August, 1870. 4to.

The Western Lancet. Monthly. Edited by E. Trenor and others. San Francisco. Vols. I.–VII. 1872–78. 8vo.

CONNECTICUT

The Monthly Journal of Medicine. Hartford. Conducted by an association of physicians. Vols. I.–VI. January, 1823, to December, 1825. 8vo.

The American Annals of the Deaf and Dumb. Quarterly. Edited by L. Ray and others. Hartford. Vols. I.–XXIII. 1847–61. Washington, D. C. 1868–78. 8vo.

The Quarterly Journal of Inebriety. Hartford. Vols. I.–II. 1876–78. 8vo.

DISTRICT OF COLUMBIA

The Register and Library of Medical and Chirurgical Science. Weekly. Edited by G. S. Pattison and J. Hagan. Washington. Vols. I.–II. 1833–36. 8vo. Vol. II. ends abruptly with page 440.

The National Medical Journal. Quarterly. Washington. Edited by C. C. Cox and others. Vols. I.–II. 1870–72. Became monthly in Vol. II. No. 10, Vol. II., last published.

National Medical Review. Walter S. Wells, Editor. Monthly. Vol. I. No. 1. December, 1878. Washington, D. C. 8vo.

GEORGIA

The Southern Medical and Surgical Journal. Monthly. Edited by M. Antony and J. A. Eve. Augusta. Vols. I.–III. 1836–39. New Series. Vols. I.– XVII. 1845–61. Third Series. Vol. I. 1866–67. 8vo.

The Georgia Blister and Critic. Monthly. Edited by H. A. Ramsay and W. T. Grant. Atlanta. Vol. I., and No. 1, Vol. II. 1854–55. 8vo.

Atlanta Medical and Surgical Journal. Monthly. Edited by J. P. Logan, W. F. Westmoreland, and others. Atlanta. Vols. I–XVII. 1855–61, 1866–78. 8vo.

The Oglethorpe Medical and Surgical Journal. Bi-Monthly. H. L. Boyd and others, Editors. Savannah. Vols. I.–III. 1858–61. 8vo.

The Savannah Journal of Medicine. Bi-Monthly. Edited by J. S. Sulli-van. R. D. Arnold, and others. Savannah. Vols. I.–IV. 1858–61. New Series, Vol. V. 1866. 8vo.

The Georgia Medical and Surgical Encyclopædia. Monthly. Edited by H. N. Hollifield and T. W. Newsome. Sandersville. Nos. 1–8, Vol. I. May to December, 1860. 8vo.

The Semi-Monthly Medical and Surgical Repertory. Edited by E. F. and J. J. Knott. Griffin, Ga. Nos. 1–4, Vol. I, 1871. 8vo.

The Georgia Medical Companion. Monthly. Edited by T. S. Powell and W. T. Goldsmith. Atlanta. Vols. I–II. 1871–72. 8vo. Continued as the fol-lowing.

The Southern Medical Record. Monthly. Atlanta. Vols. III.–VIII. 1873–78. 8vo. Continuation of preceding.

ILLINOIS

The Illinois Medical and Surgical Journal. Monthly. Edited by J. V. Z. Blaney. Chicago. Vols. I.–II. 1844–46. 8vo. Continued as the following.

The Illinois and Indiana Medical and Surgical Journal. Bi-Monthly. Edited by J. V. Z. Blaney, D. Brainard, and others. Chicago. Vols. I.–II. 1846–48. 8vo. Continuation of the preceding, and continued as the follow-ing.

The Northwestern Medical and Surgical Journal. Bi-Monthly. Edited by W. B. Herrick and J. Evans. Chicago. Vols. V.–XIV. 1848–57. 8vo. Continuation of the preceding, and continued as the following.

The Chicago Medical Journal. Monthly. Edited by N. S. Davis and W. H. Byford. Chicago. Vols. XV–XXXI. 1858–75. 8vo. Continuation of the preceding, and consolidated with the Medical Examiner, Chicago, forming the following. Vols. XXV. and XXVI. Semi-Monthly.

The Chicago Medical Journal and Examiner. Edited by W. H. Byford and others. Chicago. Vols. XXXII.–XXXVII. 1875–78. 8vo. Current. Formed by the consolidation of the preceding with the Chicago Medical Examiner.

The Northwestern Medical Intelligencer. Bi-Monthly. Chicago, 1851. 8vo. This alternated with the Northwestern Medical and Surgical Journal, of which it formed a part.

The Chicago Medical Examiner. Monthly. Edited by N. S. Davis, and E. A. Steele. Chicago. Vols. I.–XII. 1860–71. 8vo. Continued as the following.

The Medical Examiner. Chicago. Semi-Monthly. Edited by N. S. and F. H. Davis. Vols. XIII.–XVI. 1872–75. 4to. In September, 1875, united with The Chicago Medical Journal, forming The Chicago Medical Journal and Examiner.

The Military Tract Medical Reporter. L. S. and C. A. Lambert. Galesburg, Ill. Prospectus issued in August, 1871, but the journal never appeared.

The Chicago Journal of Nervous and Mental Disease. Edited by J. S. Jewell and others. Chicago. Vols. I.–II. 1874–75. 8vo. Continued as the following.

The Journal of Nervous and Mental Disease. Edited by J. S. Jewell and others. Chicago. Vols. I.–III., New Series. 1876–78. 8vo. Continuation of the preceding.

The Medical Register and Advertiser. Quarterly. Edited by J. I. Hale. Anna, Ill. Nos. 1–2, Vol. I. 1875. 8vo.

The Monthly Journal of the Southern Illinois Medical Association. Edited by C. W. Dunning and H. Wardner. Cairo. Vols. I.–II. 1877–78. Vol. I. in six numbers. Current.

The Illinois Medical Recorder. Monthly. Edited by R. E. Beach. Published under the auspices of the District Medical Society of Central Illinois. Nos. 1–6. June to November, 1878. 8vo. Current.

The American Medical Review and Index. Monthly. James I. Hale, Editor. Anna, Ill. Nos. 1–6. July to December, 1878. 8vo. Current.

INDIANA

The Indiana Medical Journal. Quarterly. Edited by W. H. Byford and H. Ronalds. Evansville. No. 1, Vol. I. 1854. 8vo. Running title of first signature is The Evansville Medical Journal, etc.

The Indiana Journal of Medicine and Surgery. Monthly. Edited by J. Jackson and T. W. Forshee. Madison. No. 1, Vol. I. 1855. 8vo.

The Indiana Journal of Medicine. Monthly. Edited by T. M. Stevens and others. Indianapolis. Vols. I.–VI. 1870–75. 8vo. After September, 1875, united with The Cincinnati Lancet and Observer.

The Western Retrospect of Medicine and Surgery. Monthly. Edited by H. M. Harvey, H. A. Lewis, and others. Evansville. Vol. I. January to December, 1872. 8vo.

IOWA

The Western Medico-Chirurgical Journal. Monthly. Edited by J. F. Sanford and S. G. Armor. Keokuk. Vols. I.–II. 1850–53, No. 1, Vol. III. 1854. 8vo.

The Iowa Medical Journal. Monthly. Edited by J. C. Hughes and W. R. Marsh. Keokuk. Five volumes. 1853–69. 8vo.

The Iowa Catlin. Monthly. Edited by E. Lawrence. Osceola, Iowa. Nos. 1 and 2. April and May, 1878. 8vo.

KANSAS

The Leavenworth Medical Herald. Monthly. Edited by C. A. Logan, T. Sinks, and others. Leavenworth. Vols. I.–III. 1867–70. 8vo. Continued as the following.

The Leavenworth Medical Herald and Journal of Pharmacy. Leavenworth. Vols. IV.–V. 1870–72. 8vo. Continuation of the preceding and succeeded by the following.

The Medical Herald. Leavenworth. Vols. VI.–IX. 1872–75. 8vo. Continuation of the preceding.

KENTUCKY

The Transylvania Journal of Medicine and the Associate Sciences. Quarterly. Edited by J. E. Cooke and C. W. Short. Lexington, Ky. Vols. I.–XII. 1828–39. 8vo.

The Louisville Journal of Medicine and Surgery. Quarterly. Edited by L. P. Yandell, H. Miller, and others. Louisville. Nos. 1 and 2, Vol. I, 1838. 8vo. January, 1840, revived, and consolidated with the Western Journal of the Medical and Physical Sciences, forming the following.

The Western Journal of Medicine and Surgery. Monthly. Edited by D. Drake and L. P. Yandell. Louisville. Thirty-two volumes. 1840–55. 8vo.

The Louisville Review. Monthly. Edited by S. D. Gross and T. G. Richardson. Louisville. Vol. I. 1856. 8vo. Continuation of the preceding. In January, 1857, united with The Medical Examiner, Philadelphia, forming the North American Medico-Chirurgical Review.

The Western and Southern Medical Recorder. Monthly. Edited by J. C. Cross. Lexington. Vol. I. 1841–42. Nos. 1–4. Vol. II. 1843. 8vo. Merged in the Western Lancet.

The Transylvania Medical Journal. Bi-Monthly. Edited by E. L. Dudley. Five volumes. 1849–54. Lexington and Louisville. Vol. III. is Vol. I. New Series. Title, The Kentucky Medical Recorder.

The Louisville Medical Gazette. Bi-Weekly. Edited by L. J. Frazee. Louisville. Nos. 1–7, Vol. I. 1859. 8vo.

The Semi-Monthly Medical News. Edited by S. M. Bemiss and J. W. Benson. Louisville. Vols. I.–III. 1859–60. 8vo. Vols. II. and III. Title, The Monthly Medical News.

The Louisville Medical Journal. Monthly. Edited by T. W. Colescott. Louisville. Nos. 1–6. Vol. I. 1860. 8vo.

The Richmond and Louisville Medical Journal. Monthly. E. S. Gaillard, Editor. Louisville. Vols. VI.–XXVI. 1868–78. 8vo. Continuation of the Richmond Medical Journal.

The American Practitioner. Formerly Western Journal of Medicine. Monthly. Edited by D. W. Yandell and T. Parvin. Louisville. Vols. I.–XVIII. 1870–78. 8vo. Current.

The Louisville Medical Reporter. Weekly. Edited by J. L. Cook and others. Henderson. No. 1, Vol. I. 1874. 8vo.

The American Medical Weekly. E. S. Gaillard, Editor. Louisville. Vols. I.–IV. 1874–76. 8vo. Continued as the following. Vol. II is paged consecutively with Vol. I.

The American Medical Bi-Weekly. E. S. Gaillard, Editor. Louisville. Vols. VI.–IX. 1877–78. 8vo. Continuation of the preceding.

The Louisville Medical News. Weekly. Edited by R. O. Cowling and others. Louisville. Vols. I.–VI. 1876–78. 8vo. Current.

LOUISIANA

Journal de la Société Médicale de la Nouvelle Orleans. Quarterly. Drs. Fortin, Daret, and others. New Orleans. Année I. 1839. 8vo.

The New Orleans Medical Journal. Bi-Monthly. Edited by E. D. Fenner and A. Hester. New Orleans. Vol. I. 1844–45. 8vo. Continued as the following.

The New Orleans Medical and Surgical Journal. Bi-Monthly. Edited by W. M. Carpenter, E. D. Fenner, and others. New Orleans. Vols. II.–XX. 1845–61 and 1866–67. 8vo. Consolidated with the Southern Journal of the Medical Sciences, forming the following.

The New Orleans Journal of Medicine. Quarterly. Edited by S. M. Bemiss and W. S. Mitchell. New Orleans. Vols. XXI.–XXIII. 1868–70. 8vo. Continued as the following in 1873.

The New Orleans Medical and Surgical Journal. New Series. Bi-Monthly. Edited by S. M. Bemiss. New Orleans. Vols. I.–IV. 1873–78. 8vo. Current.

The Louisiana Medical and Surgical Journal. Title of a periodical projected in 1845, but never issued, the New Orleans Medical and Surgical Journal taking its place.

The New Orleans Monthly Medical Register. Edited by A. E. Axon. Vols. I.–II. 1851–53. 8vo. In March, 1854, merged in The New Orleans Medical News and Hospital Gazette.

L'Union Médicale de la Louisiane. Monthly. C. Deléry, Editor. New Orleans. Vol. I. 1852. 8vo.

The New Orleans Medical News and Hospital Gazette. Semi-Monthly. Edited by S. Choppin, C. Beard, and others. New Orleans. Vols. I.–VII. 1854–61. 8vo. Continued as the following.

The New Orleans Medical Times. Monthly. Edited by A. Peniston. New Orleans. Nos. 1–3. 1861. 8vo. Continuation of the preceding.

Journal de la Société Médicale de la Nouvelle Orleans. Monthly. Edited by Dr. Thiery. Vol. I. Nos. 1–8, Vol. II. 1859–61.

The New Orleans Medical Record. Semi-Monthly. Edited by B. Dowler and S. R. Chambers. New Orleans. Nos. 1–4, Vol. I. 1866. Royal 8vo.

The Southern Journal of the Medical Sciences. Quarterly. E. D. Fenner, D. W. Brickell, and others. New Orleans. Vols. I.–II. 1866–67. 8vo. In January, 1868, consolidated with the New Orleans Medical and Surgical Journal, forming the New Orleans Journal of Medicine.

MAINE

The Journal of the Medical Society of the State of Maine. Hallowell. No. 1, Vol. I. January, 1834. 8vo.

The Maine Medical and Surgical Reporter. Monthly. Edited by W. R. Richardson and R. W. Cummings. Portland. Vol. I. 1858–59. 8vo.

MARYLAND

The Baltimore Medical and Physical Recorder. Quarterly. Conducted by T. Watkins. Baltimore. Vol. I., and No. 1 of Vol. II. 1808–09. 8vo.

The Baltimore Medical and Philosophical Lyceum. Quarterly. Edited by N. Potter. Baltimore. One volume. 1811. 8vo.

The Vaccine Inquirer. Monthly. Baltimore. No. 1, February, 1822; No. 4, May, 1822; No. 5, 1824. Announced as monthly, but published at irregular intervals.

The Baltimore Philosophical Journal and Review. Quarterly. Edited by J. B. Davidge. Baltimore. No. 1. July, 1823. 8vo.

The Maryland Medical Recorder. Quarterly. Edited by H. G. Jameson. Baltimore. Vols. I.–III. 1829–32. 8vo.

The Baltimore Monthly Journal of Medicine and Surgery. Edited by N. R. Smith. Baltimore. One volume. 1830–31. 8vo.

The Baltimore Medical and Surgical Journal and Review. Quarterly. Edited by E. Geddings. Baltimore. Vols. I.–II. 1833–34. 8vo. Continued as the following.

North American Archives of Medical and Surgical Science. Monthly. Edited by E. Geddings. Baltimore. Vols. I.–II. 1834–35. 8vo. Continuation of the preceding.

The Maryland Medical and Surgical Journal and Official Organ of the Medical Department of the Army and Navy of the United States. Quarterly. Baltimore. Vols. I.–III. 1840–43. 8vo.

The Baltimore Journal of Medicine. Bi-Monthly. Edited by E. Warren. Baltimore. Nos. 1–3, Vol. I. January to May, 1861. 8vo.

The Medical Bulletin. Semi-Monthly. Edited by E. Warren. Baltimore. Vols. I.–II. 1868–70. Folio. In 1871 merged in the following.

The Baltimore Medical Journal. Monthly. Edited by E. L. Howard and T. S. Latimer. Baltimore. Two volumes. 1870–71. 8vo. In Vol. II. title changed to Baltimore Medical Journal and Bulletin. In January, 1871, the Bulletin merged in this.

The Baltimore Physician and Surgeon. Monthly. Baltimore. Vols. I.–VI. 1872–76. 4to. The title of Vol. I., 1872–73, was The Physician and Surgeon.

Maryland Medical Journal. Monthly. H. E. T. Manning and T. A. Ashby, Editors. Baltimore. Vols. I.–III. 1877–78. 8vo. Current.

MASSACHUSETTS

The New England Journal of Medicine and Surgery and the Collateral Branches of Science. Quarterly. Boston. Vols. I.–XVI. 1812–27. 8vo. Continued as The Boston Medical and Surgical Journal. Vol. XVI., title, New England Medical Review and Journal.

The Boston Medical Intelligencer. Weekly. Edited by J. V. C. Smith. Boston. Five volumes. 1823–28. 4to. Continued as The Boston Medical and Surgical Journal.

The Boston Medical and Surgical Journal. Boston. Weekly. Ninety-nine volumes. 1828–78. 8vo. Current. Formed by consolidation of the two preceding.

American Journal of Foreign Medicine. Monthly. Conducted by an association of physicians. Boston. No. 1, Vol. I. June, 1827.

The Monthly Journal of Medical Literature and American Students' Gazette. Edited by E. Bartlett. Boston and Lowell. Nos. 1–3, Vol. I. January to March, 1832. 8vo.

The Medical Magazine. Monthly. Edited by A. L. Pierson, J. B. Flint, E. Bartlett, and others. Boston. Three volumes. 1832–35. 8vo.

The American Medical Almanac. Annual. Edited by J. V. C. Smith. Boston. Two volumes. 1839–40. 12mo.

The New England Quarterly Journal of Medicine and Surgery, Edited by C. E. Ware and S. Parkman. Boston. Vol. I. 1842–43. 8vo.

The Medical World. Weekly. Edited by J. V. C. Smith and E. S. Smith. Boston. Two volumes. 1856–57. 4to.

The Berkshire Medical Journal. Monthly. Edited by W. H. Thayer and R. C. Stiles. Pittsfield. One volume. 1861. 8vo.

The Journal of the Gynæcological Society of Boston. Monthly. Edited by W. Lewis, H. R. Storer, and G. H. Bixby. Boston. Seven volumes. 1869–72. 8vo.

MICHIGAN

The Peninsular Journal of Medicine and the Collateral Sciences. Monthly. Edited by E. Andrews, A. B. Palmer, and others. Ann Arbor and Detroit. Vols. I.–V. 1853–58. 8vo. Continued as The Peninsular and Independent Medical Journal.

The Medical Independent and Monthly Review of Medicine and Surgery. Edited by H. Goadby and others. Detroit. Three volumes. 1856–58. 8vo. Continued as The Peninsular and Independent Medical Journal.

The Peninsular and Independent Medical Journal. Monthly. Edited by A. B. Palmer, M. Gunn, and F. Stearns. Detroit. Vols. I.–II. 1858–60. 8vo. Formed by consolidation of the two preceding in April, 1858.

The Detroit Review of Medicine and Pharmacy. Monthly. Edited by G. P. Andrews and others. Detroit. Vols. I.–IX. 1866–76. 8vo. Merged in The Detroit Medical Journal.

The Michigan University Medical Journal. Monthly. Conducted by the faculty of the medical department. Ann Arbor. Three volumes. 1870–73. 8vo.

The Western Medical Advance and Progress of Pharmacy. Quarterly. W. H. Lathrop, Editor. Detroit. Vols. I.–II. June, 1871, to June 1873. 4to.

The Peninsular Journal of Medicine. Monthly. Edited by H. F. Lyster and others. Detroit. Four volumes. 1873–76. 8vo. Consolidated with The Detroit Review of Medicine and Pharmacy, forming the following.

The Detroit Medical Journal. Monthly. Edited by L. Connor and others.

Detroit. New Series. Vol. I. 1877. 8vo. Consolidation of The Peninsular Journal of Medicine with The Detroit Review of Medicine and Pharmacy.

The Detroit Lancet. Monthly. Edited by H. A. Cleland and L. Connor. Detroit. Vol. I. 1878. 8vo. Current.

The Michigan Medical News. Semi-Monthly. J. J. Mulheron, Editor. Detroit. Vol. I. 1878. 8vo. Current.

MINNESOTA

The Northwestern Medical and Surgical Journal. Monthly. Edited by W. B. Herrick and J. Evans. St. Paul. Vols. I.–IV. 1870–74. 8vo.

MISSOURI

The St. Louis Medical and Surgical Journal. Monthly. Edited by M. L. Linton, W. M. McPheeters, and others. St. Louis. Nos. 1–9, 11, 12. Vol. I. 1843–44. No. 12, Vol. II. 1844–45. Vols. III.–XIX. 1845–61. Also, New Series. Vols. III.–XV. 1866–78. 8vo. In September, 1848, The Missouri Medical and Surgical Journal was united with this.

The Missouri Medical and Surgical Journal. Monthly. Edited by R. F. Stevens, J. N. McDowell, and others. St. Louis. Vols. I.–IV. 1845–48. 8vo. In September, 1848, merged in the preceding.

The St. Louis Probe. Monthly. Edited by H. J. Coons and J. R. Atkinson. St. Louis. Vol. I. 1850. 8vo.

The St. Joseph Journal of Medicine and Surgery. Bi-Monthly. Edited by J. H. Crane, O. B. Knode, and others. St. Joseph. Nos. 4, 5, Vol. I., March, May, 1859. Nos. 1, 2, 4, 5, Vol. II. September, November, 1859, March, May, 1860. Nos. 1–3, Vol. III., September, 1860, to January, 1861. 8vo.

The Kansas City Medical and Surgical Review. Bi-Monthly. G. M. B. Maughs and T. C. Case, Editors. Kansas City, Mo. One volume. 1860. 8vo.

The Medical and Surgical Pioneer. Monthly. Edited by J. Keller. Kansas City, Mo. Nos. 1, 2, Vol. I. 1866. 8vo.

The St. Louis Medical Reporter. Semi-Monthly. Edited by J. S. B. Alleyne, O. F. Potter, and others. St. Louis. Vols. I.–IV. 1866–69. 8vo. Merged in The Medical Archives.

The Humboldt Medical Archives. Monthly. Edited by M. E. Pallen, E. F. Smith, A. Hammer, and others. St. Louis. Vol. I., in six numbers, September, 1867, to February, 1868. Vol. II., in ten numbers, March to December, 1868. Vol. III., in twelve numbers, January to December, 1869. Vol. IV., in six numbers, January to June, 1870. Vol. V., in six numbers, September, 1870, to February, 1871. Vol. VI, in six numbers, March to August, 1871. Vol. VII., in six numbers, September, 1871, to February, 1872. Vol. VIII., in ten numbers, March to December, 1872. Vol. IX., in five numbers, January to May, 1873. After Vol. II., title, The Medical Archives. In September, 1869, the preceding merged in this.

The Kansas City Medical Journal. Bi-Monthly. Edited by A. P. Lankford and others. Kansas City, Mo. Vols. I.–V. 1871–75. 8vo. Became monthly with Vol. IV.

Missouri Clinical Record. Monthly. Edited by W. A. Hardaway. St. Louis. Vol. I. 1874–75. 8vo. Continued as the following.

St. Louis Clinical Record. Monthly. Edited by W. A. Hardaway. St. Louis. Vols. II.–IV. 1875–78. 8vo. Current. Continuation of the preceding.

New Hampshire

The New Hampshire Journal of Medicine. Monthly. Edited by E. H. Parker. Concord. Vols. I.–VIII. 1850–58. 8vo. Vols. VI.–VIII., published at Manchester.

New Jersey

The New Jersey Medical Reporter and Transactions of the New Jersey Medical Society. Quarterly. Edited by Joseph Parrish. Burlington. Vols. I.–VIII. 1847–55. 8vo. Vol. V. became monthly. Continued as the following.

The Medical and Surgical Reporter. Monthly. Edited by S. W. Butler. Burlington, N. J., and Philadelphia. Vols. IX.–XI. 1856–58. 8vo. Vol. XI., and continuation published at Philadelphia. Current.

New York

A Journal of the Practice of Medicine, Surgery, and Pharmacy in the Military Hospitals of France. Published by order of the king. Reviewed and digested by M. De Horne. Translated by Joseph Browne. No. 1, Vol. I. New York. No date. 1783 or 1790.

The Medical Repository. Quarterly. Conducted by S. L. Mitchell, E. Miller, and E. H. Smith. New York. Vols. I.–XXIII. 1797–1824. 8vo. Slight change of title.

The New York Medical and Philosophical Journal and Review. Semi-Annual. New York. Vols. I.–III. 1809–11. 8vo.

The American Medical and Philosophical Register. Quarterly. Conducted by David Hosack and John W. Francis. New York. Vols. I.–IV. 1810–14. 8vo. Two editions of Vol. I.

The New York Medical Magazine. Annual. Edited by V. Mott and H. M. Onderdonk. New York. Vol. I. (in two numbers). 1814–15. 8vo.

The Medical and Surgical Register. Edited by J. Watts, Jr., V. Mott, and A. H. Stevens. New York. Vol. I. 1818–20. 8vo.

The New York Medical and Physical Journal. Quarterly. Edited by J. W. Francis and others. New York. Vols. I.–IX. 1822–30. 8vo.

The New York Monthly Chronicle of Medicine and Surgery. By an Association of Physicians. New York. Vol. I. 1824–25. 8vo.

The New York Medical Journal. Quarterly. Conducted by D. L. M. Peixotto, J. R. Rhinelander, and J. J. Graves. New York. Two volumes. 1830–31. 8vo.

The New York Medico Chirurgical Bulletin. Monthly. Edited by George Bushe. New York. Two volumes. 1831–32. 8vo.

The United States Medical and Surgical Journal. Monthly. Edited by an Association of Physicians. New York. Vols. I.–III. 1834–36. 8vo. After No. 2, September, 1834, published at New York and Philadelphia.

The New York Journal of Medicine and Surgery. Quarterly. New York. Vols. I.–IV. 1839–41. 8vo.

The New York Medical Gazette. Weekly. Published by U. Turner. New York. Vols. I.–II. 1841–42. 8vo.

The New York Lancet. Weekly. Edited by J. A. Houston. New York. Vols. I.–II., and Nos. 1–4, Vol. III. 1842–43. 8vo.

Albany Journal of Neurology. Monthly. By an Association of Physicians. Albany. No. 1, Vol. I. July, 1843. 8vo.

The New York Journal of Medicine and the Collateral Sciences. Bi-Monthly. Edited by S. Forry and others. New York. Thirty-four volumes. 1843–60. 8vo. For continuation, see The American Medical Times. Vol. I. Third Series. In 1856, the words "and the Collateral Sciences" dropped from the title-page. The New York Medical Times merged in this journal.

The American Journal of Insanity. Quarterly. Edited by medical officer of the New York State Lunatic Asylum, Utica, N. Y. Vols. I.–XXXIV. 1844–78. 8vo. Current.

The New York Medical and Surgical Reporter. Bi-Weekly. Edited by C. T. Collins. New York. Vol. I., 1845–46, and Nos. 1–18. Vol. II., 1847. 8vo.

The Buffalo Medical Journal. Monthly. Edited by A. Flint. Buffalo. Fifteen volumes. 1845–60. 8vo. In July, 1860, merged in The American Medical Monthly.

The Annalist. Bi-Weekly. Edited by W. C. Roberts and N. S. Davis. New York. Three volumes. 1846–49. 8vo.

Wood's Addenda to the Medico-Chirurgical Review. Quarterly. New York. Two volumes. 1847–49. 8vo. Also issued in somewhat different form as Wood's Quarterly Retrospect of American and Foreign Practical Medicine and Surgery.

The New York Register of Medicine and Pharmacy. Semi-Monthly. Edited by C. D. Griswold. New York. Two volumes. 1850–51. 8vo.

The Northern Lancet and Gazette of Legal Medicine. Monthly. Edited by F. J. D'Avignon and H. Nelson. Plattsburgh, N. Y. Vols. I.–XII. 1850–56.

8vo. Vols. IV.–VI., title, Nelson's Northern Lancet, etc.; Vols. VII–XII., title. Nelson's American Lancet, etc.

The New York Medical Gazette and Journal of Health. Weekly and Monthly. Edited by D. M. Reese. New York. Twelve volumes. 1850–61. 4to and 8vo. Vols. VI.–VIII., title, The American Medical Gazette and Journal of Health. Vols. IX.–XII., title, The American Medical Gazette.

The New York Medical Times. Monthly. Edited by J. G. Adams and others. New York. Vols. I.–V. 1851–56. 8vo. Merged in The New York Journal of Medicine.

New Yorker Medicinische Monatsschrift. Edited by J. Herzka, E. Krakowitzer, and W. Roth. New York. Jahrg. I. 1852–53. 8vo.

The American Medical Monthly. Conducted by Horace Green and others. New York. Vols. I.–XVIII. 1854–62. 8vo.

The North American Medical Reporter. Quarterly. Edited by W. Elmer. New York. Vol. I, 1858–59. 8vo.

The New York Medical Press. Weekly. Edited by J. L. Kiernan and W. O. Meagher. New York. Vols. I.–III. 1859–60. Royal 8vo. Four preliminary numbers were issued in 1858. In July, 1860, merged in The American Medical Times.

The Buffalo Medical and Surgical Journal and Reporter. Monthly. Edited by J. F. Miner. Buffalo. Vols. I.–XVII. 1860–78. 8vo. Current. In Vol. II., 1860, the words "and Reporter" dropped from title.

The American Medical Times. Weekly. Edited by Stephen Smith. New York. Vols. I.–IX. 1860–64. 4to. Continuation of The New York Journal of Medicine. In July, 1860, The New York Medical Press merged in this.

Summary of Medical Science. Semi-Annual. Edited by W. S. Wells. New York. Part I. April, 1861. 8vo.

American Journal of Ophthalomology. Bi-Monthly. Edited by J. Homberger. New York. Vol. I. 1862–63, and Nos. 1–2, Vol. II. 1864. 8vo. Vol. II. became quarterly.

Nord Americanische Deutsch' medizinische Zeitschrift für praktische Heilkunde. Bi-Monthly. Edited by W. Meisburger. Buffalo. Nos. 1–3. Vol. I. 1865. 8vo.

The New York Medical Journal. Monthly. Edited by W. A. Hammond, E. S. Dunster, and others. New York. Twenty-eight volumes. 1865–78. 8vo. Current.

The Medical Record. Semi-Monthly. Edited by G. F. Shrady. New York. Fourteen volumes. 1866–78. 4to. Current. Vol. X., 1875, became weekly.

The Quarterly Journal of Psychological Medicine and Medical Jurisprudence. Edited by W. A. Hammond. New York. Vols. I.–III. 1867–69. 8vo. Continued as the following.

The Journal of Psychological Medicine. Quarterly. New York. Vols.

IV.–VI. 1870–72. 8vo. Continuation of the preceding. In July, 1874, the publication was resumed as The Psychological and Medico-Legal Journal.

The Medical Gazette. Weekly. Edited by A. L. Carroll and others. New York. Vols. I.–VI., and Nos. 1–6. Vol. III. 1867–71. 4to.

Revista médico quirurgica y dentistica de los Sres. Wilson y Gonzales. Quarterly. Nueva York. Nos. 1–3. Tom I. 1868. 8vo.

The Physician and Pharmaceutist. Quarterly. Edited by G. J. Fisher and others. New York. Vols. I.–III. 1868–71. 4to. Continued as the following.

The Physician and Pharmacist. Quarterly. New York. Vols. IV.–XI. 1871–78. 4to. Current. Continuation of the preceding.

The American Journal of Obstetrics and Diseases of Women and Children. Quarterly. Edited by E. Noeggerath, B. F. Dawson, and others. New York. Vols. I.–XI. 1868–78. 8vo. Current.

The Archives of Ophthalmology and Otology. Semi-Annual. Edited and published simultaneously in English and German by H. Knapp, in New York, and S. Moos, in Heidelberg. New York. Vols. I.–VII. 1869–78. 8vo. Current. Vol. IV. became quarterly.

The American Journal of Syphilography and Dermatology. Quarterly. Edited by M. H. Henry. New York. Vols. I.–V. 1870–74. 8vo.

The Medical World. Monthly. Edited by R. A. Vance. New York. One Volume. 1871–72. 8vo.

Archives of Scientific and Practical Medicine and Surgery. Monthly. Edited by C. E. Brown-Séquard and E. C. Seguin. New York. Nos. 1–5. Vol. I. 1873. Royal 8vo.

The Sanitarian. Monthly. Edited by A. N. Bell and others. New York. Vols. I.–VI. 1873–78. 8vo. Current.

Archives of Electrology and Neurology. Semi-Annual. Edited by G. M. Beard. New York. Two volumes. 1874–75. 8vo.

The Psychological and Medico-Legal Journal. Monthly. Conducted by W. A. Hammond and T. M. B. Cross. New York. New Series. Vols. I.–III. 1874–76. 8vo. For First Series see The Quarterly Journal of Psychological Medicine. Vol. III. 1875–76, title, The American Psychological Journal. Quarterly. Conducted by Allan McLane Hamilton and others.

Archives of Dermatology. Quarterly. Edited by L. D. Bulkley. New York. Vols. I.–IV. 1874–78. 8vo. Current.

Proceedings of the Medical Society of the County of Kings. Monthly. Conducted by the Council of the Society. Brooklyn. Vols. I.–III. 1876–78. 8vo. Current.

Archives of Clinical Surgery. Monthly. Edited by E. J. Bermingham. New York. Vol. I. 1876–77. 8vo. In October, 1877, united with the following forming the Hospital Gazette and Archives of Clinical Surgery.

The Hospital Gazette. Monthly. Edited by F. A. Lyons. New York. Nos.

1–6. Vol. I. 1877. 4to. In October, 1877, united with the preceding, forming the following.

The Hospital Gazette and Archives of Clinical Surgery. Semi-Monthly. Edited by E. J. Bermingham and F. A. Lyons. New York. Four volumes. Whole series. 1876–78. 8vo.

Revista mensual medico-quirurgica de Nueva York. A. de Tejada, Editor. Nueva York. No. 1, Vol. I. October, 1878. 8vo. Current.

The New York Medical and Surgical Brief. Monthly. E. J. Fisk, Editor. New York. No. 1, Vol. I. November, 1878. 8vo. Current.

NORTH CAROLINA

The Medical Journal of North Carolina. Bi-Monthly. E. Warren, Editor. Edenton and Raleigh. Four volumes. 1858–61. 8vo.

The North Carolina Medical Journal. Monthly. M. J. DeForrest and Thomas F. Wood, Editors. Raleigh. Vols. I.–II. 1878. 8vo. Current. The same was running title of preceding.

OHIO

The Western Quarterly Reporter of Medical, Surgical, and Natural Science. Edited by J. D. Godman. Cincinnati. Vols. I.–II. 1822–23.

Ohio (The) Medical Repository of Original and Selected Essays and Intelligence. Bi-Monthly. Edited by G. W. Wright and J. M. Mason. Cincinnati. Vol. I. 1826–27. Folio. Completed. Merged into the following in April, 1827.

Western (The) Medical and Physical Journal. Original and eclectic. Monthly. Edited by Daniel Drake and Guy W. Wright. Cincinnati. Vol. I. 1827–28. No. 1, Vol. II. May, 1828. 8vo. No. 1, Vol. II., believed to be the last published. In April, 1828, the Western Journal of the Medical and Physical Sciences was commenced by Daniel Drake, and was subsequently represented and regarded as continuation of the above, the volume for April, 1828, to March, 1829, being reckoned Vol. II. of the periodical.

Western (The) Journal of the Medical and Physical Sciences. Monthly. Edited by Daniel Drake. Cincinnati. Vols. II.–XII. 1828–33. 8vo. No. 1, Vol. XII. believed to be the last published. For Vol. I. see preceding. In 1835, The Western Medical Gazette merged in this journal, January 1, 1840, revived and consolidated with the Louisville Journal of Medicine and Surgery, forming The Western Journal of Medicine and Surgery.

Western (The) Medical Gazette. Semi-Monthly and Monthly. Edited by Eberle and others. Vols. I.–II. 1832–35. 8vo. Completed. Suspended from September 1, 1833, to February 1, 1834. In 1835 merged into the preceding.

Ohio (The) Medical Repository. Monthly. Edited by J. M. Mason. Cincinnati, Nos. 1–5, Vol. I. 1835–36. 8vo.

Western (The) Quarterly Journal of Practical Medicine. Edited by John Eberle and others. No. 1, Vol. I. June, 1837. Cincinnati. 8vo. No more published.

Western (The) Lancet. Devoted to medical and surgical science. Monthly. Vols. I.–XVIII. Cincinnati and Lexington, 1842–1857. After April, 1843, The Western and Surgical Medical Recorder merged in this journal. In January, 1858, united with The Cincinnati Medical Observer, forming the Cincinnati Lancet and Observer.

Ohio (The) Medical and Surgical Journal. Bi-Monthly. Edited by John Butterfield. Columbus. Vols. I.–XVI. 1848–64. 8vo. Completed.

American (The) Psychological Journal. Devoted chiefly to the elucidation of mental pathology and the medical jurisprudence of insanity. Bi-Monthly. Conducted by Edward Mead, Cincinnati. One volume. 1853. 8vo. Completed. Prospectus for a new series to be published in Boston issued in 1874.

Medical (The) Counsellor. A weekly gazette of the medical and physical sciences. R. Hills, Editor. Columbus, Ohio. Vols. I.–II. 1855–56. 8vo. Completed. The Ohio Medical Gazette was running title of this journal.

Cincinnati (The) Medical Observer. Edited by G. Mendenhall, J. A. Murphy, and E. B. Stevens. Monthly. Vols. I.–II. 1856–57. 8vo. In January, 1858, united with The Western Lancet, forming the Cincinnati Lancet and Observer.

Cincinnati (The) Medical News. Devoted to the dissemination of truth. Edited by A. H. Baker. Monthly. Vol. I., Nos. 1 and 2. Vol. II., August 15, 1858, November 15, 1859. Folio. Continued as the Cincinnati Medical and Surgical News.

Belmont (The) Medical Journal. A monthly periodical published under the patronage of the Belmont Medical Society. Bridgeport, Ohio. Two volumes. 1858–60. 12mo. Completed.

Cincinnati (The) Lancet and Observer. Edited by G. Mendenhall, J. Murphy, and E. B. Stevens. Monthly. Vols. I.–XXI. 1858–78. 8vo. Completed. Formed by consolidation of the Cincinnati Medical Observer with the Western Lancet. Consolidated with The Clinic, forming the Cincinnati Lancet and Clinic.

Cleveland (The) Medical Gazette. A monthly journal for the advancement and review of the Medical Sciences. Edited by G. C. E. Weber. Vols. I.–III. 1859–61. 8vo. At end of Vol. I., consolidated with Cincinnati Lancet and Observer, but each journal retained its own name, and they were issued simultaneously.

Columbus (The) Review of Medicine and Surgery. Edited by W. L. McMillen. Bi-Monthly. Nos. 1–5. Vol. I. August, 1860, to April, 1861. 8vo. Completed.

Cincinnati (The) Medical and Surgical News. Edited by A. H. Baker. Monthly. Four volumes. 1860–63. 8vo. Completed. Continuation of the Cincinnati Medical News.

Cincinnati (The) Journal of Medicine. Edited by G. C. Blackman, T. Parvin, and R. Bartholow. Monthly. Vols. I.–IV. Cincinnati, Ohio, and Indianapolis. 1866–69. 8vo. After No. 6 of Vol. II., title, The Western Journal of Medicine. For continuation see The American Practitioner.

Cincinnati (The) Medical Repertory. Edited by J. A. Thacker. Monthly. Vols. I.–IV. 1868–71. 8vo. For continuation see The Cincinnati Medical News.

Clinic (The). Edited by J. T. Whittaker. Weekly. Cincinnati. Fourteen volumes. 1871–78. 4to. Completed. Merged in Cincinnati Lancet and Clinic, July 1, 1878.

Cincinnati (The) Medical News. Edited by J. A. Thacker and others. Monthly. Vols. I.–VII. 1872–78. 8vo. Continuation of The Cincinnati Medical Repertory.

Ohio (The) Medical and Surgical Journal. Edited by J. H. Pooley. Bi-Monthly. New Series. Columbus. Vols. I.–III. 1876–78. 8vo.

Ohio (The) Medical Recorder. Edited by J. W. Hamilton and J. F. Baldwin. Monthly. Columbus. Vols. I.–II. 1876–78. 8vo.

Toledo Medical and Surgical Journal. Edited by J. Priest. Monthly. Vols. I.–II. 1877–78. 8vo.

Cincinnati Lancet and Clinic. Weekly. J. C. Culbertson and J. G. Hyndman, Editors. No. 1. July 6, 1878. 8vo. Current. Formed by consolidation of The Clinic with The Cincinnati Lancet and Observer.

The Obstetric Gazette. Monthly. E. B. Stevens, Editor. Vol. I. 1878. Cincinnati. 8vo.

OREGON

The Oregon Medical and Surgical Reporter. Monthly. Edited by E. R. Fiske and H. Carpenter. Salem. Two volumes. 8vo. Completed.

The Oregon Medical Journal. A quarterly journal of medicine and surgery. Published by the Marion County Medical Society. Salem. Nos. 1–4. Vol. I. 1876–77. 8vo.

PENNSYLVANIA

The Philadelphia Medical and Physical Journal. Quarterly. Collected and arranged by Benjamin Smith Barton. Vols. I–III. 1804–09. 8vo.

The Philadelphia Medical Museum. Quarterly. Conducted by John Redman Coxe. Seven volumes. 1804–11. 8vo. Completed. A subdivision of each number, entitled Medical and Philosophical Register, is, after Vol. II, paged separately.

The Eclectic Repertory and Analytical Review. Medical and philosophical. Quarterly. Philadelphia. Vols. I–X. 1811–20. 8vo. For continuation see Journal of Foreign Medicine.

The Journal of Foreign Medical Science and Literature. A continuation of the Eclectic Repertory. Quarterly. Conducted by S. Emlen, Jr., and William Price. Vols. I–IV. 1821–24. Philadelphia. 8vo.

The American Medical Recorder. Quarterly. Philadelphia. Vol. I–XV. 1818–29. 8vo. Completed. Merged in the American Journal of the Medical Sciences, after No. 2, Vol. XV. Vols. VII–XII., title, The Medical Recorder, etc.

The Philadelphia Journal of Medical and Physical Sciences. Quarterly. Supported by an association of physicians, and edited by N. Chapman, W. P. Dewees, J. D. Goodman, and Isaac Hays. Fourteen volumes. 1820–27. 8vo. Continued as the American Journal of the Medical Sciences.

The American Journal of the Medical Sciences. Quarterly. Edited by Isaac Hays. Philadelphia. One hundred and two volumes. 1827–78. 8vo.

The AEsculapian Register. Weekly. Edited by several physicians. Philadelphia. Vol. I. June 17 to December 9, 1824. 8vo.

The Medical Review and Analectic Journal. Quarterly. Conducted by John Eberle and George McClellan. Philadelphia. Three volumes. 1824–26. 8vo. Completed. Vols. II–III., title, The American Medical Review and Journal of Original and Selected Papers in Medicine and Surgery.

North American Medical and Surgical Journal. Quarterly. Conducted by H. L. Hodge and others. Philadelphia. Vols. I–XII. 1826–31. 8vo. Completed.

The Philadelphia Monthly Journal of Medicine and Surgery. Edited by N. R. Smith. Vol. I and Nos. 1–3, Vol. II. 1827–28. 8vo. After February, 1828, merged in The American Journal of the Medical Sciences.

The Monthly Journal of Foreign Medicine. Edited by S. Littell. Philadelphia. Vols. I–III. 1828–29. 8vo.

The Cholera Gazette. Weekly. Philadelphia. Nos. 1–16. Vol. I. July 11. No. 21, 1832.

The American Lancet. Bi-Weekly. Edited by F. S. Beattie. Philadelphia. Nos. 1–7. Vol. I. 1833.

American Cyclopedia of Practical Medicine and Surgery. A digest of medical literature. Philadelphia. Two volumes. 1834–36. 8vo.

The American Medical Library and Intelligencer. A concentrated record of medical science and literature. Edited by G. S. Pattison and R. Dunglison. Philadelphia. Specimen sheet November, 1836. Continued as The American Medical Intelligencer.

The Eclectic Journal of Medicine. Monthly. Edited by John Bell. Philadelphia. Vols. I–IV. 1836–40. 8vo.

The American Medical Intelligencer. A concentrated record of medical science and literature. Semi-Monthly and Monthly. Edited by Robley Dunglison. Philadelphia. Five volumes. 1837–42. 8vo. Continued as the Medical News and Library.

Medical News and Library. Monthly. Philadelphia. Thirty-six volumes. 1843–78. 8vo. Current. A continuation of the preceding.

The Medical Examiner. Bi-Weekly and Monthly. Edited by J. B. Biddle, M. Clymer, and W. W. Gerhard. Philadelphia. Vols. I–VII. 1838–44. Royal 8vo. Vols. I–XII. New Series. 1845–56. 8vo. In January, 1857, united with the Louisville Review, forming the North American Medico-Chirurgical Review.

The Bulletin of Medical Sciences. Monthly. Edited by John Bell. Philadelphia. Four volumes. 1843–46. 8vo. Completed.

Nordamerikanischer Monatsbericht für Natur und Heilkunde. Philadelphia. Four volumes. 1850–52. 8vo.

The Philadelphia Medical and Surgical Journal. Semi-Monthly. Edited by James Bryan. Vols. I–VI. 1853–58. 8vo.

The Medical Reporter. A quarterly journal, published under the direction of the Chester and Delaware County Medical Societies. West Chester, Pennsylvania. Vols. I–III. 1853–56. 8vo.

The North American Medico-Chirurgical Review. Edited by S. D. Gross and T. G. Richardson. Bi-Monthly. Philadelphia. Vols. I–V. 1857–61. 8vo. Completed, formed by consolidation of The Medical Examiner, Philadelphia, and the Louisville Review.

The Medical and Surgical Reporter. A weekly journal. Edited by S. W. Butler and R. J. Levis. Philadelphia. Vols. I–XXXIX. 1858–78. 8vo.

Compendium of Medical Science. Half-Yearly. Edited by S. W. Butler, D. G. Brinton, and G. H. Napheys. Philadelphia. Eleven volumes. 1868–78. 8vo.

The Photographic Review of Medicine and Surgery. A bi-monthly illustration of interesting cases, accompanied by notes. Edited by F. F. Maury and L. A. Duhring. Philadelphia. Two volumes. 1870–72. 8vo. Completed.

The Medical Times. A semi-monthly journal of medical and surgical science. Edited by J. H. Hutchinson and J. Tyson. Philadelphia. Two volumes. 1870–72. Royal 8vo. Continued as the following.

The Philadelphia Medical Times. A weekly journal of medical and surgical science. Philadelphia. Vols. III–VII. 1872–1878. 8vo. Current. See The Medical Times, for Vols. I–II. Vol. VI became bi-weekly.

The Medical Cosmos. A monthly abstract of medical science and art. G. J. Zeigler, Editor. Vol. I. Nos. 1–5. Vol. II. Philadelphia. 1871–72. 8vo.

The Obstetrical Journal of Great Britain and Ireland: including midwifery and the diseases of women and children. Monthly. Edited by J. H.

Aveling and A. Wiltshire. With an American supplement, edited by Wm.
F. Jenks. Philadelphia. Vols. I–VI. 1873–78. 8vo.

The Monthly Abstract of Medical Science. Philadelphia. Vols. I–V. 1874–
78. 8vo.

SOUTH CAROLINA

Charleston Medical Register. Annual, by David Ramsay. 1802.

The Carolina Journal of Medicine, Science, and Agriculture. Quarterly.
Conducted by T. Y. Simons and W. Michel. Charleston. Vol. I. 1825. 8vo.

The Southern Journal of Medicine and Pharmacy. Bi-Monthly. Edited
by J. L. Smith and S. D. Sinkler. Charleston. Vols. I.–II. 1846–47. 8vo. Continued as the following.

The Charleston Medical Journal and Review. Bi-Monthly. Edited by
P. C. Gaillard and H. W. De Saussure. Charleston. Vols. III.–XV. 1848–60.
8vo. Continuation of the preceding.

The Charleston Medical Journal and Review. Quarterly. New Series.
Edited by F. P. Porcher and R. A. Kinloch. Charleston. Vols. I.–IV. 1873–77.
8vo.

TENNESSEE

The East Tennessee Record of Medicine and Surgery. Quarterly. Edited
by F. A. Ramsey. Knoxville. 1 Vol. 1852–53. 8vo. After May, 1853, merged
in The Southern Journal of the Medical and Physical Sciences.

The Memphis Medical Recorder. Bi-Monthly. Edited by A. P. Merrill.
C. T. Quintard, and others. Memphis. Vols. I.–VI. 1852–58. 8vo.

The Southern Journal of the Medical and Physical Sciences. Bi-Monthly.
Conducted by J. W. King and W. P. Jones. Nashville and Knoxville. Vols.
I.–VI. 1853–57. 8vo. In 1853, The East Tennessee Record of Medicine and
Surgery merged in this Journal. In December No., 1857, The East Tennes-
see Medical Times announced as a continuation.

The East Tennessee Medical Times. Announced by R. O. Currey in
1857, to be issued monthly as a continuation of the Southern Journal of
the Medical and Physical Sciences, but never appeared, so far as I can
learn.

The Nashville Monthly Record of Medical and Physical Science. Edited
by D. F. Wright, R. O. Currey, and others. Vols. I.–II., and Nos. 1, 2, Vol.
III. 1858–60. 8vo.

The Medical and Surgical Monthly. Edited by F. A. Ramsey. Memphis.
Nos. 1–6, Vol. I., 1866. 8vo.

The Nashville Journal of Medicine and Surgery. Bi-monthly and
monthly. Edited by W. K. Bowling, P. F. Eve, and others. Nashville. Vols.

I.–XXI. 1851–61. New Series, Vols. I.–XXI. 1866–78. 8vo. Current. Vol. II., became monthly.

TEXAS

The Galveston Medical Journal. Monthly. Greensville Dowell, Editor. Galveston. 5 vols. 1866–71. 8vo.

The Texas Medical Journal. Monthly. Edited by J. D. Rankin. Galveston. Nos. 1–7, 10, Vol. I.; Nos. 2, 9, Vol. II.; Nos. 1, 2, 4, Vol. III.; Vols. V.–VII. 1873–78. 8vo. Current. Vol. III., became quarterly.

VERMONT

Vermont Medical Journal. Bi-Monthly. J. M. Currier, Editor. Burlington. Nos. 1, 2, Vol. I. 1874. 8vo.

VIRGINIA

The Stethoscope and Virginia Medical Gazette. Monthly. Edited by T. P. Atkinson, R. W. Haxall, and others. Richmond. Vols. I.–V. 1851–55. 8vo. Vols. IV.–V.; title, The Stethoscope. In January, 1856, united with The Virginia Medical and Surgical Journal, forming The Virginia Medical Journal.

The Monthly Stethoscope and Medical Reporter. Edited by G. A. Wilson and R. A. Lewis. Richmond. Vol. I. Nos. 1–5, Vol. II. 1856–57. 8vo.

The Virginia Medical and Surgical Journal. Monthly. Edited by G. A. Otis, and others. Richmond. Vols. I.–V. 1853–55. 8vo. Continued as the following.

The Virginia Medical Journal. Monthly. Richmond. Vols. VI.–XIII. 1856–59. 8vo. Formed by the union of The Stethoscope with the Virginia Medical and Surgical Journal. Continued as the following.

The Maryland and Virginia Medical Journal. Monthly. Richmond. Vols. XIV.–XVI. 1860–61. 8vo. Continuation of the preceding.

The Confederate States Medical and Surgical Journal. Published under the auspices of the Surgeon-General C. S. A. Monthly. Vol. I. Nos. 1, 2, of Vol. II. January, 1864, to February, 1865. 4to.

The Richmond Medical Journal. Monthly. Edited by E. S. Gaillard and W. S. McChesney. Richmond. Vols. I.–V. 1866–68. 8vo. Continued as The Richmond and Louisville Medical Journal, *q. v.*

The Virginia Clinical Record. Monthly. Edited by J. S. Dorsey Cullen. Richmond. Vols. I.–III. 1871–74. 8vo.

Virginia Medical Monthly. L. B. Edwards, Editor. Richmond. Vols. I.–V. 1874–78. 8vo. Current.

The Southern Clinic. Monthly. Edited by C. A. Bruce and J. R. Wheat. Richmond. No. I., Vol. I., October, 1878. 8vo. Current.

WEST VIRGINIA

The West Virginia Medical Student. Monthly. J. E. Reeves, Editor.
Wheeling. Vol. I. 1875–76. 8vo.

The following table shows by countries the number of medical journals
and transactions received at the library of the surgeon-general's office and
regularly indexed. This list does not include pharmaceutical, chemical,
dental, veterinary, homœopathic, hydropathic, eclectic, or popular journals.

Countries	Journals	Transactions
United States	57	60
Mexico	2	—
South America		
Argentine Confederation	1	—
Brazil	4	—
Chile	1	—
Venezuela	1	—
Great Britain and Colonies	36	37
France	64	29
Germany	96	38
Belgium	10	12
Netherlands	7	5
Spain	21	1
Portugal	3	—
Italy	35	4
Switzerland	5	5
Russia	10	4
Sweden and Norway	6	2
Denmark	4	—
Turkey	2	—
China	1	1
Poland	6	3
Total	372	201

There are now in existence the following medical journals of equal or
greater age than the Boston Medical and Surgical Journal, and a study of
the causes why these have survived so long would be a valuable contribution to the literature of journalism, but this study cannot be undertaken
here.

The Philadelphia Journal of the Medical and Physical Sciences. Philadelphia. 1820–27.

The American Journal of the Medical Sciences. Philadelphia. 1820–78.

Annales d'Hygiène publique et de Médecine légale. Paris. 1829–78.

Annali universali di Medicina. Milano. 1817–78.
Archives générales de Médecine. Paris. 1823–78.
Bibliothek for Læger. Kjöbenhavn. 1821–78.
Bullettino delle Scienze mediche, pubblicato per cura della Società medico-chirurgica di Bologna. 1829–78.

Gazette de Santé, contenant les nouvelles Découvertes sur les Moyens de se bien porter, et de guérir quand on est malade. Paris. 1773–1829. Gazette de Médecine de Paris; journal de Médecine et des Sciences accessoires. Paris. 1773–1878.

The Edinburgh Medical and Surgical Journal. Edinburgh. 1805–55. The Edinburgh Medical Journal; combining the Monthly Journal of Medicine with the Edinburgh Medical and Surgical Journal. Edinburgh. 1805–78.

Gemeinsame deutsche Zeitschrift für Geburtskunde. Weimar. 1826–32. Neue Zeitschrift für Geburtskunde. Berlin. 1834–52. Monatsschrift für Geburtskunde und Frauenkrankheiten. Berlin. 1853–69. Archiv für Gynæ-kologie. Berlin. 1826–78.

Journal de Chimie médicale, de Pharmacie et de Toxicologie. Paris. 1825–78.

Recueil périodique de la Société de Santé de Paris. (1797.) 2d ed. Recueil périodique de la Société de Médecine de Paris. 1797–1802. Journal général de Médecine, Chirurgie, et de Pharmacie, ou recueil périodique de la Société de Médecine de Paris. 1802–30. Transactions médicales; Journal de médecine pratique et de Litterature médicale, dans lequel sont publiés les Actes de la Société de Médecine de Paris. 1830–33. Revue médicale française et ètrangère. Paris. 1797–1878.

Journal de Médecine, de Chirurgie, et de Pharmacie militaires. Paris. 1815–16. Recueil de Mémoires de Médecine, de Chirurgie, et de Pharmacie militaires, faisant suite au journal qui paraissait sous le même titre. Paris. 1815–78.

The Lancet. A Journal of British and Foreign Medical and Chemical Science, Criticism, Literature, and News. London. 1823–78.

The London Medical Gazette; a Weekly Journal of Medicine and the Collateral Sciences. London. 1827–51. The Medical Times and Gazette. A Journal of Medical Science, Literature, Criticism, and News. London. 1827–78.

Pamietnik Lekarski Warszawski. Warszawie. 1828–29. Pamietnik Towarzystwa Lekarskiego Warszawskiego. Warszawa. 1828–78.

Voyenno-medtisinskii Journal, isdavayemwi Meditsinskim Departamentom Voyennavo ministerstva. St. Petersburg. 1823–78.

Kritisches Repertorium für die gesammte Heilkunde. Berlin. 1823–33. Wochenschrift für die gesammte Heilkunde. Berlin. 1833–51. Vierteljahrsschrift für gerichtliche und öffentliche Medicin. Berlin. 1852–71. Vierteljahrsschrift für gerichtliche Medicin und öffentliches Sanitätswesen. Berlin. 1823–78.

Reil's Archiv für die Physiologie. Halle. 1796–1815. Deutsches Archiv für die Physiologie. Halle. 1815–23. Archiv für Anatomie und Physiologie. Leipzig. 1826–32. Archiv für Anatomie, Physiologie, und Wissenschaftliche Medicin. Leipzig. 1834–76. Archiv für Anatomie und Physiologie. Leipzig. 1796–1878.

Who Founded the National
Medical Library?

Washington, February 3, 1880

To the Secretary of the Medical Society of the County of New York:

Dear Doctor—As my attention has several times been called to the communication by Dr. Wm. A. Hammond relative to the library of this office, read at the annual meeting of the Society, October 27, 1879, and more especially to the report of this communication given on page 472 of the New York MEDICAL RECORD for November 15, 1879, with requests for explanations, I deem it proper to make a statement on the matter to the Society.

From the report in the RECORD, some have inferred that I claim to have been the founder of the National Medical Library, although the letter of Dr. Hammond, as printed on page 40 of the minutes of that meeting, makes it very plain that I have made no such claim.

The facts of the case are simply as follows:

For many years there was a small collection of medical books and journals in the Surgeon-General's office at Washington, which collection was commenced by Surgeon-General Lovell prior to 1836.

At the commencement of the war this collection amounted to between three and four hundred volumes.

Dr. Hammond entered on his duties as Surgeon-General April 28, 1862, and left Washington August 30, 1863, after which date he was not on duty in this office. During this interval three hundred and fifty-nine volumes were purchased for the use of the office, the principal works being a set of the "Annales d'Hygiène" and a set of the "Boston Medical and Surgical Journal." During the years 1864 and 1865 about 1,000 volumes were added to the library, mainly works selected by Drs. Woodward and Otis.

When the library came under my charge, in the fall of 1865, it contained, as shown by a catalogue made at the time, about 1,800 volumes. At this date it contains about 50,000 volumes and 60,000 pamphlets.

Very respectfully and truly yours,

JOHN S. BILLINGS
Surgeon U. S. Army

Medical Record (NY) 17: 298–9 (1880).

Our Medical Literature

When I was surprised by the honour of an invitation to address this Congress, my first thought was that it must be declined, for the simple, but sufficient reason that I had nothing to say that would be worth occupying the time of such an assemblage as it was evident this would be. But while thinking over the matter, and looking absent-mindedly at a shelf of catalogues and a pile of new books and journals awaiting examination, it occurred to me that perhaps some facts connected with our medical literature, past and present, from the point of view of the reader, librarian, and bibliographer, rather than from that of the writer or practitioner, might be of sufficient interest to you to warrant an attempt to present them; and, the wish being probably father to the thought, I decided to make the trial.

When I say "Our Medical Literature," it is not with reference to that of any particular country or nation, but to that which is the common property of the educated physicians of the world as represented here to-day —the literature which forms the intra- and international bond of the medical profession of all civilized countries; and by virtue of which we, who have come here from the far West and the farther East, do not now meet, for the first time, as strangers, but as friends, having common interests, and though of many nations, a common language, and whose thoughts are perhaps better known to each other than to some of our nearest neighbours.

It is usual to estimate that about one-thirtieth part of the whole mass of the world's literature belongs to medicine and its allied sciences. This corresponds very well to the results obtained from an examination of bibliographies, and catalogues of the principal medical libraries. It appears from this that our medical literature now forms a little over 120,000 volumes properly so called, and about twice that number of pamphlets, and that this accumulation is now increasing at the rate of about 1,500 volumes and 2,500 pamphlets yearly.

Let us consider the character of this annual growth somewhat in detail, first giving some figures as the numbers of those who are producing it.

There are at the present time scattered over the earth about 180,000 medical men, who, by a liberal construction of the phrase, may be said to be educated; that is, who have some kind of a diploma; and for whose edification this current medical literature is produced. Of this number about 11,600 are producers of, or contributors to, this literature, being

Delivered in London, August 5, 1881, before the International Medical Congress. *Transactions of the International Medical Congress* (7th, London, 1881). v. 1, pp. 54–70.

divided as follows: United States, 2,800; France and her Colonies, 2,600; the German Empire and Austro-Hungary, 2,300; Great Britain and her Colonies, 2,000; Italy, 600; Spain, 300; all others, 1,000. These figures should be considered in connection with the number of physicians in each country; but this I can only give approximately, as follows: United States 65,000; Great Britain and her Colonies, 35,000; Germany and Austro-Hungary, 32,000; France and her Colonies, 26,000; Italy, 10,000; Spain, 5,000; all others, 17,000.

It will be seen from these figures that the number of Physicians who are writers, is proportionately greatest in France and least in the United States. As regards France, this is largely due to the requirement of a printed thesis for graduation, which of itself adds between six and seven hundred annually to the number of writers.

Excluding popular medicine, pathies, pharmacy and dentistry, all of which were included in the figures for the annual product just given, we find that the contributions to medicine, properly so called, form a little over 1000 volumes and 1600 pamphlets yearly.

For 1879, Rupprecht's Bibliotheca gives as the total number of new medical books, excluding pamphlets, periodicals and transactions, 419; divided as follows, viz.: France, 187; Germany, 110; England, 43; Italy, 32; United States, 21; all others, 26. These figures are, however, too small, and especially so as regards Great Britain and the United States. The Index Medicus for the same year shows by analysis that the total number of medical books and pamphlets, excluding periodicals and transactions was 1643; divided as follows: France, 541; Germany, 364; United States, 310; Great Britain, 182; all others, 246. This does not include the inaugural theses, of which 693 were published in France alone.

The special characteristics of the literature of the present day are largely due to journals and transactions, and this is particularly true in medicine. Our periodicals contain the most recent observations, the most original matter, and are the truest representations of the living thought of the day, and of the tastes and wants of the great mass of the medical profession, a large part of whom, in fact, read very little else. They form about one-half of the current medical literature, and in the year 1879 amounted to 655 volumes, of which the United States produced 156; Germany, 129; France, 122; Great Britain, 54; Italy, 65; and Spain, 24. This is exclusive of journals of pharmacy, dentistry, &c., and of journals devoted to medical sects and isms. These are given in an appended table from which it appears that the total number of volumes of medical journals and transactions of all kinds was for the year 1879,—850 and for 1880,—864. The figures for 1880 are too small, but the real increase is slight. During the year 1879, the total number of original articles in medical journals and transactions

TABLE I

The Number of Volumes of Medical Journals and Transactions Published in the Years 1879 and 1880.

Subjects	Journals and Transactions	United States		Gt. Brit. and Colonies		France & Colonies		Germany		Spain		Italy		All Others		Total	
		1879	1880	1879	1880	1879	1880	1879	1880	1879	1880	1879	1880	1879	1880	1879	1880
General and Miscellaneous, Practical Medicine, etc.	Journals	75	83	26	26	60	63	41	43	22	26	42	42	70	72	336	355
	Transactions	56	54	11	12	30	19	31	31	1	1	9	7	31	27	169	151
Anatomy, Physiology, Morphology, Biology	Journals			4	4	5	5	15	17	1		1			1	26	27
	Transactions	1	1			4	2									5	3
Diseases of Nervous System and Insanity	Journals	3	5	4	4	2	3	5	5			3	4			17	21
	Transactions					1										1	
Surgery	Journals		1					3	3							3	4
	Transactions	1					1	1	1							2	2
Ophthalmology	Journals	1	1	1	2	4	4	5	5	3	3	3	3	2	2	19	20
	Transactions							1	1			1				2	1
Skin Diseases	Journals	1	1	1	1	1	1	1	1			1	1			5	5
	Transactions	1	1													1	1
Otology	Journals	2	2			1	1	3	3							6	6
	Transactions	1														1	
Gynaecology and Obstetrics	Journals	2	2	1	1	5	7	6	6	1		2	2	1	2	18	20
	Transactions	3	1	2	1											5	2

This statistical table is rotated on the page and continues from the preceding page; the column headings are not printed on this page. Values are given for Journals and Transactions across sixteen columns, with a final "Total" column.

Subject	Type	1	2	3	4	5	6	7	8	9	10	11	12	13	14	15	16 (Total)
Hygiene and Medical Jurisprudence	Journals	40	36	6	6	4	3	3	1	13	13	5	5	3	2	6	6
	Transactions	13	13	1	1					13	4	2	3	4	2	3	3
Pharmacy and Medical Chemistry	Journals	54	53	9	9	5	5	5	5	15	15	5	5	6	7	9	7
	Transactions	4	8								1	1	3			3	4
Dentistry	Journals	15	10							3	2	2	2			10	6
	Transactions																
Homœopathy	Journals	36	33	3	3	2	3	1	1	7	7	3	3	4	4	16	12
	Transactions	4	5									1	2			3	3
Eclectic, Botanic, Physio-Medical, etc.	Journals	13	11													13	11
	Transactions	2	2													2	2
Popular, Advertising, Mineral Waters, etc.	Journals	33	35	2	2	2	2	2	2	5	5	8	12	4	4	10	8
	Transactions	1	1									1	1				
Veterinary	Journals	29	27	4	4	5	4			10	11	4	4	3	3	3	1
	Transactions																
Laryngology	Journals	2														1	1
	Transactions	1														1	1
Total	Journals	680	635	101	97	70	69	40	36	136	132	112	109	58	57	163	135
	Transactions	184	215	28	32	7	10	1	1	36	38	27	45	17	15	69	74

which were thought worth noting for the Index Medicus was a little over 20,000. Of these there appeared in American periodicals 4781, in French, 4608; in German, 4027; in English, 3592; in Italian, 1210; in Spanish, 703; in all others, 1248. The figures for 1880 are about the same. It will be seen that at present more of this class of literature appears in the English language than in any other, and that the number of journal contributions is greatest in the United States. The actual bulk of periodical literature is, however, greatest in Germany, owing to the greater average length of the articles. With regard to the mode of publication, I will only say that in all countries except Spain, the greater number of medical periodicals are monthly, while in Spain they are semi-monthly. It is this periodical literature which, more than anything else, makes medicine cosmopolitan, and although as regards new discoveries or methods of treatment, it is still somewhat farther from London or Berlin or Paris to New York, than it is from New York to either of these places, the discrepancy is gradually becoming less.

Many of the medical journals are very short lived, but the total number is increasing. In 1879, 23 such journals ceased, but 60 new ones appeared, and in 1880 there were 24 deaths and 78 births in this department of literature. Over one-third of this fluctuation occurs in the United States alone, France being next in the scale, Spain third and Italy fourth, while Great Britain is the most stable of all.

This merely quantitative classification gives of course no idea as to the character, and very little as to the value of the product. Let us now consider it by subjects. During 1879 there were published 167 books and pamphlets and 1543 articles relating to anatomy, physiology and pathology—that is, to the biological or scientific side of medicine. Dividing this again by nations, we find that Germany produced a majority of the whole, France being second. The proportionate production by nations of this class of literature is perhaps better shown by an analysis of the bibliography of physiological literature for the year 1879, as published by the Journal of Physiology. This shows 59 treatises and 500 articles in German, 17 treatises and 227 articles in French, 5 treatises and 77 articles from Great Britain, 8 treatises and 41 articles from Italy, and 2 treatises and 24 articles from the United States. The number of authors for this product was, German, 393, French, 119, English, 59, Italian, 39, United States, 19, all others, 41. For the year 1880 the same journal reports 62 treatises and 452 articles from Germany, 23 treatises and 216 articles from France, 12 treatises and 76 articles from Great Britain, 4 treatises and 51 articles from Italy, 6 treatises and 25 articles from the United States, and 10 treatises and 31 articles from all other countries.[1]

---

[1] The difference between these figures and those of the Index Medicus, is due, on the

When we turn to the literature of the art, or practical side of the profession the figures are decidedly different. We find over 1200 treatises and 18,000 journal articles which come under this head, and the order of precedence of countries as to quantity is: France, United States, Germany, Great Britain, Italy and Spain. The appended tables give still further subdivisions, showing by nations the number of works and journal articles upon the practice of medicine, surgery, obstetrics, hygiene, etc., for the years 1879 and 1880, and some of the figures will be found interesting. A marked increase has occurred in the literature of hygiene during the last two years, and this especially in England, France, Germany and the United States. The literature of diseases of the nervous system, of ophthalmology, otology, dermatology, and gynæcology, is also increasing more rapidly than that of the more general branches.

It would of course be extremely unscientific to use these figures as if they represented positively ascertained and comparable facts, the accuracy of which, as well as of the classification, could be verified. They represent merely the opinions of an individual—first as to whether each treatise or pamphlet included in these statistics was worth noting, and second as how it should be classed. Had everything been indexed the figures, for journal articles at least, might have been nearly doubled; while if the selection had been made by a more severe critic they might have been reduced one-half.

If I had to do the work again I should not obtain the same results. The prevailing error is that, as regards journal articles, the figures are too large, for some of those included are of so little value or interest that they are, I fear, never read by more than two persons.

Be that as it may, I think we can take them as indicating certain differences in the direction of work of the medical authors of the great civilized nations of the earth; but they must be considered as approximations only; and the statistical axiom must be remembered that the results obtained from a large number of facts are applicable to an aggregate of similar facts but not to single cases. There will be a certain number of medical books and papers printed next year, just as there will be a certain number of children born;—and as we can within certain limits predict the number of these births and the proportion of the sexes, or even of monsters;—so we can within certain limits predict the amount and character of literature that is yet to come, the ideas that are yet unborn. The differences are due to race, political organization, and density of population. As Dr. Chadwick

---

one hand, to the fact that the Journal of Physiology includes articles which are placed under other headings in the Index Medicus, and on the other hand, to the fact that the Journal has a different standard of excellence from that of the Index, rejecting many articles which the latter must accept as original.

TABLE II
THE MEDICAL LITERATURE OF 1879 AND 1880

Subjects	No. of	United States 1879	United States 1880	England 1879	England 1880	France 1879	France 1880	Germany 1879	Germany 1880	Italy 1879	Italy 1880	Spain 1879	Spain 1880	Others 1879	Others 1880	Total 1879	Total 1880
Anatomy and Physiology	Books	7	17	19	18	60	32	54	31	5	2	1	1	26	8	172	106
	Theses					25	24	4							6	29	30
	Jour. Articles	162	177	157	176	385	351	458	420	109	105	26	32	74	68	1371	1329
Pathology	Books	2	3		2	13	5	7	6					2	1	22	16
	Theses					11	7	3	1							16	9
	Jour. Articles	32	32	25	27	36	51	35	56	13	12	5	5	12	19	158	202
Practice of Medicine	Books	52	27	39	51	132	104	78	56	7	12	9	2	55	12	372	264
	Theses					248	216	7	12					2	7	257	235
	Jour. Articles	1454	1154	1085	918	1340	1056	1001	812	316	257	198	171	405	348	5799	4716
Diseases of Nervous System	Books	38	32	19	30	33	48	32	23	1	4	1		11	7	135	144
	Theses					56	51	3	4					4	4	63	59
	Jour. Articles	406	410	342	303	380	355	372	332	112	124	50	43	99	100	1761	1667
Surgery	Books	18	27	5	23	62	63	36	29	2	4	5	4	16	15	135	150
	Theses					144	144	15	6	1				5	11	165	161
	Jour. Articles	894	823	844	706	706	597	539	513	198	180	136	123	160	145	3477	3087
Ophthalmology	Books	10	15	7	7	13	18	20	17		1	5		5	5	60	64
	Theses					41	32	1	1					2	1	44	34
	Jour. Articles	187	228	81	101	310	252	254	271	59	58	52	52	49	45	992	1007
Otology	Books	3	9	3	1	2	7	2	6					2		12	23
	Theses					7	9	1								8	9
	Jour. Articles	114	185	38	74	31	73	102	158	11	9	5	16	12	20	313	535

Category	Type	C1	C2	C3	C4	C5	C6	C7	C8	C9	C10	C11	C12	C13	C14	C15	C16
Skin Diseases	Books	3	9	2	8	11	12	15	10	1	2		2	1	1	33	44
	Theses					21	24	1								22	24
	Jour. Articles	63	95	115	101	62	138	99	109	51	53	20	27	31	24	441	547
Venereal	Books	1	2	4	4	19	13	5	6		3			6	1	35	29
	Theses					19	19									19	19
	Jour. Articles	76	72	45	31	106	96	94	56	42	31	17	22	19	32	399	348
Gynaecology	Books	12	16	2	6	12	13	13	12	3	2	1		4	1	47	50
	Theses					40	25	3	2					1		44	27
	Jour. Articles	364	416	239	189	200	200	192	186	60	66	27	27	48	48	1130	1132
Obstetrics	Books	6	7	6	8	17	16	8	13		5	1	1	7	1	45	52
	Theses					33	47	2	1					1	1	37	49
	Jour. Articles	435	430	216	195	293	211	173	142	80	55	22	30	51	57	1270	1114
Hygiene	Books	62	80	29	48	39	80	29	28	3	5		2	16	4	178	247
	Theses					2	13								3	2	16
	Jour. Articles	173	239	161	237	186	271	235	202	27	26	33	30	76	56	891	1061
Jurisprudence	Books	2	2	1	1	9	18	2	4		4				1	15	30
	Theses					8	9		2							8	11
	Jour. Articles	72	167	44	103	85	173	80	160	33	46	18	28	36	49	368	726
Genral and Miscellaneous	Books	94	96	46	52	119	144	61	64	6	6	2	2	52	13	382	377
	Theses					22	50	2	7					5	6	29	63
	Jour. Articles	349	476	200	274	488	556	393	411	99	142	94	79	176	178	1799	2116
Total by Countries	Books	310	339	182	259	541	573	364	306	28	50	21	11	197	58	1643	1596
	Theses					677	670	42	36	1				23	40	743	746
	Jour. Articles	4781	4904	3592	3443	4608	4380	4027	3828	1210	1164	703	685	1248	1183	20,169	19,587

has pointed out, in speaking of the statistics of obstetric literature, one of the chief causes of the multiplication of medical societies is geographical. "In England it is possible for those who are specially interested in gynæcology and obstetrics to attend the meetings of the Obstetrical Society of London, whereas in America the distances are so great that this is impossible." Speaking broadly we may say that at present Germany leads in scientific medicine both in quantity and quality of product, and that the rising generation of physicians are learning German physiology. But the seed has gone abroad and scientific work is receiving more and more appreciation everywhere.

Seven years ago Professor Huxley declared that if a student in his own branch showed power and originality he dared not advise him to adopt a scientific career, for he could not give him the assurance that any amount of proficiency in the biological sciences would be convertible into the most modest bread and cheese. To-day I think he might be bolder, for such a fear would hardly be justifiable; at all events, in America; where such a man as is referred to could almost certainly find a place, bearing in mind the Professor's remark that it is no impediment to an original investigator to have to devote a moderate portion of his time to giving instruction either in the laboratory or in the lecture room.

Within the last ten years the literature of France, Germany, Great Britain, and the United States has contained much with regard to medical education and the means for its improvement. In all these countries there is more or less dissatisfaction with the existing condition of things, although there is no general agreement as to the remedy. Solomon's question, "Wherefore is there a price in the hands of a fool to get wisdom, seeing he hath no heart to it?" is now easily answered, for even a fool knows that he must have the semblance of wisdom, and a diploma to imply it, if he is to succeed in the practice of medicine; but to ensure the value of a diploma as a proof of education is the difficulty.

This evidence of discontent and tendency to change is a good sign. In these matters stillness means sleep or death—and the fact that a stream is continually changing its bed shows that its course lies through fertile alluvium and not through sterile lava or granite.

I have said that as regards scientific medicine we are at present going to school to Germany. This, however, is not the case with regard to therapeutics either external or internal,—in regard to which I presume that the physicians of each nation are satisfied as to their own pre-eminence. At all events it is true that, for the treatment of the common diseases, a physician can obtain his most valuable instruction in his own country; among those whom he is to treat. Just as each individual is in some respects peculiar and unique, so that even the arrangement of the minute ridges and furrows at the end of his forefinger differs from that of all other forefingers, and is sufficient to identify him; and as the members of certain families require special care to guard against hæmorrhage, or insanity, or phthisis; so it is with nations and races. The experienced military surgeon knows this well, and in the United States, which is now the great mixing ground, illustrations of race peculiarities are familiar to every practitioner.

Neither the tendency nor the true value of this current medical literature can be properly estimated by attending to it alone. It is a part of the thought of the age—of that wonderful kaleidoscopic pattern which is unrolling before us, and must be judged in connection with it. From several sources of high authority there have come of late years warnings and laments that science is becoming too utilitarian. For example, Prof. Du Bois-Reymond in his address upon civilization and science, says that that side of science which is connected with the useful arts is steadily becoming more prominent, each generation being more and more bent on material interests. "Amid the unrest which possesses the civilized world men's minds live as it were from hand to mouth. * * * And if industry receives its impulse from science it also has a tendency to destroy science. In short, idealism is succumbing in the struggle with realism and the kingdom of material interests is coming." Having laid down this rather pessimistic platform, he goes on to state that this is especially the case in America which is the principal home of utilitarianism, and that it has become the custom to characterize as "Americanization" the dreaded permeation of European civilization by realism. If this characterization be correct it would seem that Europe is pretty thoroughly Americanized as regards attention to material interests and appreciation of practical results. But the truth of the picture seems to me doubtful. Science is becoming popular, even fashionable, and some of its would be votaries rival the devotees of modern Æstheticism in their dislike and fear of the sunlight of comprehensibility and common sense. The languid scientific swell who thinks it bad style to be practical, who takes no interest in any thing but pure science, and makes it a point to refrain from any investigations which might lead to useful results lest he might be confounded with mere "practical men" or "inventors," exists and has his admirers. We have such in medicine, and their number will increase.

The separation of biological study from practical medicine, which has of late years become quite marked in the literature of the subject, has its advantages and disadvantages. Thus far the former have far outweighed the latter, and both the science and the art of medicine have been promoted thereby. But are not the physiologists, or as I believe they prefer to be called, the biologists, separating themselves too completely from medicine for the best interests of their own science, in that they are neglecting human pathology? In our hospital wards and among our patients, nature is continually performing experiments which the most dexterous operator cannot copy in the laboratory—she is, as Professor Foster says, "a relentless and untrammelled vivisector, and there is no secret of the living frame which she has not, or will not, at some time or place, lay bare in misery and pain."

Now while it is true that Professor Foster, in his address before the British Medical Association last year, (which address is the clearest exposition of the aims of the physiology of the present day that I have seen) insists upon the fact that all distinctions between physiology and pathology are fictitious, and declares that attempts to divide them are like attempts to divide meteorology into a science of good and a science of bad weather, his conclusion that the pathologist should be trained in methods of physiological investigation seems to me to be only a part of the truth. The tacit assumption is that all, or at least the most important, phenomena of human disease may be reproduced in the physiological laboratory. If this were only true, what a tremendous stride would have been taken towards making medicine a science. Unfortunately it is not so. Many of the most interesting of these phenomena—the most interesting because as yet the most unexplainable—can only be observed in the sick man himself. Nor have the physiologists as yet made much use of that field which ought to be specially inviting to them—namely: comparative pathology; although the literature of the present time already indicates that a change has begun in this respect.

While it is true that to the graduate of thirty years ago much of the physiological literature of the present day is in an unknown tongue, it is also true that the physiologist of the present, who confines himself to laboratory work, will find himself distanced by the man who keeps his clinical and pathological studies and his experimental work well abreast.

The increase in both the amount and value of the literature of the several specialities in medicine is readily seen by a comparison of recent catalogues and bibliographies with those of twenty or thirty years ago, and this increase still continues at a greater rate than prevails in the more general branches. There are great differences of opinion as to the relative value of this increase and as to its future effect upon the profession, but there can be no doubt as to the fact. There must be specialities and specialists in medicine, and the results will be both good and evil; but the evils fall largely upon those specialists who have an insufficient general education,—who attempt to construct the pyramid of their knowledge with the small end as a foundation. It has been said by Dr. Hodgen that "in medicine a specialist should be a skilled physician and something more, but that he is often something else—and something less." There is truth in this: truth which the young man will do well to consider with care before he begins to specialize his studies; but on the other hand it is also true that the great majority of men must limit their field of work very much and very clearly if they hope to achieve success. The tool must have an edge if it is to cut. It is by the labour of specialists that many of the new channels for thought and research have been opened, and if the flood has sometimes seemed to spread too far, and to lose itself in shallow and sandy places, it has nevertheless tended to fertilize them in the end.

The specialists are not only making the principal advances in science but they are furnishing both strong incentives and valuable assistance towards the collection and preservation of medical literature and the formation of large public libraries.

Burton declares that a great library cannot be improvised, not even if one had the national debt to do it with—thinks that 20,000 volumes is about the limit of what a miscellaneous collection can bring together, and refers especially to the difficulty in creating large public libraries in America. My experience would show that these statements do not apply to medical books. Of these the folios and quartos of three and four hundred years ago seem to have had great capacity for resistance to ordinary destructive forces. Perhaps much of this is due to the fact that they are not usually injured by too much handling or perusal. True, they are gradually becoming rarer, but at the same time by means of properly organized libraries they are becoming more accessible to all who wish to really use them, and not merely to collect and hide them away. They drift about like the sea weed, but the survivors are gradually finding secure and permanent resting-places in the score of great collections of such literature which the world now possesses. At present the currents of trade are carrying them in relatively large numbers to the United States, where medical collectors and specialists are among the best customers of the antiquarian booksellers of Europe. I could name a dozen American physicians who have given to European agents almost unlimited orders for books relating to their several specialties, and upon their shelves may be found books of the 15th and 16th centuries, which may be properly marked as "rarissime."

Not that the rarest books are by any means the oldest. The collector who seeks to ornament his shelves with the "Rose of John of Gaddesden," or the "Lily of Bernard de Gordon," the first folios of "Avicenna" or "Celsus," or almost any of the eight hundred medical incunabulæ described by Hain, will probably succeed in his quest quite as soon as the one who has set his heart on the first editions of Harvey or Jenner, the American tracts on inoculation for small-pox, or complete sets of many of the journals and transactions of the present century.

Whatever may be the chosen line of the book collector, he is the special helper of the public library, and this whether he intend it or not. In most cases his treasures pass through the auction room, and sooner or later the librarian, who can afford to wait, will secure them from further travel. Thanks to the labours of such collectors, I think it is safe to say,—what certainly would not have been true twenty years ago,—that if the entire medical literature of the world with the exception of that which is collected in the United States, were to be now destroyed, nearly all of it that is valuable could be reproduced without difficulty.

What is to be the result of this steadily increasing production of books? What will the libraries and catalogues and bibliographies of a thousand, or even of a hundred years hence be like, if we are thus to go on in the ratio of geometric progression, which has governed the press for the last few decades? The mathematical formula which would express this, based on the data of the past century, gives an absurd and impossible conclusion, for it shows that if we go on as we have been going there is coming a time when our libraries will become large cities, and when it will require the services of every one in the world, not engaged in writing, to catalogue and care for the annual product. The truth is, however, that the ratio has changed, and that the rate of increase is becoming smaller. In western Europe, which is now the great centre of literary production, it does not seem probable that the number of writers or readers will materially increase in the future, and it is in America, Russia, and southern Asia, that the greatest difference will be found between the present amount of annual literary product and that of a century hence.

The analogies between the mental and physical development of an individual, and of a nation or society, have been often set forth and commented on, but there is one point where the analogy fails as regards the products of mental activity,—and that is that as yet we have devised no process for getting rid of the exuviæ. Growth and development in the physical world imply the changes of death as well as of life—that with the increase of the living tissues there shall also be the excretion and destruction of dead, outgrown and useless matters which have had their day and served their purpose. But *litera scripta manet*. There is a vast amount of this effete and worthless material in the literature of medicine, and it is increasing rapidly. Our literature is in fact something like the inheritance of the golden dustman, but with this important difference, viz: that when the children raked a few shells or bits of bone from the dust-man's heap,—and, after stringing them together and playing with them a little while, threw them back,—they did not thereby add to the bulk of the pile,—whereas our preparers of compilations and compendiums, big and little, acknowledged or not, are continually increasing the collection, and for the most part with material which has been characterized as "superlatively middling, the quintessential extract of mediocrity." A large medical library is in itself discouraging to many inquirers, and I have become quite familiar with the peculiar expression of mingled surprise, awe and despair which is apt to steal over the face of one not accustomed to such work when he first finds himself fairly in the presence of the mass of material which he wishes to examine for the purpose of completing his ideal bibliography of,—let us say epilepsy,—or excisions,—or the functions of the liver.

Let such enquirers, as well as those who regret that they have no access to large libraries, and must therefore rely on the common text books and current periodicals for bibliography, console themselves with the reflection that much the larger part of all of our literature which has any practical value belongs to the present century, and indeed will be found in the publications of the last 20 years.

There are a few books written prior to 1800 which every well educated medical man should,—I will not say read but—dip into, such as some of the works of Hippocrates and Galen, of Harvey and Hunter, of Morgagni and Sydenham—but this is to be done to learn their methods and style rather than their facts or theories, and by the great majority of physicians it can be done with much more profit in modern translations than in the originals. The really valuable part of the observations of these old masters has long ago become a part of the common stock, and the results are to be found in every text book.

If, perchance, among the dusty folios there are stray golden grains yet ungleaned, remember that just in front are whole fields waiting the reaper. There is not, and has not been any lack of men who have the taste and time to search the records of the past, and the man who has opportunities to make experiments or observations for himself wastes his time, to a certain extent, if he tries to do bibliographical work so long as he can get it done for him. He wishes to know whether this problem has been attacked before, and with what result—whether there are accounts of any other cases like the one he has in hand. In ninety-nine instances out of a hundred if the answer to these questions is not given in the current text books or monographs it is not worth prolonged search by the original investigator. Yet he should know how to make this search, if only to enable him to direct others, and it is for this reason that a little acquaintance with bibliographical methods of work ought to be obtained by the student.

When a physician has observed or (thinks he has observed), a fact, or has evolved from his inner consciousness a theory which he wishes to examine by the light of medical literature, he is often very much at a loss to know how to begin, even when he has a large library accessible for the purpose.

The information he desires may be in the volume next his hand, but how is he to know that? And even when the usual subject-catalogue is placed before him he finds it very difficult to use it, especially when, as is often the case, he has by no means a well defined idea as to what it is he wishes to look for. Upon the title page of the Washington City Directory is printed the following aphorism, "To find a name you must know how to spell it." This has a very extensive application in medical bibliography. To find accounts of cases similar to your own rare case you must know what your own case is.

To return to the Subject-Catalogue. If it is a classed catalogue, a catalogue raisonnée—it will often seem to be a very blind guide to one who is not familiar with the classification and nomenclature adopted by the compiler. And certainly some of these classifications are very curious—reminding one of Heine's division of ideas into reasonable ideas, unreasonable ideas, and ideas covered with green leather. But if the enquirer has mastered the arrangement of the catalogue it is two to one that it will not help him. It is a catalogue of the titles of books, but very often the title of a book gives very little information as to its contents, if indeed it is not actually misleading. Now suppose the particular case he has in hand is one of a new-born infant having one leg much larger and longer than the other. He will find no book title relating to this. There may be a book in the library on diseases of the lymphatics which contains just what he wants, but unless he knows that his case is one affecting the lymphatics he will hardly get the clue. There may also be in the library twenty papers, in as many different volumes of journals and transactions, the titles of which show that they probably relate to similar cases, but the titles of such papers do not appear in the catalogue.

It should also be observed that Subject-Catalogues may easily be put to improper uses, or thought to give more information than they really do. They are not bibliographies, but mechanical aids in bibliographical work.

You will, perhaps, pardon me for taking as an illustration the Index Catalogue of the library of the Surgeon-General's office in Washington, as being one with which I am familiar, and which I can venture to comment on without risk of its being thought that I wish to depreciate its value. Taking any given subject in medicine, it is possible for a fairly educated physician to obtain from this catalogue a large proportion of all the references which have any special value, and by so doing to save a vast amount of time and labour. On the other hand, he will find when he comes to examine the books and articles referred to, that at least one-half of them are of no value so long as the other half are accessible, seeing that they are dilutions and dilatations, re-hashes and summaries of the really original papers. If the seeker is in the library itself, this does not cause a great waste of time, as he can rapidly examine and lay aside those that do not serve his purpose. But if he is using this catalogue in another library—say here in London, the case is different. It is highly improbable that he will find in any other collection all the books referred to, and then comes the annoyance of the doubt as to whether he may not be missing some very valuable paper. How is he to know whether or not Smith, in his pamphlet on the functions of the pneumogastric, has anticipated his own theory of its relations to enlarged tonsils? And in all such cases "omne ignotum est pro magnifico." In a bibliography of the subject, prepared from the same material as the catalogue, he would either find no mention of Smith's paper, or, better still, a note that his paper is merely an abstract, or compilation. The fact that he does not find Smith's book in the London library, nor any allusion to it in the best works on the subject, ought to induce him to ignore it altogether.

In proportion to the energy of the young writer, and his determination to not only note everything that has been written about his subject, but to carry out the golden rule of verifying all his references, he is apt to be led off from his direct research into the many attractive by-paths of quaint and curious speculation which he will find branching off on every side, and this danger must be guarded against, or he will find that he is wasting his time and energy in turning over chaff which has long ago been pretty thoroughly threshed and winnowed.

It is, however, no part of my present purpose to set forth the methods and principles of bibliography; it is sufficient to point out their importance, and to call attention to the point that a knowledge of how and where to find the record of a fact is often of more practical use than a knowledge of the fact itself, just as we value an encyclopædia for occasional reference, and not for the purpose of reading through from cover to cover.

Instruction in the history and literature of medicine forms no part of the course of medical education in English and American schools; nor should I be disposed to recommend its introduction into the curriculum if it were to be based on French and German models but it does seem possible to take a step in this direction which would be of great value, not only as a means of general culture, as teaching students how to think, but from a purely practical point of view, in teaching them how to use the implements of their profession to the best advantage—for books are properly compared to tools of which the index is the handle. Such instruction should be given in a library, just as chemistry should be taught in a laboratory. The way to learn history and bibliography is to make them—the best work of the instructor is to show his students how to make them.

In the absence of some instruction of this kind the student is liable to waste much time in bibliographical research. There has been much more done in this direction than many writers seem to suppose, and there are not many subjects in medicine which have not been treated from this point of view. Of course all is not bibliography which pretends to be such. Very many of the exhaustive and exhausting lists of references which are now so common in medical journal articles have been taken largely at second-hand, and thereby originate or perpetuate errors. It is well to avoid false pride in this matter. To overlook a reference is by no means discreditable, —but a wrong reference, or an unwitting reference to the same thing twice, gives a strong presumption of carelessness and second-hand work. Journal articles, however, and especially reports of cases, undergo strange trans-mogrifications sometimes, and I have watched this with interest in the case of a French or German paper, translated and condensed in the London Record, then appearing in abstract under the name of the translator in a leading journal, then translated again, with a few new circumstances, in a continental periodical, and finally perhaps reversed and appearing as an original contribution in the pages of the "Little Peddlington Medical Universe."

In this connection it is well to remember that a mere accumulation of observations, no matter how great the number, does not constitute science, especially if these observations have been recorded under the influence of the same theories and in essentially similar conditions.

Science seeks the law which governs or explains the phenomena, and when this is found the records of isolated instances of its action usually become of small importance so far as that law is concerned. We care little now for the records of the chemical experiments of a century ago, and the many detailed accounts of the earlier cases of the use of ether or chloroform are of so little interest at the present time that it is not worth while to refer to them in a bibliography of the subject. And although much has been done towards classifying and indexing our medical records (more in fact than most physicians suppose) still, as Helmholtz points out, such knowledge as this hardly deserves the name of science, since it neither enables us to see the complete connection nor to predict the result under new conditions yet untried.

Do I seem to depreciate the value of the thoughts which our masters have left us, and which have furnished the foundations on which we build?— or to undervalue the importance of the great medical libraries in which are stored these thoughts?—or to speak slightly of the utility of the catalogues, and indexes, and bibliographies, without which such libraries are trackless and howling wildernesses? If so, I have said what I did not mean to say. The subject has been considered from the point of view of what used to be called the division of labour, but which now I suppose should be called evolution and differentiation, and this has been done because life is short and the art is long,—with fair prospect of becoming longer. It is surely unnecessary for me to enter upon any panegyric of books or libraries. As

Dr. Holmes says: "It is not necessary to maintain the direct practical utility of all kinds of learning. Our shelves contain many books which only a certain class of medical scholars will be likely to consult. There is a dead medical literature, and there is a live one. The dead is not all ancient, the live is not all modern. There is none, modern or ancient, which, if it has no living value for the student, will not teach him something by its autopsy. But it is with the live literature of his profession that the medical practitioner is first of all concerned."

In medicine, as in social science, we must depend for many facts upon the observation of conditions which occur very rarely, and which cannot be repeated at pleasure. I have already alluded to the importance of Nature's vivisections to the physiologist, and a record of a case written a century ago may be just the link that is needed to correlate the results of his experiments of yesterday with existing theories. The case, which at first seems unique and inexplicable, both receives and furnishes light when compared with ancient records.

A science of medicine, like other sciences, must depend upon the classification of facts, upon the comparison of cases alike in many respects, but differing somewhat either in their phenomena or in the environment. The great obstacle to the development of a science of medicine is the difficulty in ascertaining what cases are sufficiently similar to be comparable—which difficulty is in its turn largely due to insufficient and erroneous records of the phenomena observed. This defect in the records is largely due—first, to ignorance on the part of observers; second, to the want of proper means for precisely recording the phenomena; and third, to the confused and faulty condition of our nomeclature and nosological classification.

Let us consider each of these points briefly. Very, very few are the men who can, by and for themselves, see and describe the things that are before them. Just as it took thousands of years to produce a man who could see what now any one can see when shown him, that the star Alpha in Capricorn is really two separate stars, so we had to wait long before the man came who could see the difference between measles and scarlatina, and still longer for the one who could distinguish between typhus and typhoid. Said Plato, "He shall be as a god to me, who can rightly divide and define." Men who have this faculty—the "Blick" of the Germans—we cannot produce directly by any system of education; they come we know not when or why, "forming a small band, a mere understanding of whose thoughts and works is a test of our highest powers. A single English dramatist, and a single English mathematician have probably equalled in scope and excellence of original work in their several fields all the like labours of their countrymen put together." [2]

---

[2] Iles, Mathematics in Evolution. Pop. Sci. Monthly, 1876, IX. p. 207.

But cannot we do something to increase the number of observers by tell-ing them what to observe? It is probable that much may be accomplished in this direction provided that care be taken to limit the field. Manuals of "what to observe at the bedside and in the post-mortem room" are very well in their way, but can never be made to reach the great majority of the profession, nor would they be of much use if they did. If a few, a very few, distinct specific questions are brought to the attention of the general prac-titioner, he will often be on the alert for their answer. And it should be remembered that chance may present to the most obscure practitioner an opportunity for observation which the greatest master may never meet.

The great difficulty is to get such questions prepared. They must relate to matters that are just in the nebulous region between the known and unknown—to points not yet clear, but of which we know enough to make it probable that by observing in a definite direction they can be made clear; and to prepare them requires not only knowledge, but a certain reaching out beyond knowledge. It usually happens that the man who has this faculty strives to answer his questions himself; and no doubt he can usually do it better than another. But much can be done towards defining and marking out what we do not know, and this has been a powerful aid to the progress of physiology in recent years.

I have had occasion to refer to this in speaking of Professor Foster's work on physiology, in each section of which an attempt is made to separate that which may be considered as proved from that which is merely prob-able; and thus almost every page becomes suggestive of work to be done.

Another example of what I mean will be found in a paper on the collec-tion of data at autopsies by Professor H. P. Bowditch of Boston (Trans. Mass. Med. Legal Soc. 1, 1880, p. 139). Taking the results of an investiga-tion into the absolute and relative size of organs at different periods of life, and in connection with different morbid tendencies, recently published by Professor Beneke of Warburg—Dr. Bowditch urges the securing as large a number as possible of such data, and selects certain of Professor Beneke's results for special inquiry; as for instance that "the cancerous diathesis is associated with a large and powerful heart, capacious arteries, but a relatively small pulmonary artery, small lungs, well developed bones and muscles, and tolerably abundant adipose tissue." It can hardly be doubted that those who read the papers of Professors Bowditch and Beneke will be induced to examine things which before would have had for them no interest, and therefore to make and record observations in pathological anatomy which otherwise would have been lost.

The second difficulty referred to—viz.: the want of means for making accurate records, is one that is yearly growing less. It behoves us to be modest in our predictions as to what may be accomplished in the future towards the solution of our Sphynx's riddle. We see as through a glass darkly, and except through the glass, in no wise; but at least we have made such progress that what we do see, we can to a great extent so record that our successors yet unborn can also see—and it is owing to this fact that a part of the medical literature of the last quarter of a 19th century will be more valuable than all that has preceded it.

The word-pictures of disease traced by Hippocrates and Sydenham, or even those of Graves and Trousseau, interesting and valuable as they are, are not comparable with the records upon which the skilled clinical teacher of the present day relies. Yet how imperfect in many cases are even the best of these records as compared with what might be given with the resources which we have at our command. The temperature chart has done away with the errors which necessarily follow attempts to compare the memory of sensations perceived last week with the sensations of to-day—and the balance and the burette enable us to estimate with some approach to precision the tissue changes of our patients by the records of change in the excretions which they furnish; but we must still trust to our memory, or to the imperfect descriptions of what others remember, when we attempt to compare the results obtained on successive days by auscultation or percussion, although the phonograph and microphone strongly hint to us the possibility of either accurately reproducing the sounds of yesterday, or of translating them into visible signs, perhaps something like the dot and dash record of the telegraph code, which could then be given to the press, and so compared with each other by readers at the Antipodes.

We are beginning to count the blood corpuscles, and to use photomicography, but we do not yet apply the latter process to the former so as to enable every reader to count for himself.

The connections of medicine with the physical sciences are yearly becoming closer, and the methods by which these sciences have been brought to their present condition are those by which progress has been, and is to be, made in therapeutics as well as in diagnosis or in physiological research. These methods turn mainly upon increasing the delicacy and accuracy of measurements: of expressing manifestations of force in terms of another force, or of dimension in space or time. The balance and the galvanometer, the microscope and the pendulum, the camera, the sphygmograph and the thermometer are some of the means by which investigators, at the bedside and in the laboratory, are seeking to obtain records which shall be independent of their own sensations or personal equations; which shall be taken and used as expressing not opinions but facts; and with every addition to or improvement in these means of measurement and record, the field of observation widens, and new and more reliable materials are furnished for the application of logical and mathematical methods.

Upon the third difficulty which has been referred to,—viz: our confused and defective terminology I need not dwell. "Science," said Condillac, "is a language well made," and though this is far from being the whole truth, it is an important part of it. In examining medical reports and statistics, it is necessary to bear constantly in mind that to understand many terms you must know what the individual writer means by them. When, for example, we find in such statistics a certain number of deaths attributed to gastro-enteritis, or croup, or scrofula, we have to take into account the country, the period and the individual author in order to get even a fair presumption as to what is meant.

The three difficulties which have been referred to, although the most important, are by no means the only causes of the confusion and imperfection of our records.

Prominent among the minor troubles of the investigator are defective or misleading titles;—and in behalf of the readers and bibliographers of the future I would appeal to authors, and more especially to editors, to pay more attention than many of them do to the matter of titles and indexes. The men to whom your papers are most important, and who will make the best use of them provided they knew of their existence, are for the most part hard workers, busy men, who have a right to demand that their literary table shall be provided with properly prepared materials and not with shapeless lumps.

The editors of transactions of societies, whether these are sent to journals, or published in separate form, often commit numerous sins of omission in the matter of titles. The rule should be that every article which is worth printing is worth a distinct title, which should be as concise as a telegram, and be printed in a special type. If the author does not furnish such a title it is the editors business to make it, and he should not be satisfied with such headings as "Clinical Cases," "Difficult Labour," "A Remarkable Tumour," "Case of Wound, with Remarks." The four rules for the preparation of an article for a journal will then be: 1. Have something to say; 2. Say it; 3. Stop as soon as you have said it; 4. Give the paper a proper title.

Some societies and editors do not seem to appreciate fully their responsibility for the articles which they accept for publication, a responsibility which cannot be altogether avoided by any formal declaration disclaiming it. This is due to the fact that while the merits of a paper can usually be determined by examination, this is by no means always the case. In every country there are writers and speakers whose statements are received with very great distrust by those best acquainted with them. Supposing these statements to be true, the papers would be of much interest and importance; but the editor should remember that a certain number of readers, and especially those in foreign countries, have no clue to the character of the author, beyond the fact that they find his works in good company. In medical literature, as in other departments, we find books and papers from men who are either constitutionally incapable of telling the simple literal truth as to their observations and experiments, although they may not write with fixed intention to deceive, or from men who seek to advertise themselves by deliberate falsehoods as to the results of their practice. Such men are usually appreciated at their true value in their immediate neighbourhood, and find it necessary to send their communications to distant journals and societies in order to secure publication.

I presume that you are all familiar with the peculiar feeling of distrust which is roused by too complete an explanation. The report of a case in which every symptom observed, and the effect of every remedy given, is fully accounted for, and in which no residual unexplained phenomena appear, is usually suspicious, for it implies either superficial observation, or suppression, or distortion of some of the facts. A diagrammatic representation is usually much plainer than a good photograph, but also of much less value as a basis for further work.

No fact is more familiar to this audience than the vast extent of the field of the science of to-day—so vast that few may hope to master more than a small part of it, and yet so closely connected that even the small part cannot be fully grasped without some acquaintance with a much wider field.

But little over a hundred years ago, Haller in Göttingen was professor of anatomy, botany, physiology, surgery, and obstetrics, and lecturer on medical jurisprudence. At the same time he was writing one review a week, and summing up existing medical science in his Bibliothecæ. To-day any one of these branches requires all the time of the most energetic and learned of our contemporaries; but, on the other hand, the well-educated medical graduate of to-day could give Haller valuable instruction in each of the branches of which he was professor. It is also true, as I have pointed out, that our actual progress is by no means in proportion to the work done, nor as great as these merely quantitative statements would seem to make it.

Science has been termed "the topography of ignorance." "From a few elevated points we triangulate vast spaces, enclosing infinite unknown details. We cast the lead and draw up a little sand from abysses we shall never reach with our dredges. If it is true that we understand ourselves but imperfectly in health, it is more signally manifest in disease, where natural actions imperfectly understood, disturbed in an obscure way by half seen causes, are creeping and winding along in the dark toward their destined issue, sometimes using our remedies as safe stepping stones, occasionally, it may be, stumbling over them as obstacles." [3]

---

[3] "Border Lines of Knowledge," etc., by O. W. Holmes, Boston, 1862, pp. 7–8.

In days of old, when the profession of medicine, or of a single medical specialty was an inheritance in certain families, a large part of their knowledge, and the efficiency of their remedies was thought to depend upon these being kept a profound mystery. Among the precepts of magic there was no more significant one than that which declared that the communication of the formula destroyed its power, and that hence attempts to reveal the secret must always fail. We have changed all that. Every physician hastens to publish his discoveries and special knowledge, and a good many do the same by that which is not special, or which is not knowledge. For the individual, in a degree—for the nation or the race in a much greater degree —the literature produced is the most enduring memorial. The whole result of civilization has been cynically defined as being roughly, "Three hundred million Chinese, two hundred million natives of India, two hundred million Europeans and North Americans, and a miscellaneous hundred million or two of Central Asians, Malays, South Sea Islanders, &c., and over and above all the rest the Library of the British Museum. This is the net result of an indefinitely long struggle between the forces of men and the weights of various kinds in the attempts to move which these forces display themselves." [4]

And thus in our great medical libraries each of the folios or quaint little black letter pamphlets which mark the first two centuries of printing, or of the cheap and dirty volumes of more modern days with their scrofulous paper and abominable typography, represents to a great extent the life of one of our profession and the fruit of his labours, and it is by the fruit that we know him.

After stating that modern physicists have concluded that the sun is going out, that the earth is falling into the sun, and therefore that it and all things in it will be either fried or frozen, Professor Clifford concludes that "our interest lies so much with the past as may serve to guide our actions in the present, and with so much of the future as we may hope will be affected by our actions now. Beyond that we do not know and ought not to care. Does this seem to say let us eat and drink for tomorrow we die? Not so, but rather let us take hands and help for this day we are alive together." To this I join a verse from the Talmud which will remind you of the first aphorism of Hippocrates, and is none the worse for that. "The day is short, and work is great,—the reward is also great, and the master presses. It is not incumbent on thee to complete the work, but thou must not therefore cease from it."

---

[4] "Liberty, Equality and Fraternity," by James Fitz James Stephen, N.Y., 1873, p. 178.

Address to the Graduating Class of Bellevue Hospital Medical College

I vaguely remember that once upon a time—a long while ago it seems, for I look back at it across the gulf of a great war, in which the days were like weeks, and the months almost counted for years—I spent one evening on a platform in a large hall, in the character of a new graduate in medicine. A part of the ceremonies on that auspicious occasion consisted of a valedictory address to the graduates, delivered by the most eloquent member of the faculty—an address which was highly praised, but of which I have vainly tried to remember either the ideas or the phraseology. Fearing that this specially localized loss of memory might be a symptom of a new nervous disease which I should have to name and describe, I have consulted several of my medical friends as to their experience in this respect, and I am much pleased to be able to say that I have found very few who have not totally forgotten the words of congratulation and of counsel given to them when they received their diplomas.

Nor is the reason of this far to seek. The new doctor, in the pride and vigor of youth, just stepping out of leading-strings, and realizing that he is really his own man at last—standing at the threshold of that wonderful, glittering world which beckons him on so enticingly, and in which fame, and love, and wealth await his coming—this learned and skilful physician is held back yet another hour, and compelled to listen to advice from one whom he does not know, but who can surely have nothing to tell him beyond some well-worn platitudes about the dignity and honor of the profession which he has chosen, and that if he will be virtuous he will be happy, or words to that effect. Small wonder then that, after a moment's attention, his thoughts wander, and he drifts away on that beautiful river of revery upon whose banks are Spanish castles unmatched by those of the Rhine or the Danube, and which are in strange contrast to the practical, prosaic, warehouse sort of a view which his orator is trying to present. If, therefore, I observe five minutes hence that some of my special audience here, the new graduates, are gazing reflectively upon some point of infinite distance, or are evidently magnetized by some particular wave in the sea of this other audience before me, I shall know that it is all quite as it should be, and that my remarks are fulfilling their purpose.

Being unable, as I have just explained, to remember what was said to

Delivered March 15, 1882. *Medical News* (Phila) 40: 285–8 (1882).

me by way of valedictory, and never having been present at a similar cere-
mony from that day to this, I thought it would be prudent to consult the
literature of the subject and find out what is usually said upon such occasions. For this purpose I have examined about a hundred valedictory addresses, and have obtained from them a vast amount of instruction, and
some little amusement. From them I gather that this is an epoch in your
lives, that you are entering a remarkable age of the world's history (it is
customary here to allude to steam and electricity), that you live in the most
wonderful country under the sun, and that the eyes of the world are upon
you. All are agreed upon these points, and also as to the importance and
dignity of the science and art of medicine, and the necessity of continued
study on your part to keep pace with its advances. But the addresses are not
equally harmonious on all points. Some of them assert that the condition of
medical education in this country is not altogether satisfactory, that there
are some medical colleges (not, of course, the college of the graduates, but
some other medical college) which might be spared, that there are too many
doctors now, and more coming, and that some of these not only have not as
clear ideas about the precession of the equinoxes, or the authorship of the
book of Job, as a member of one of the learned professions should have, but
that there are even graduates in medicine (of other schools, of course), to
whom the addition of vulgar fractions is a stumbling-block, and correct
spelling vexation of spirit. On the other hand I find some who assert, first,
that the above statements are unfounded; second, that it is not necessary to
know how to spell correctly in order to cure the chills or set a broken leg;
and third, that the demand for higher medical education is essentially a
pernicious aristocratic movement, calculated to oppress the poor, and prevent them from obtaining the sheepskins so desirable to cover their naked-
ness. As, however, I am sure that all of you are just now strongly in favor
of higher medical education, without regard to what you may have thought
about it a few weeks ago, or what you may think of it a few years hence,
when you get a little steam-hatching machine of your own, I feel that I shall
most contribute to the harmony which this occasion demands by—entirely
agreeing with you.

Upon the whole, I came to the conclusion that on this occasion it is
safest to talk platitudes; in fact, I must do this if I am to advise you as a
body. The inexorable laws of statistics tell me that among you are those
having the most diverse capacities, purposes, and destinations. Two or
three of you will go on with your studies for the next ten or fifteen years,
observing, experimenting, reading, and comparing, until some fine day
you will know something that other people don't know, and will become
writers and teachers, leaders in your profession, famous in your day and
generation. One or two of you may become popular physicians, for whom
being called in consultation is an everyday matter, and a large income a

matter of course. Many of you will become plain, solid, common-sense practitioners, who will do a vast amount of good, be indispensable to the comfort and safety of the community, and be happy because satisfied, which is more than I can predict of the others. A few will abandon medicine because it does not pay, and turn to some occupation of better promise. And one or two will slip farther and faster down the broad, smooth path of dissipation on which their feet have already taken the first step, and will pass on to the inevitable end.

Fortunately for all of us, nobody knows who are to be the black sheep and who are to win the prizes. Each of you must live out that which is in your brains and blood, the result of generations gone before; but, you have also to live out that which you yourselves add to the inheritance.

Now you are going out to Vanity Fair duly armed and equipped, and provided with maps and guide-books of the latest and most approved editions. Probably you will never again be so fully conscious of, or so thoroughly satisfied with, your knowledge of the science and art of medicine as you are to-night. What would I not give now to know as much as I thought I knew the day I received my diploma. And yet the seven world problems of Du Bois-Reymond are still unsolved.

I congratulate you on your prospects. Shall I tell you what some of them are? Our American life will present to you as much variety, as vivid contrasts, as subtle mysteries, and as many giants, demons, and sirens to be overcome or outwitted as any that the legends of old depict. No doubt you will soon come across some of that curious sect, the *antis*, who are beginning to make their appearance amongst us; antivaccinationists, antivivisectionists, anti-anything, so that it gives them an excuse to keep their names before the public. And when you are asked how you account for the voluminous statistics and startling facts which some of these antis produce so rapidly and easily, you may hesitate a little, unless you have heard the celebrated conundrum which I am about to give you. A little boy said, "That girl is the daughter of my father and my mother, but she is not my sister. How do you account for that?" And the answer is (this is strictly confidential), that the little boy lied. Taking them all in all, these antis are a curious class of cranks, worthy of careful study on the part of some of our experts in mental diseases, during the brief intervals in which they have no medico-legal case on hand. Some of them are quite honest in their convictions, and all are very theological and emotional in their appeals, and to this they owe what success they have in achieving notoriety; and yet, while professing the most humane sentiments, they are unscrupulous even to cruelty in carrying out their fantastic ideas. They will not greet your coming on the stage of action with any particular enthusiasm, but you must not be discouraged on that account.

You will find, also, that the manufacturing pharmacist is abroad in the land, and that he, on the other hand, will be very glad to make your acquaintance. He will not only supply you with toothsome preparations, neatly put up in artistic packages, but he will tell you what they are good for, in what doses to use them, and, most important of all, which of them are in accordance with the code of ethics. He will ornament your office with innumerable samples, and pleasantly interrupt and variegate the perusal of your medical journals by means of blue, green, and yellow advertising sheets, unexpectedly and neatly inserted. Under his friendly guidance the path of medicine becomes a flowery one, for all that you have to do is to decide upon the name of the disease of your patient, and then look over the advertisements and samples to see what will cure it.

Moreover, there are some canvassers, and publishers and editors, who are prepared to be your best friends if you will only permit it. They want you in the first place to subscribe, and then to write; to produce from the stores of your knowledge, items, and essays, and papers, to help them to raise the standard of American medical literature, until it shall be high above that of the effete despotisms of Europe. Nor are these the only persons who await your coming. You are wanted in Medical Societies, the advocates of higher medical education rely on your support, Boards of Health and Registrars are looking to you to make their statistics perfect and complete, and Army and Navy Medical Examining Boards are preparing fresh lists of questions for your benefit. But perhaps you flatter yourselves that you have now passed your final examination. Never was a greater mistake. Your most severe and continued ordeal is just about to begin. And it may be that the result will give rise in some of your minds to serious doubts as to the value of the Darwinian theory about the survival of the fittest. But at all events I can assure you that you need have no fear as to there not being room for you, or that the world has not work enough for you to do. You know the old saying, "There is always plenty or room on top." But even in the lower stories there is plenty of standing room. There are to-day between one and two millions of sick persons in the United States, and the deaths for this year will certainly be a million. You see, therefore, that the sanitarians, whom some of you may, unwisely, look upon as enemies, since they are trying to do away with some of the causes which necessitate your services, have, at all events, not yet seriously injured the business of the profession. And for your further encouragement I will predict that it will be a long time before they succeed in doing this, for whatever variations the changing seasons bring to our other harvests, the fool crop continues with almost unvarying regularity.

While I am on this subject, however, let me advise you from the business point of view, as well as on account of your interests as citizens and humanitarians, to look into this matter of preventive medicine a little more closely than you have yet probably had time to do. It is going to be a very important matter in your day and generation, and you will be examined and cross-questioned on it to an extent which you little suspect. Some of you will no doubt be called to act as members of Boards of Health, and all of you are sure to be appealed to on questions of ventilation, house drainage, school hygiene, pure water, adulterated food and drugs, and the means of shunning or putting away the pestilences, which will consume, not only the children of other people, but your own also, if you cannot answer the sphinx's riddle.

You will find that public health legislation is a matter to which you cannot remain indifferent, for you will become part of the machinery whether you wish to or not, and if you are wise you will study the subject so that you can aid in shaping this legislation to what it should be, for in this respect knowledge is power. If you leave the matter to sentimental enthusiasts and professional office-seekers, you will find that it will turn out like the Irishman's ale—it will thicken as it clears. One of the matters just alluded to touches your professional work very nearly, and that is the adulteration of drugs. If you practice in a large city, this is not of so much importance, since you can always readily find first-class pharmacists, upon whose preparations you can rely, but away from the great centres, the case is different. Unless you can depend upon getting what you call for in your prescription, what success can you hope for? and yet unless you know what apothecary is to fill that prescription, you cannot rely upon it. And it is always wise not to conclude that your treatment has failed until you have made sure that what you ordered has really been given.

And in this immediate connection, permit me to remind you why the hyrax has no tail. It is written in the mystic volume of St. Nicholas that when the world was about being completed, notice was issued to all the beasts that, if they would go to the Court of the King on a certain day, they would be handsomely finished off with tails. All were pleased with the prospect, but the hyrax was especially delighted. Now when the appointed day came, it was cold and rainy, and the hyrax did not like to go out in bad weather. So he stood in his door and asked the lion and the wolf and several others to bring him his tail, and they all promised to attend to it. But they all forgot it; and when the hyrax went himself the next day to see about it, he found that the supply of tails was exhausted. That is why the hyrax has no tail, and if you rely on what other people tell you that they have done, or are going to do, for you, the result will probably be about the same.

And just here permit me to give you an entirely new bit of advice; at least, I did not find it in any of the valedictories I read. You will, of course, never ask a man who is not acquainted with you personally to give you recommendations or testimonials; but see to it that you yourselves never sign a recommendation for a man whom you do not know. Do not be persuaded or bullied into doing this by people whom you know, for people whom they know, but you do not. If you wish your name and opinion to have any value in the eyes of other people, respect them yourself.

Do not be in a hurry to write or teach. The American press has been said to be chronically premature, and the same may be said of a good many graduates—not, of course, of this school, but of some other schools; and not only in this country, but in other countries. There are a great number of men, in all professions, and in all parts of the world, of whom it may be truly said, that if they knew more, they would say less. Try to know something of all branches of science, for they all throw light upon your work; and at the same time try in some one branch in your own special field of study to know more than anybody else, and to be sure that you really do know it. This is not so difficult as it may seem. You will not have to go far in any direction before you will come upon that which is doubtful or unknown—questions which as yet have no answers. And if, during your pupilage, you have learned to think, and are not, as Holmes phrases it, merely "phonographs on legs," the rest is a mere matter of detail, and this advice is not difficult to follow. Hesiod said that in his day there were three kinds of men—those who understand things of themselves, those who understand things when they are explained to them, and those who neither understand things of themselves nor when they are explained to them. That was the classification in Greece over two thousand years ago, but it is a convenient one for use even now; and when a man has settled for himself to which class he belongs, his education has taken a long stride.

Each of you has his aspirations—a little vague, no doubt, but none the less real. Keep them as long as possible, and, above all things, do not assume or affect a cynicism which belongs neither to your age nor your experience. Second-hand misanthropy is like a second-hand Chatham Street coat: it never fits. No doubt you all desire to make money; not for the money's sake, but for what you can do with it. It is not a desire to be ashamed of, and the business side of your profession demands your careful attention. But mark this: The best works in this world are not done for money, or from selfish motives of any kind. And if you are to achieve true success—the success which brings happiness, and is the only kind worth seeking—you must do a vast amount of work, not for money, but in part because you like it, and in part because it will do good and help others. Do not wait for the opportunity to do some great thing. Take hold of the work that lies next your hand; work which you can do, and which ought to be done—it will be very strange if there is not always something of that sort waiting for you; and do not dawdle, and defer, and lose the good, in a vain waiting and longing for the best.

Be healthy, brave-hearted, and joyous. Physical health is unfortunately not contagious, but mental and moral health is. Avoid second-hand philosophy, sickly complainings about the evils and miseries of life, and small beer of all kinds. No doubt you will find many of your golden dreams fading into gray mists; but, on the other hand, you will be continually stumbling against solid realities, which are quite as good as any dreams if you only recognize the opportunity. Labor and trouble you must meet; but of the first you can for the most part make a pleasure, and the second should not be pampered and made a luxury of. Never pity yourselves. Do not waste your time in vain speculations as to the why. Remember that bitter little poem of Heine's:

"By the sea, by the dreary, darkening sea, stands a youthful man,
His head all questioning, his heart all doubting,
And with gloomiest accent he questions the billows.
Oh, solve me life's riddle, I pray ye, the torturing ancient enigma
O'er which full many a brain hath long puzzled....
Tell me, what signifies man? Whence came he hither?
                    Where goes he hence?....
"The billows are murmuring their murmur unceasing,
Wild blows the wind, the dark clouds are fleeting,
The stars are still gleaming so calmly and cold,
And a fool is awaiting an answer."

In the majority of valedictory addresses which I have examined, there was more or less special advice about medical ethics, and a word or two on this subject is therefore not out of place. The code—or perhaps I should now rather say the codes—of medical ethics are great mysteries to the public at large. By many it is supposed to be a sort of trades-union set of rules designed to protect the business interests of physicians, without any particular regard to the rest of the world. I need hardly say to you that this is not true. It may be summed up in this, that a physician should be a gentleman, and should treat other physicians and his patients as he would wish to be treated under like circumstances. And your duty in this matter is to attend to your own ethics and not those of other people. Medicine is not a rigid system of rules and formulæ as it was in ancient Egypt; a fixed creed to which you are to subscribe, and from which you must not vary. It is a living, growing thing, making use of every resource which the progress of science brings; it is truly eclectic and catholic, testing all things, and holding fast to that which is good. It is not a system which forbids the use of any particular remedy, or limits its followers within the narrow bounds of any sect or ism. There are such systems, and there are a few men who advertise themselves as followers of such systems, and who really do follow them. There are also many men who so advertise, but who really do not follow them. Some of these last are well-educated physicians, "but they are—that is to say, from the point of view of a gentleman, they must be considered as—in short, the more you know of their methods the more fervidly you will assent to what I have not said about them."

One of the latest authoritative expressions of opinion on this subject is the following resolution recently adopted by the Royal College of Physicians in London:

"While the College has no desire to fetter the opinion of its members in reference to any theories they may see fit to adopt in connection with the practice of medicine, it nevertheless considers it desirable to express its opinion that the assumption or acceptance by members of the profession of designations implying the adoption of special modes of treatment is opposed to those principles of the freedom and dignity of the profession which should govern the relations of its members to each other and to the public. The College, therefore, expects that all its fellows, members, and licentiates will uphold these principles by discountenancing those who trade upon such designations." This last sentence touches the root of the difficulty. *Those who trade upon such designations.* Let us take a concrete example. You treat a case of pemphigus with arsenic. You may theorize as you like about the essential nature of pemphigus; you may select arsenic because you think it would produce the disease, or because you think it produces something contrary to the disease, or for no reason whatever beyond the empirical fact that you have seen a case of pemphigus recover under the use of arsenic. Also, you may give this arsenic alone or combined with other substances, and in any doses that you please, from the decillionth of a grain to a grain, and you may explain the results as you like. But as an educated physician, and a gentleman, you may not advertise yourself as an arsenio-pemphigist, and denounce every one who does not adopt your theory and practice, and as there is a good deal of common-sense truth in the old adage, that a man may be known by the company he keeps, you will not have more to do than you can help with the men who do so advertise themselves; and still less will you have to do with those who advertise themselves as antiarsenio-pemphigists, and then treat their cases with arsenic after all, and claim the results as due to dynamized brickdust.

And please observe that this is all that you have to do. You are not to enter into controversies with them or about them, you are not to repine over their success or exult over their failures. They have another code of ethics from your own; that is all that need be said about it. Thus far I have been speaking of fairly educated sectarian physicians. As to the ordinary, uneducated, and bill-distributing quack, with his sure cure for cancer, or his pure vegetable specific for coughs, rheumatism, and dyspepsia, you may be sure that in the long run he will make rather more business for you than he takes away. Do not fall into the error of supposing that legislation can prevent the existence of this class of men, or that you need the protection of the law against them. The public interest demands such protection, if for no other reason than to secure a proper registration of the causes of death of all citizens, and it is not only your right, but your duty, to call the attention of legislators to these interests, but never seek protection on your own account.

Be honest to yourselves as well as to other people, and do not be afraid of admitting that you do not know, or feel bound to attempt an explanation of all that you see or do. He who would know anything thoroughly must be content to be ignorant of many things. Try to define to yourselves, as clearly as possible, your own ignorance; it is the first step towards remedying it, and be sure that the modest student, whether he be undergraduate or learned professor, will everywhere meet with helping hands in the great brotherhood of science.

There are many men who are honest in purpose, and yet who are constantly, although not consciously, untruthful; they see that which they think they ought to see, and not that which is.

I am reminded that this is a valedictory address, and that in it I must bid you farewell. This I do in behalf of your teachers, whose unavailing regrets that they are not to have another opportunity of meeting you in the examination-room, you can imagine much better than I can describe. What they could do for you they have done. And now, as Emerson says, "We have accompanied you with sympathy, and manifold old sayings of the wise, to the gate of the arena, but 'tis certain that not by strength of ours, or of the old sayings, but only on strength of your own, unknown to us or to any, that you must stand or fall." You may be sure of our best wishes for your success and happiness.

"Who misses or who wins the prize, go lose or conquer as you can;
But if you fall or if you rise, be each, pray God, a gentleman."

But while I bid you farewell as students, I also bid you welcome to the ranks of the profession. And I can assure you, that upon the whole, you are coming into very good company. If in anything I have said this evening I have seemed to speak lightly of the medical profession or its adjuncts, I hope it will not be construed as more than the ordinary banter in which we boys sometimes indulge when we get off in a corner by ourselves.

I have much faith in the advice of that anonymous writer who said—

"Oh, never wear a brow of care, or frown with rueful gravity,
For wit's the child of wisdom, and good humor is the twin.
No need to play the Pharisee, or groan at man's depravity;
Let one man be a good man, and let all be fair within.

Speak sober truth with smiling lips; the bitter wrap in sweetness,
    Sound sense in seeming nonsense, as the grain is hid in chaff.
And fear not that the lesson e'er may seem to lack completeness,
    A man may say a wise thing, though he say it with a laugh."

It is true that you are entering, nay, in your medical studies you have already entered, a world of labor, and pain, and sorrow. You will see how the destruction of the poor is their poverty, and how the sins of the fathers are visited upon the children; how neither culture, nor wealth, nor power, can forever put off the evil day; and how there is, at last, one event to all sons of men.

You must be prepared to deal with anxiety, fear, grief, and despair, as well as fever and physical pain; you are to be not only physician, but friend, confessor, guide, and judge, and you cannot avoid these responsibilities if you would, nor should you if you could.

Nevertheless, I can assure that you are also entering a beautiful world, where the very shadows prove that plenty of sunshine exists, a world of brave men and good women, whose best and noblest characteristics are brought out most clearly and vividly in such scenes as those in which you will be called to act. But remember, that as a rule, you will find only what you seek and believe in. Remember, also, that this knowledge which you have acquired, and are yet to acquire, is entrusted to you as a power, a power none the less real, and involving no less responsibility because it is accompanied by no special outward insignia of authority or rank.

By the help of this knowledge you are to get wisdom—that wisdom which always lingers, and sometimes comes too late; that wisdom of which it is written that for all the children of men "length of days are in her right hand, as in her left hand riches and honor."

Medical Bibliography

Mr. President and Gentlemen of the Faculty:

First of all, permit me to return thanks for the honor of being called upon to address you at this Annual Meeting, and also for the distinction of an election as an Honorary Member of this body. As regards the latter, my thanks are unqualified; as regards the former, I am reminded of the comparison of such honors to that little book described in Revelation as being "sweet in the mouth but bitter in the belly," since the preparation of such an address as one would wish to present to this assemblage, is by no means an unmixed pleasure; and if my reflections while hesitating in the choice of a subject for this occasion could be given in full, they would illustrate this capitally.

I thought of a number of things which would probably interest you, at all events I should very much like to hear something about them myself; but, unfortunately, I knew just enough about them to deprive me of that unhesitating confidence with which one can advise about matters of which he is quite ignorant,—and yet not enough to feel that I had anything to say about them which would be worth listening to.

Once upon a time—many years ago it was—I had a patient! This patient was a locomotive engineer, who ran the night express on one of our great Western through-lines. He told me that on dark and stormy nights he drove his engine into the blackness ahead without special anxiety or fear, but on the moonlight nights, when the vista into which vanished the glittering rails in front was half revealed, and when the bars of shadow across the track seemed like missing rails or fallen tree-trunks, he was fearful and hesitating, and that the nervous strain then became great and exhausting. It was a new illustration of the old proverb, "Where ignorance is bliss," etc.

But to return to my subject, or rather to my want of a subject. I thought of matters of local interest, of the relations of physicians to public health, the management of smallpox epidemics, and the Baltimore Ordinance for the Control of Contagious Diseases; of the vital statistics of Maryland, and a comparison of the results obtained by the census with those which may be deduced from a multiplication of the supposed number of houses by the estimated number of persons per house; of

Address at the 85th Annual Session of the Medical and Chirurgical Faculty of Maryland, held at Baltimore, April 1883. *Transactions of the Medical and Chirurgical Faculty of Maryland*, 1883. pp. 58–80.

higher medical education, and the probable relations the Medical Department of the Johns Hopkins University will have to it and to other
medical schools in this city; of hospitals in general, and the merits and
demerits of the Johns Hopkins Hospital in particular; of quarantine
versus scientific investigation, and the National Board of Health *versus*
the Marine Hospital Service; and the result of these reflections was that
the progress of science and the harmony of this auspicious occasion would
be best aided and preserved by letting all these subjects carefully
alone. "Let us remember," said Whewell, "that we are not infallible, not
even the youngest of us," and in all these matters let each abide in his own
belief; that is, of course, provided that we cannot persuade or drive
him out of it.

Finally, I decided to occupy the time with a talk about medical bibliography and how this Faculty can promote it. The trouble did not end,
however, with the selection of a subject; far from it. Do you remember
Fuseli's description of his method of painting a picture? He said, "First I
sits myself down; then I works myself up; then I puts in my shades; then
I drags out my lights." This sounds simple and easy; but, in the first
place, I could find no time or opportunity to sit down to this business
until a few days ago. As to the working up—let me take you behind
the scenes for a moment, and in the strictest confidence show you how it
was done.

In the first place, a sheet of foolscap was covered with notes of headings, such as "definition," "utility," "history," "necessity for truthfulness," "difference between a bibliography and an index," "method of
work," "how to use a library," etc., etc. Then I wrote out more fully the
few ideas I had derived from personal experience. Then I took up the
Index Catalogue of the Washington library and turned to the heading
"Bibliography (Medical)." In this particular case I happened to know
pretty well what I wanted, which was a list of three or four of the first
attempts at medical bibliography, and the precise reference to a paper
on "errors in medical bibliography," by Dr. A. Petit, which I had
found very interesting. I also knew that I had read, within the past year,
another article on the same subject by the same author, being a reply to
an article by M. Richet in the *Revue Scientifique*. To find the precise
reference for this I went to the *Index Medicus*, and in five minutes I
had it. Having examined these various papers, I found half a dozen more
references which were neither in the *Index Catalogue* nor the *Index
Medicus*, and, especially, one to a preface written by Prof. Verneuil to a
treatise on gastrostomy, by M. Petit, to which I shall have occasion to
refer presently, and which is probably in about the last place where
one would have thought of looking for one of the most eloquent
eulogiums of medical bibliography with which I am acquainted.

Having read these various papers, together with the very excellent article on Bibliography in the last edition of the *Encyclopædia Britannica*, I discovered three things, all of which previous melancholy experiences had led me to anticipate. First, I found a number of fresh references; second, that I had more material than could be used in an hour's address, and third, that most of the ideas contained in my preliminary notes had been very much better expressed by previous writers, and that they must either be dropped, or quotations substituted for what I had thought might possibly be something new.

I shall not trouble you with further details, my object being merely to indicate one method of commencing a bibliographical research; and also to indicate why it is that such researches tend so strongly to destroy originality of expression, since one so often finds a sentence or paragraph in which his idea is so well stated that any change in it would be the reverse of an improvement, and the impulse to quote becomes irresistible, although the quotation is by no means always acknowledged.

Now, like the fine old Scotch gentlewoman quoted by John Brown, one often finds that the best way to get the better of temptation is just to yield to it; which is simply another way of stating what some modern philosophers would express as the importance of following the lines of least resistance; and therefore you are duly warned that I shall make no special attempt at originality, either in matter or form; and while I do hereby formally apologize for not having prepared a set oration, I do, at the same time, beg that you will shift the greater part of the blame for this failure from my shoulders to those of the gentlemen who are responsible for my being in this position.

Bibliography is defined by the *Encyclopædia Britannica* as "the science of books, having regard to their description and proper classification," the meaning having been greatly modified from that which it had a hundred and fifty years ago, when it signified "skill in deciphering and judging of ancient manuscripts," which is now called palæography. This definition of the Encyclopædia, comprehensive as it is, does not fairly include the most usual sense in which the term bibliography is now used as applied to a particular subject, that is, as giving references to all the literature of that subject: including not only the titles of books and pamphlets specially treating of it, but also articles in periodicals and transactions, and even single paragraphs which furnish information with regard to the matter in hand. Perhaps I can best illustrate this by giving a few specimens of the inquiries made at the Library of the Surgeon General's Office in Washington, such as: "for the literature of hydrophobia"; "for all cases of epilepsy reported as cured by burns"; "for a complete list of all books and papers written by Dr. John Jones"; "for materials for the life of Dr. John Morgan"; "for a list of the printed medical theses of the graduates of the University of Pennsylvania"; "for materials for a history of the Medical Schools of Baltimore, including all catalogues, announcements, etc."; "for all accounts of epidemics occurring in Memphis"; "for data relative to the diseases of Georgia"; "how many editions have been published of the treatise of the school of Salernum?" "Which is the best edition of Galen?" "Who was the author of *Sechs Bücher ausserlesene Artzney, etc.*, published at Torgau in 1600?" "Where can I find a paper 'On the voice' by Dr. H. H. Hayden, published in some journal or transactions forty or fifty years ago?" "Where can I find a paper 'On the differences between dead and living protoplasm,' recently published, author's name not remembered?" "What is a copy of Bagellardus *de Egritudinibus infantium* worth?" "What will you give for a perfect manuscript in good condition, written in 1429, being extracts from and commentaries on Almansor and Isaac, and making 160 leaves folio?" The answers to these and similar questions come under the head of medical bibliography, and you will see that it is not easy to give a definition which will include them all, unless you make it so general and vague as to be useless, as, for instance, that it is the science of medical literature. It may be viewed and studied either as a means or as an end. The greater part of medical bibliography does not go beyond the titles of books or articles. The first distinct and separate work on the subject is that of Pascal Lecoq, better known by his Latinized name of Paschalis Gallus. His *Bibliotheca Medica*, published at Basle in 1590, gives a list of about thirteen hundred medical authors, the titles of whose works are stated vaguely and indefinitely, usually only one edition being given. It is arranged alphabetically by the first, not the last names of the authors. It gives, also, lists of writers on certain subjects or in certain languages, and as the system of classification is brief and curious, I give it in full: Works in French, works in German, works on Hippocrates, on Galen, on Avicenna, on Dioscorides, on Surgery, Anatomy, Materia Medica, Pharmacopœias, on Practice, on Consilia Medica (or what we would call clinical medicine), on Pest and on Lues.

In the following year, namely, 1591, Israel Spachius published, at Frankfort, his *Nomenclator Scriptorum Medicorum*. This is a subject-catalogue with an index of authors, of whom 1436 are mentioned. The data for both these books appear to have been derived mainly from the *Bibliotheca* of Conrad Gesner. Cuvier, in his life of Gesner, in the *Biographie Universelle*, mentions that Gesner never permitted the section "Medicine" of his *Bibliothèque Universelle* to be printed, as he could never get it arranged to his satisfaction. If this rule were to be generally applied, bibliographies and catalogues would be exceedingly rare. I shall not inflict upon you an account of the various attempts at medical bibliography which have been published from the time of Spachius to the present day. You will find their titles down to 1874 in the very complete and accurate *Bibliographie des Sciences Médicales*, by Paully, which is itself a book worth knowing, being a bibliography of medical bibliography, history and biography, making a volume of over 1800 pages. I must, however, say a word upon one series of works, not to mention which would be unpardonable, for an address on medical bibliography which contained no allusion to the *Bibliothecæ* of Haller would be like a political speech of the present day with no allusion to reform or the tariff. The quarto volumes which contain Haller's *Bibliothecæ Anatomica, Chirurgica* and *Medicinæ*, comprise a remarkable piece of work, which only those who have been engaged in similar pursuits can fully appreciate. They form a history of medicine rather than a bibliography; but it is wonderful that remote as he was from great libraries, he should have been able to make such a complete enumeration of existing medical books as he did. These works are, however, much more generally praised than consulted for bibliographical purposes; the arrangement in order of dates, instead of by subjects, or alphabetically by authors, being very inconvenient, and the index being imperfect. Their great value is in the clear, brief analyses and pithy criticisms which are given of a large number of books, and in the fact that he clearly indicates the books which he himself has seen and examined, as distinguished from those of which he knew only the titles. With reference to these last he usually indicates his authority, but, unfortunately, in printing he forgot to give the key to his abbreviations, and some of these are now unexplainable.

Mr. Thomas Windsor, of Manchester, one of the most learned and accurate of living medical bibliographers, has pointed out an amusing error resulting from misinterpreting Haller's abbreviations. "Speaking of Peter Lowe's work, *The Whole Course of Chirurgie*, Haller gives the editions as follows: 'London 1597. 4. Tr. 1612. 4. Port. 1614. 4. Gunz. 1634. 4. Port. 1657. 4. Gunz.' That is, there were five editions, published in the years 1597, 1612, 1614, 1634 and 1657. All were issued in London, and all were quartos. The abbreviations Tr., Port., Gunz., signify the authorities for Haller's statements, he himself not having seen any copy of the work. Watt, in his *Bibliotheca Britannica*, vol. I, p. 618, has amplified Haller in the following extraordinary manner: 'Lowe, Peter . . . *The Whole Course of Chirurgerie*. . . . Lond. 1596, 1597, 1612, 1634, 1654, 4to. This is considered to be a book of very great merit, and was translated into a variety of languages, and printed in Fr. 1612, Port. 1614, Gunz. 1634, Port. 1657.' Allibone, in his *Critical Dictionary of English Literature*, has carefully copied Watt." [1]

---

[1] Index Medicus, Vol. I, 1879, p. 372.

It is not my purpose to indicate or comment on the various systematic works on medical bibliography which have appeared since the days of Haller, all of which are largely indebted to his works for information. Most of them are more useful to a librarian or bookseller than they are to a physician seeking for information on a particular subject, unless that subject is bibliographical. The best medical bibliography will be found in the French dictionaries or encyclopædias of medicine, in monographs, and articles in medical journals. I shall presently, however, have a word or two to say with regard to one source of information, namely, catalogues of medical libraries; but first let us consider some of the methods used in medico-bibliographical work.

First, there is the old-fashioned way, in which the student searches the books immediately at his command, using their indexes and making notes of all references to other works. He then goes to a library—asks for these books, gets more references from them, and so on—his time and patience being usually exhausted some time before the supply of references fails. It is in this way that bibliographical research becomes a pleasure by and for itself, and it is thus also that the best of this work has been done, but it requires much time.

Second, there is the modern mechanical way, the extreme type of which is to pay some one else to make a list of references for you, and then print this list as a bibliography of the subject without taking the trouble to consult the works themselves. Some writers, in fact, seem to desire to finish their article with an imposing string of references, without caring much whether they have any special relation to the matter in hand or not, something like the retired merchant who bought a country place and resolved to have a cow because he was so fond of new-laid eggs.

Do not suppose, however, that I object to mechanical bibliographical work; it is of great use as saving the time of those who can be more usefully employed, and it is now in fact a necessity,—since the mass of material to be dealt with is too great in most cases to be handled in any other way. I only wish to reiterate warnings which have already been given by others. Sir James Paget, for example, thinks that "there is now a danger that in the multiplication of scientific pursuits, and in the superabundance of means of publication, we shall lose the accuracy which should be at the foundation of our work. The publishing of error is quite as easy as the publishing of truth, and there will always be a large number of persons who will believe a statement because it is in print."

Again, in an excellent article signed "Ch. R.," in the *Revue Scientifique* for July 1, 1882, it is urged that an indispensable condition in bibliographical work is sincerity. "It is almost a lie to quote a book which one has not had in his hands," and, again, "It is a part of elementary scientific honesty to cite only the books which one has read. . . . Of course one can neither consult all authors nor have at his disposal all the collections and books which contain desirable information; but if one cannot consult the original record, there is certainly nothing to prevent stating that a given bibliographical note is given at second-hand, and noting the authority for it. A good bibliography, however, should merit more praise than the mere statement that it is not deceptive. After all the data and materials have been collected it will be found that many items are useless, and it is the elimination of these useless references which forms an important part of true erudition." M. Richet would not have such references mentioned at all, he would have the writer ignore them entirely. This view, however, does not appear to me to be correct, so far as concerns the titles of books or papers which might seem to a person unacquainted with them to relate to the matter in hand. When in the course of his researches a writer has examined such a book or pamphlet and found that it contains nothing original, or that the contents do not correspond with the title, or that for other reasons it is a waste of time to consult it, he should give the reference and note the fact distinctly. It is often just as important to indicate that there is no thoroughfare as to point out the direct road. It is precisely this critical indication of the value of a paper which makes the difference between good and bad bibliography, or between bibliography, properly so called, and catalogues or indexes. Consider for a moment what is, or should be, the main purpose for which a writer gives bibliographical details, namely, to save his reader time and trouble in case he wishes to verify or enlarge upon the author's statements. But if the writer has consulted John Smith's book or article and found that it gives no information in regard to the subject in hand, although its title seems to indicate it; that it is a mere rehash of opinions without any new facts, any intelligent criticism, or anything else which would induce one to look at it if he had no other sources of information, he should say so, and spare his successors in the same path the labor of looking up and reading John Smith's work, and the moral deterioration which the feelings excited by the examination of such a work are apt to produce.

It is very true that when one is speaking of the works of contemporaries and friends there is a very natural and even commendable reluctance to publish unfavorable criticisms or comments, and that it is much easier to refrain from all mention in such cases; but at least it should be done for the older writers when an attempt is made to present a bibliography properly so called. The article of M. Richet, to which reference has just been made, gave rise to an interesting comment by M. Petit upon the method to be pursued in bibliographical researches, in which he points out the impossibility of preventing literary thefts in bibliographical work, and refers to the "wrath of Broca and Jaccoud at this factitious erudition, and at the fact that their work has been used by others without acknowledgment." (Petit (L. H.) Sur la méthode à suivre dans les recherches bibliographiques. Gaz. hebd. de méd., Paris, 1882, 2e sér., tome XIX, pp. 537; 585.)

Jaccoud prefaces his bibliography of diabetes as follows: "The general bibliography of diabetes has been thus far a little neglected. I have taken special pains in preparing the following, and have arranged it on a new plan which I think will much increase its usefulness. I hope that whoever does this bibliography the honor of copying from it, will at the same time indicate the original of the copy."

On reading this note I was naturally led to an examination of the bibliography thus commended, and certainly it shows extensive research and is a very useful compilation. I note in it, however, some errors of matter and form, and as by these I can illustrate one or two rules of bibliography, I will occupy two minutes with some remarks on the first of the ten pages of which this list consists. The merits of a bibliography are to be judged of: 1st, as to its accuracy; 2d, as to its completeness; 3d, as to absence of redundancy or repetition; 4th, as to its form; the most important rules for which last are, that it should be such that a librarian or a bookseller can find the books called for with the least expenditure of time and trouble, and that the classification shall be such as will direct the inquirer most readily to the especial information which he seeks.

First, then, are the names, titles, dates, etc., accurately given? I find that the title of the work of Trnka de Kr'zowitz, which is given as "Commentarius de diabete," is really "De diabete commentarius"; that "Rollo. Cases of diabetes, etc., 1797," should be "Rollo. Two cases," etc., or else the date should be changed; that "Bennet (J. B.) 1801," should be spelled with two t's instead of one; that the paper of "Dupuytren et Thenard," which is said to have been published in the *Bulletin de la Société de médecine,* 1806, was really published in the *Journal de médecine, chirurgie, pharmacie, etc.,* for that year, p. 83, and that only an extract from it is given in the *Bulletin de la Faculté de médecine de Paris* (etc.), which is what Jaccoud intended to refer to, but of which he did not give the correct title; that the date of the dissertation of Salomon, which he gives as 1809, is really 1808; that the article referred to as by "Renaudin" in 1818, is by "Renauldin" in the volume of the *Dictionnaire des sciences médicales,* dated 1814; that the dissertation given as by "Siegmeyer" is by "Siegmayer," and that the title of the thesis of Dusseaux is "Sur le diabète," and not "Du diabète," as given. Here, then, are at least eight errors on this page, comparatively trivial, it is true, but of such a character as to make it doubtful whether Professor Jaccoud had himself examined all of these books whose titles he quotes.

Second, let us look at the completeness of the list. It gives five titles of works on Diabetes published prior to 1800. If its compiler had consulted the bibliography given at the end of the article by Renauldin, above referred to, he would have found over thirty titles of works published prior to 1800, which should have been included, and he would also have found a large number in Ploucquet's work, which is one of which no medical bibliographer should be ignorant.

Third, as to absence of duplication or redundancy. From this fault Dr. Jaccoud's *Bibliography* is free, and it is one not likely to occur in a list of general treatises. It is a very common one, however, in lists of references to cases, and it is one which requires minute examination of each case to avoid; many specimens of it will be found in those sections of the *Index Catalogue* of your Washington library which refer to cases of a given disease, injury or operation.

Fourth, we come to the form in which Dr. Jaccoud gives his references. As regards the individual items, judged by the rules given above, this form is very bad. The size of the books is not given, nor the volume of the journal, nor the page. The various medical encyclopædias are referred to as "the Dictionary in thirty volumes," "the Dictionary in fifteen volumes," &s., and the number of the volume is given in only one instance, and that for a German encyclopædia. On the other hand, unnecessary space is occupied by giving the titles of journals in full instead of using well-recognized abbreviations. The classification adopted is a very good one—it is into treatises on the general subject, on complication with gangrene, with disordered vision, etc., on pathological anatomy and etiology, chemistry, theories and treatment.

Now, probably, this seems to you very petty criticism, and so it would be if it were intended for criticism, which it is not. I simply wish to call your attention to the fact that there is a systematic way of giving bibliographical references with which medical writers should be familiar, and incidentally to suggest that when one calls attention to his own bibliographical work as being especially fine, it is a sort of challenge which some carper and doubter is sure to take up sooner or later. Taking all things into consideration, the best specimens of medical bibliographical work with which I am acquainted are those given by my colleague, Dr. Woodward, in the medical volume of the second part of the

Medical and Surgical History of the War; and the work of Petit presently to be alluded to.

M. Richet concludes his article in the *Revue Scientifique* as follows: "Perhaps it is unwise to attribute so much importance to bibliography. Perhaps the turning over the pages of many books and the consulting of many authors has a tendency to destroy orginality. But on the whole I do not think so. Moreover, those who have the rare gift of scientific originality are altogether excused. They are creators and have no need of being erudite. Those who need to be such are those who are neither discoverers nor inventors, and it appears to me that such are in the majority." This does not fully accord with the opinions of Prof. Verneuil, who in his preface to the treatise on gastrostomy, by L. H. Petit (Paris, 1879), introduces the book with the statement that it is a work of pure erudition, compiled by a bibliographer who never has performed, and probably never will perform, the operation of which he gives the history; and yet that he has contributed as much to its future success as those who have devised or practised it. He says: "Scientific progress is due to three things of equal importance, namely, erudition, observation and experiment. There is a bibliographical method which is distinct, independent, worthy of cultivation for its own sake, and in no way inferior to its two rivals in the amount and value of the information which it furnishes. . . . While erudition certainly creates nothing, it leads to creation. To discountenance research in literature is like advising travellers who visit regions not yet fully explored, to refrain from making use of the maps prepared by their predecessors. The great objection to such work is the amount of time which it requires, if it is to be done thoroughly and accurately. This time is, moreover, the greater since each bibliophile must serve his apprenticeship almost alone, for the bibliographical method has not been taught yet, nor have its rules been laid down. Certainly no one can do such work for himself upon all subjects. A lifetime would be insufficient to thus study the hundredth part of pathology; but we may ask of those who cannot do such work, that at least they shall not disdain those who labor at it. Certainly we do not wish to depreciate either observation or experiment, but we desire that erudition should be honored as it merits, and that bibliographical work should be recognized as of public utility. With us to call a man erudite implies rather the idea of narrow specialization and professional inaptitude."

I have quoted thus fully from Professor Verneuil's eulogium as giving the views of a French master upon the state of French professional opinion on this subject. With us I think the feeling is rather one of undue, uncritical admiration of bibliographical matters than of contempt or dislike; but, until quite recently, American physicians had not at their command the means of research in medical literature possessed by their transatlantic brethren, and even now the physicians of large portions of the country find it very difficult to get access to the original material of literary research.

The members of the Medico-Chirurgical Faculty of Maryland, and especially those who reside in Baltimore, are more favorably situated in this respect than their professional brethren elsewhere. Possibly this may be news to some of you, and I had better explain. You are all aware that your society has a library here in Baltimore, a library which contains for the most part only old books, and is practically little used, except by a very few persons, and of which it might, until within the last few years, have been said that its strongest characteristic was its feebleness, being, as a Kentuckian would say, "powerful weak." Recently, however, by the exertions of a few members, and especially through the energy and zeal of your librarian, Dr. Cordell, the collection has been put in order and made accessible, a certain number of current medical journals are regularly received, and other improvements have been effected. Permit me, however, to suggest to you that one of the most important uses to which you can put your library here is to so arrange it that it may be the means of your getting the full benefit of your other collection over in Washington, which you may consider as a sort of branch library of the Faculty. You all know that what is called the Library of the Surgeon-General's Office is a large and valuable one, but probably you have not all fully realized that it is your library, intended for your benefit and use, and that it is not a Bureau Library intended only for the use of officials. Such, however, is the fact, and therefore it comes within the limits of my subject to offer you some suggestions as to how you can best use both of your libraries, and what should be done to maintain and increase their completeness and usefulness.

First, then, your library in Baltimore should be made, and kept, as complete as possible in the local medical history of the city and State. It should contain every medical book, pamphlet, etc., published in or relating to the State. The great majority of these will cost nothing but watchfulness and prompt application for them at the time of publication, but if they be not then obtained, the acquisition soon becomes difficult. You want every report of a hospital, asylum, or dispensary, every announcement or catalogue of a medical school, every mortality report, order or hand-bill issued by sanitary authorities for the State or city, and, as far as possible, you want to obtain at least two copies of each, one for the Baltimore and one for the Washington branch. It is a matter of interest, also, to keep in the library a scrap-book for local newspaper cuttings of all matters of medical or sanitary interest which should be promptly and systematically inserted. A small scrap-book, properly indexed, to certain newspaper medical advertisements, especially those of the various quacks who infest this, as they do all other large cities, will be found in years to come very interesting, and, it may be, useful.

The limited amount of funds available for increasing your Baltimore collection will naturally be for the most part applied to the purchase of medical journals. The main thing which you have to do is to perfect the system of care and storage of your books, in order that they may be perfectly secure against, let us say, unauthorized borrowing. This is necessary, not only to preserve your own books, but to make it possible for the Washington library to loan freely to the Baltimore library. The Washington collection is a reference, and not a circulating, library. It does not as a rule lend books to individuals, although in the case of modern books, which can be readily replaced, it will do so upon a deposit sufficient to amply cover their value, its rules in this respect being the same as those of the Library of Congress; but it will lend freely to other libraries which are so constructed, located, and managed that the books in them are secure from fire, theft, etc.

Now, suppose that a member of the Faculty desires to prepare a somewhat elaborate article upon some medical subject for a society or journal, and that for this purpose he wishes to compare his own experience and observations with those of others: how is he to proceed? Before attempting to answer this, permit me to suggest one or two things which he should not do. In the first place, he should not as the first step write a note to the Washington librarian, somewhat as follows:

Dear Sir:—I am preparing a paper on fractures and wish to obtain the bibliography of the subject. Can you favor me with a copy of all the references which you have collected upon this head? I shall be happy to pay the expense of the copy.

Very truly yours,

This will no doubt seem to some to be not an unreasonable request, and yet it is one with which it is impossible to comply. The librarian is busy with his current work—cataloguing, printing, furnishing books, etc. He has no clerical force available for making copies, and he cannot employ an unskilled clerk and give him access to his manuscript cards. He cannot himself spare much time to assort and arrange references for these special demands. For a subject which has only half a dozen references he can furnish them, he can verify a quotation, and is glad to furnish information which a brief examination of a few volumes will provide. If the inquirer will visit Washington he can see and examine the reference cards and make such notes as he desires, provided always that this does not interfere with the catalogue work.

In the second place, the man who proposes to write a paper or a book should not as a rule issue a circular informing the world at large of his intention, and calling upon physicians generally to report to him at once all cases which they may have had of the particular disease or injury which he proposes to discuss. I say *as a rule*, for I admit that a certain amount of interesting and useful information may be obtained in this way when it is requested by one who is recognized as having himself already contributed largely to our information on the matter in hand, and who is therefore an authority on the subject who may be well intrusted with the classifying, comparing and judging of the results of the work of others. But when a comparatively unknown man makes such a demand upon the profession at large, his success will probably be small—and properly so. A man should show that he has some money of his own before calling on the public to bank with him.

This is, however, a digression from medical bibliography, which seems to be a subject with regard to which it is extraordinarily difficult to keep to the point. To obtain as much as possible from a library you should bring as much information there as you can, and have it in as clear and definite a form as possible. Note upon a slip of paper the books you wish to see, giving their titles concisely, but clearly, so that the man who is to find the books will not have to waste ten minutes of his time in deciphering your references. Consult the *Index Catalogue* so far as published, the *Index Medicus*, and the bibliographies attached to the articles in the modern French and German encyclopædias, and it will be strange if you can find no titles which will put you on the right road. Remember that the *Index Catalogue* is not a bibliography. The question is sometimes asked why an attempt, at least, was not made to make it such. Why the comparatively few medical journals, etc., which the library does not contain, could not have been found in other libraries and indexed there, and in like manner the titles of books have been taken from other catalogues and the whole combined into a huge bibliography. It is said "You have got so much, it is a pity you cannot give it all." I shall not detain you with the various reasons why this could not be done with the means and opportunities we had. When the *Index Catalogue* is finished, if Congress will provide the funds necessary for the preparation of a supplement to contain the titles of all medical books and papers which are not in the library, it would no doubt be a very good thing; but, for the present, we must console ourselves with the reflection that when we look down a string of references in the catalogue, we can at all events promptly verify all of them by examining the books; whereas, when we have consulted a bibliography, we have next the very serious task of discovering in what libraries and collections the various books are to be found, and we are nearly sure to be made unhappy by being unable to discover some of them anywhere. The fact that those which we cannot find are probably worthless is small consolation, for we want to determine that fact for ourselves. My experience is, that by the time one has examined all the books on a particular subject, to which references are given in the *Index Catalogue*, and has followed out the various clues given in these books to others not indexed but which are in the collection, he is usually rather pleased than otherwise that he knows of no more references and therefore does not feel bound to consult them. A large number indeed of those who use the library select only the most recent literature relating to the subject of their studies, and, so long as they can get this, care little or nothing for the historical side of the matter. Perhaps I may some day have occasion to write about the uses and abuses of the *Index Catalogue*, in which case the main point I shall insist on is that it is a tool which must be used for a time before you can judge of its merits. It is by no means a perfect work, and although as yet I have only discovered, or had pointed out, some half dozen errors which are specially discreditable as indications of ignorance on the part of its compiler, I am nevertheless quite sure there must be a number of others, and I hope those who discover them will point them out to me, although I cannot truly say that I shall be happy to receive this information.

Having prepared the list of references to be consulted, which it will be found most convenient to arrange on card slips of uniform size—that of an ordinary postal card is very good—the next thing is to get the books. It is best to go to Washington and visit the library in person, when this is possible. If the list of the books which it is desired to consult be sent to the librarian so that he can have it the day before the visit, some time and confusion will be avoided, and the visitor will find the books which he desires to see laid out ready for his examination. If, however, it is impossible to visit Washington, the inquirer had best get some library which has the means of safely caring for the books, and will be responsible in case of loss or damage, to borrow the books for him through its librarian, the borrower of course paying the expense of transportation. Now, in order that the library of the Faculty may be able to borrow freely from your Washington branch, it must be so managed and arranged that the books in it will be perfectly secure against loss. At present this is not the case, and one of your first cares should be to improve matters in this respect. Until this is done books can only be obtained freely from the Library of the Surgeon-General's Office by the Library of the Peabody Institute, or that of the Johns Hopkins University.

Permit me next to call your attention to the fact that it is a part of your duty to see that your Washington library is made and kept as complete as possible. In the first place it should have every new medical book, journal, report, or thesis, in every language, as soon as possible after its publication. You ought to be certain of finding in this, our National medical collection, the latest literature upon any subject connected with medicine, and everything noted in the *Index Medicus* should be upon its shelves. Now, to effect this would require an appropriation of from seven to eight thousand dollars a year. The journals and transactions relating to medicine and the allied sciences will alone cost about $2500 per annum. In the second place, the deficiencies in the library should be gradually supplied as opportunity offers. The amount and character of these deficiencies are matters of some interest. In order to obtain some data on this point I have compared the catalogue of the Washington library with those of the two largest collections of books in existence, viz. the British Museum of London, and the Bibliothèque Nationale of Paris. Taking the fasciculi of the catalogue printed by the British Museum in 1881–82, I find that on 1140 pages, containing about 34,000 titles exclusive of cross references, there are the titles of 657 books and 880 inaugural theses relating to medicine. Comparing these with the corresponding portions of the Washington catalogue it is found that the British Museum has 262 medical books, 372 medical theses and 118 different editions which are not in the Surgeon-General's Library. On the other hand the Surgeon-General's Library has 285 books, 342 theses and 88 different editions which are not in the British Museum. There are common to both libraries 277 books and 508 theses. The two libraries therefore appear to be nearly equal as regards medical books. This is exclusive of medical journals, transactions and reports, in which the Washington library is much the richer. The tables, I and II, show in detail, by countries and periods, the difference between the two collections as regards medical books.

The catalogue of the medical section of the Bibliothèque Nationale in Paris is arranged by subjects and not by authors, does not include inaugural theses or dissertations, and was published in 1857–73; hence it is not possible to make an exact comparison between it and the *Index Catalogue* or that of the British Museum. But taking the general subjects, anatomy, fevers, diseases of the eye, and cholera, I have prepared a table showing the results of a comparison of the two catalogues, from

TABLE I

TABLE SHOWING RESULTS OF COMPARISON OF THE MEDICAL SECTION OF THE CATALOGUE OF THE BIBLIOTHÈQUE NATIONALE, PARIS, WITH THE INDEX CATALOGUE OF THE LIBRARY OF THE SURGEON-GENERAL'S OFFICE, U. S. ARMY, FOR THE SUBJECTS "ANATOMY," "FEVERS," "EYE DISEASES," AND "CHOLERA"

	United States			England			France			Germany			Italy			Spain			Others			Total		
	Both	Surgeon General's Office only	Paris Catalogue only	Both	Surgeon General's Office only	Paris Catalogue only	Both	Surgeon General's Office only	Paris Catalogue only	Both	Surgeon General's Office only	Paris Catalogue only	Both	Surgeon General's Office only	Paris Catalogue only	Both	Surgeon General's Office only	Paris Catalogue only	Both	Surgeon General's Office only	Paris Catalogue only	Both	Surgeon General's Office only	Paris Catalogue only
Anatomy, Fevers and Eye Diseases.																								
Prior to 1600				1	2			3	17		2	2	17	10	24		1	4	6	6	11	36	23	58
1600–1799		1		18	40	13	5	13	65	7	31	30	10	7	16		4	5	27	23	27	90	116	156
1800–date	1	46		5	45	2	21	8	60	13	62	6	7	9	5	1	3	2	2	18	13	73	192	88
Different Editions		7	1		24	14	41	11	91	17	18	27		2	21			1		20	26		85	181
Total	1	54	1	24	111	29	67	35	233	37	113	65	34	28	66	1	8	12	35	67	77	199	416	483
Cholera	2	85		18	130	11	142	79	219	17	272	5	10	64	39		4		5	111	7	194	745	272
Grand total	3	139	1	42	241	40	209	114	452	54	385	70	44	92	105	1	12	12	40	178	84	393	1161	755

Note.—Theses and reprints excluded.

TABLE II

TABLE GIVING RESULTS OF A COMPARISON OF 1140 PAGES OF THE BRITISH MUSEUM CATALOGUE IN THE LETTERS A AND C, WITH THE CORRESPONDING PAGES OF THE INDEX CATALOGUE OF THE LIBRARY OF THE SURGEON-GENERAL'S OFFICE, U. S. ARMY, WASHINGTON, D. C.

	United States			England			France			Germany			Italy			Spain			Others			Total		
	Both	S.G.O. only	B.M. only	Both	S.G.O. only	B.M. only	Both	S.G.O. only	B.M. only	Both	S.G.O. only	B.M. only	Both	S.G.O. only	B.M. only	Both	S.G.O. only	B.M. only	Both	S.G.O. only	B.M. only	Both	S.G.O. only	B.M. only
Books—Prior to 1600							3		3	5	3	12	7	5	14			2	1		3	16	8	34
1600–1799		63	3	20	8	17	10	4	9	29	9	16	6	2	12		3	4	1	2	4	66	25	62
1800–date	13	32	4	80	41	64	32	57	42	57	52	43	3	14	7	1	2	3	6	22	4	192	252	166
Editions not in Library but of which it has the book.					30	71		8	9		12	14		3	12					1	8	3	88	118
Total Books	13	95	7	100	79	152	45	69	63	91	76	85	16	24	45	1	5	9	8	25	19	277	373	380
Theses Prior to 1600												4									2			4
1600–1799	1	1	1	6	18	1	3	1	21	89	60	76							5	11	16	104	91	116
1800–date	1	4		3	14	2	412	69	223	39	177	11								47	6	404	251	252
Total Theses	2	5	1	9	32	3	415	70	244	128	237	91			9				5	58	24	508	342	372

Note.—Periodicals, Transactions and Reports of Medical Institutions excluded.

which it appears that in the first three subjects named 199 books are common to both, 416 are in the Washington collection only, and 483 in the Paris collection only. On the subject of cholera (excluding treatment) 194 books are common to both, 745 are in the Washington library only, and 272 in the Paris library only. The books which the Paris library has, and our own library has not, are for the most part old books dating before 1800, or French books which have come to the library under the law which requires one copy of every publication to be deposited there. This law is not strictly obeyed, for we have in our library 79 French works on cholera which are not in the Paris catalogue, but it is due to this law that the medical section of the National library of France is essentially French and not cosmopolitan.

As the result of these comparisons I think it is safe to conclude that the Library of the Surgeon-General's Office in Washington not only contains more medical literature than the British Museum or the National library of France, but that it covers a wider field, represents better the medical literature of the whole world, and is decidedly a better practical reference and working collection for medical purposes than either of the great libraries referred to. Each library is, as might be expected, richest in the literature of its own country; but the French library is comparatively poor in English and German medical books, and has almost nothing in American medical literature, while the English library is also poor in American literature, and comparatively weak in German medicine of the present century. Both of them are rich in the literature of the fifteenth and sixteenth centuries, and have many editions of older works of which the Washington library has only one or two. Both of them have been in existence for over three hundred years, and have had almost unlimited funds for the purchase of books. Why then is it that they do not contain all medical books which have ever been printed; and that your medical library in Washington, which is only about twenty years old and has never had in any one year funds sufficient to purchase more than two-thirds of the medical books printed in various parts of the world during that same year, should already be equal if not superior to them in practical value? It appears to me that it is very largely due to the fact that while the Washington library is the National collection, it has been kept separate from the general National library. The result of this has been that the medical profession has taken much more interest in it than they would do if, as is the case with the English and French medical collections, it became merely a section of the National library.

As a matter of fact, comparatively little use is made by medical writers of the collection in the British Museum or the Bibliothèque Nationale.

They consult, in preference, the special medical libraries in London and Paris, which are under the direction of medical bibliographers, such as the libraries of the Royal College of Surgeons, or of the Royal Medical and Chirurgical Society, or those of the Faculty of Medicine, or of the Academy of Medicine, of Paris. It is to such special libraries that physicians give their books and pamphlets; and the rapid growth of the Washington library is largely due to this cause. There is pouring into it ι steady stream of literature the sources of which are by no means conined to this country, although, of course, the largest part comes from the United States. Those who incline to pessimistic views of human nature, and to attribute all the actions of men to selfish motives, would not find their views confirmed by my experience. I could name a number of gentlemen who take almost as much interest in the library as if it were their own, and who are constantly on the lookout to supply its deficiencies. Now, so long as the library can preserve and extend this feeling of interest in its completeness, so long it is sure to grow in value and usefulness, but if it be merged into a general National library this interest will rapidly diminish. It is not to be expected that the manager of a large miscellaneous library, if well fitted for his position by a knowledge of general literature, should also be familiar with the various departments of scientific literature; as the modern Greeks say, "two watermelons cannot be carried under one arm," and no subordinate or assistant will have the same stimulus to do good work that the man who is responsible in the eyes of the public will have. I think therefore that you will do well to see that a proper and commodious fire-proof building is provided for your Washington collection, that it is not merged into the Congressional Library, and that it is granted sufficient funds to enable it to secure all new medical books as they are published, and gradually to collect the best of the older literature.

It is supposed by some that this library receives a copy of every medical book published in the United States. This is not the case. Under the copyright law, two copies of every copyrighted medical book are deposited in the Library of Congress, but no copy comes to the Library of the Surgeon-General's Office. It seems to me that the law should be so amended as to make our library the place of deposit for one of the copyright copies, and this is a matter to which I invite your attention.

It may perhaps seem to some of you that this Washington library of yours is not after all such an important matter as I make it out to be, and it must be confessed that I am not an impartial judge; nevertheless it does seem to me that the making and keeping this library complete is one of the most valuable means of advancing medical science in this country which at present is within our grasp, and that it is within our grasp if the medical profession of the country choose to exert their influence for the purpose.

It is also well to remember that the opportunity which is now presented for placing this matter on a proper and permanent basis will not occur again. There are not two springs in the year, nor in the life of a nation, and if the spring work is not done in time the fruits of summer and autumn will be correspondingly deficient.

It is true that the successful practitioner is rarely a book-worm, but it is also true that "improvements are made by those who know well the old methods." The toast of the Pure Mathematical Society of England as given by Sir James Paget, namely, "Prosperity to pure mathematics, may it never be of use to any man," is one with which I have no special sympathy, but in so far as it is a plea for amusement, and for mental exercise without reference to pecuniary results, it applies to bibliomania as well. I like to see on the doctor's shelves a little group of books such as Sprengel's or Daremberg's or Haeser's Histories of Medicine, the letters of Guy Patin, the Medical Portrait Gallery of Pettigrew, the works of John Brown of Edinburgh, or a collection of pamphlets relating to local medical history; and it certainly does not cause a lower estimate of his ability as a practical physician and surgeon to know that he reads something else beside manuals and text-books.

I like the quaint, old-timy name which the physicians of this State have preserved for their society, "The Medical and Chirurgical Faculty of Maryland." Do you know why for the last three hundred years and more physicians have been known as *the* Faculty? All universities, properly so called, have other faculties—Faculties of Arts, of Law, of Theology; but by the world at large, when one speaks of "the Faculty," he is understood as referring only to the medical profession. You will remember that in the old University of Paris, where this special meaning of the term originated, those who graduated as doctors graduated also as teachers; in other words, the Faculty of Medicine in Paris was composed of all the graduated doctors of medicine of the University. Now, as Dr. Raynaud points out in his admirable little book, "Les médecins au temps de Molière" (which should be added to the list of books above mentioned), the other Faculties of the University were composed purely and simply of learned men, whose sole object and work was to teach. "The physicians, on the contrary, formed both a corps for instruction and a body exercising a liberal profession of which they had the monopoly, a profession lucrative and honored, accessible as a rule only to the upper middle class and brought into continual relations with the public." It was therefore the Faculty whose affairs were of the most interest to the world at large, and it is for this reason, according to Raynaud, that in the world of Paris and France it became known as *the* Faculty.

As the Faculty of Maryland has preserved the name, let it also preserve the best of the traditions, such as for example that the doctor should be what his name implies, an educated gentleman. It is to be hoped that the scheme of higher medical education which your University is about to organize will include instruction in bibliographical and historical methods as well as in those of the laboratory and clinic. If this be done, your Washington library will become a very important aid to the University, and your Baltimore collection will also be more used and require more looking after.

I have occupied more time than I had intended, and yet I have said very little of what I had in my mind to say when I prepared that memorandum which was mentioned at the commencement of this address. I shall be quite satisfied, however, if I can arouse some interest in providing proper means for good medico-bibliographical work for the direct benefit of our teachers and writers, and through them for the benefit of every one, not only in this country, but in the whole world; and if the result shall prove to be that "Our University" and "Our Library" have been both helpful to and helped by "Our Medical and Chirurgical Faculty of Maryland."

Scientific Men and Their Duties

Mr. Chairman and Fellow-Members of the Philosophical Society:

The honor of the presidency of such a society as this—carrying with it, as it does, the duty of giving at the close of the term of office an address on some subject of general interest, has been aptly compared to the little book mentioned in the Revelations of St. John—the little book which was "sweet in the mouth but bitter in the belly." I can only thank you for the honor, and ask your indulgence as to the somewhat discursive remarks which I am about to inflict upon you.

There is a Spanish proverb to the effect that no man can at the same time ring the bell and walk in the procession. For a few moments tonight I am to ring the bell, and being thus out of the procession I can glance for a moment at that part of it which is nearest. At first sight it does not appear to be a very homogeneous or well-ordered parade, for the individual members seem to be scattering in every direction, and even sometimes to be pulling in opposite ways; yet there is, after all, a definite movement of the whole mass in the direction of what we call progress. It is not this general movement that I shall speak of, but rather of the tendencies of individuals or of certain classes; some of the molecular movements, so to speak, which are not only curious and interesting of themselves, but which have an important bearing upon the mass, and some comprehension of which is necessary to a right understanding of the present condition and future prospects of science in this country.

The part of the procession of which I speak is made up of that body or class of men who are known to the public generally as "scientists," "scientific men," or "men of science." As commonly used, all these terms have much the same significance; but there are, nevertheless, shades of distinction between them, and in fact we need several other terms for purposes of classification of the rather heterogeneous mass to which they are applied. The word "scientist" is a coinage of the newspaper reporter, and, as ordinarily used, is very comprehensive. Webster defines a scientist as being "one learned in science, a savant"—that is, a wise man—and the word is often used in this sense. But the suggestion which the word conveys to my mind is rather that of one whom the public suppose to be a wise man, whether he is so or not, of one who claims to be scientific.

The President's Address before the Philosophical Society of Washington, December 4, 1886. *Bulletin of the Philosophical Society of Washington* 9: xxxv-lvi (1886–7).

I shall, therefore, use the term "scientist" in the broadest sense, as including scientific men, whether they claim to be such or not, and those who claim to be scientific men whether they are so or not.

By a scientific man I mean a man who uses scientific method in the work to which he specially devotes himself; who possesses scientific knowledge, —not in all departments, but in certain special fields. By scientific knowledge we mean knowledge which is definite and which can be accurately expressed. It is true that this can rarely be done completely, so that each proposition shall precisely indicate its own conditions, but this is the ideal at which we aim. There is no man now living who can properly be termed a complete savant, or scientist, in Webster's sense of the word. There are a few men who are not only thoroughly scientific in their own special departments, but are also men possessed of much knowledge upon other subjects and who habitually think scientifically upon most matters to which they give consideration; but these men are the first to admit the incompleteness and superficiality of the knowledge of many subjects which they possess, and to embrace the opportunity which such a society as this affords of meeting with students of other branches and of making that specially advantageous exchange in which each gives and receives, yet retains all that he had at first.

Almost all men suppose that they think scientifically upon all subjects; but, as a matter of fact, the number of persons who are so free from personal equation due to heredity, to early associations, to emotions of various kinds, or to temporary disorder of the digestive or nervous machinery that their mental vision is at all times achromatic and not astigmatic, is very small indeed.

Every educated, healthy man possesses some scientific knowledge, and it is not possible to fix any single test or characteristic which will distinguish the scientific from the unscientific man. There are scientific tailors, bankers, and politicians, as well as physicists, chemists, and biologists. Kant's rule, that in each special branch of knowledge the amount of science, properly so called, is equal to the amount of mathematics it contains, corresponds to the definition of pure science as including mathematics and logic, and nothing else. It also corresponds to the distinction which most persons, consciously or unconsciously, make between the so-called physical, and the natural or biological sciences. Most of us, I presume, have for the higher mathematics, and for the astronomers and physicists who use them, that profound respect which pertains to comparative ignorance, and to a belief that capacity for the higher branches of abstract analysis is a much rarer mental quality than are those required for the average work of the naturalist. I do not, however, propose to discuss the hierarchy of the sciences; and the term science

is now so generally used in the sense of knowledge, more or less accurate, of any subject, more especially in the relations of causes and
effects, that we must use the word in this sense, and leave to the future
the task of devising terms which will distinguish the sciences, properly
so called, from those branches of study and occupation of which the most
that can be said is that they have a scientific side. It is a sad thing that
words should thus become polarized and spoiled, but there seems to be
no way of preventing it.

In a general way we may say that a scientific man exercises the intellectual more than the emotional faculties, and is governed by his reason
rather than by his feelings. He should be a man of both general and
special culture, who has a little accurate information on many subjects
and much accurate information on some one or two subjects, and who,
moreover, is aware of his own ignorance and is not ashamed to confess it.

We must admit that many persons who are known as scientists do not
correspond to this definition. Have you never heard, and perhaps assented to, some such statements as these: "Smith is a scientist, but he
doesn't seem to have good, common sense," or "he is a scientific crank?"

The unscientific mind has been defined as one which "is willing to
accept and make statements of which it has no clear conceptions to
begin with, and of whose truth it is not assured. It is the state of mind
where opinions are given and accepted without ever being subjected to
rigid tests." Accepting this definition, and also the implied definition of a
scientific mind as being the reverse of this, let us for a moment depart
from the beaten track which presidential addresses usually follow, and
instead of proceeding at once to eulogize the scientific mind and to re-
capitulate the wonderful results it has produced, let us consider the unscientific mind a little, not in a spirit of lofty condescension and ill-
disguised contempt, but sympathetically, and from the best side that we
can find. As this is the kind of mind which most of us share with our
neighbors, to a greater or less degree, it may be as well not to take too
gloomy a view of it. In the first place, the men with unscientific minds
form the immense majority of the human race.

Our associations, habits, customs, laws, occupations, and pleasures are,
in the main, suited to these unscientific minds; whose enjoyment of
social intercourse, of the every-day occurrences of life, of fiction, of art,
poetry, and the drama is, perhaps, none the less because they give and
accept opinions without subjecting them to rigid tests. It is because there
are a goodly number of men who do this that the sermons of clergymen,
the advice of lawyers, and the prescriptions of physicians have a market
value. This unscientific public has its uses. We can at least claim that
we furnish the materials for the truly scientific mind to work with and

upon; it is out of this undifferentiated mass that the scientific mind supposes itself to be developed by specialization, and from it that it obtains the means of its own existence. The man with the unscientific mind, who amuses himself with business enterprises, and who does not care in the least about ohms or pangenesis, may, nevertheless, be a man who does as much good in the world, is as valuable a citizen, and as pleasant a companion as some of the men of scientific minds with whom we are acquainted.

And in this connection I venture to express my sympathy for two classes of men who have in all ages been generally condemned and scorned by others, namely, rich men and those who want to be rich.

I do not know that they need the sympathy, for our wealthy citizens appear to support with much equanimity the disapprobation with which they are visited by lecturers and writers—a condemnation which seems in all ages to have been bestowed on those who have by those who have not.

So far as those who actually are rich are concerned, we may, I suppose, admit that a few of them—those who furnish the money to endow universities and professorships, to build laboratories, or to furnish in other ways the means of support to scientific men—are not wholly bad. Then, also, it is not always a man's own fault that he is rich; even a scientist may accidentally and against his will become rich.

As to those who are not rich, but who wish to be rich, whose chief desire and object is to make money, either to avoid the necessity for further labor, or to secure their wives and children from want, or for the sake of power and desire to rule, I presume it is unsafe to try to offer any apologies for their existence. But when it is claimed for any class of men, scientists or others, that they do not want these things it is well to remember the remarks made by old Sandy Mackay after he had heard a sermon on universal brotherhood: "And so the deevil's dead. Puir auld Nickie; and him so little appreciated, too. Every gowk laying his sins on auld Nick's back. But I'd no bury him until he began to smell a wee strong like. It's a grewsome thing is premature interment."

I have tried to indicate briefly the sense in which the terms "scientist" and "scientific man" are to be used and understood, and you see it is not an easy matter. The difficulty is less as regards the term "man of science." By this expression we mean a man who belongs to science peculiarly and especially, whose chief object in life is scientific investigation, whose thoughts and hopes and desires are mainly concentrated upon his search for new knowledge, whose thirst for fresh and accurate information is constant and insatiable. These are the men who have most advanced science, and whom we delight to honor, more especially in these later days, by glowing eulogiums of their zeal, energy, and disinterestedness.

The man of science, as defined by his eulogists, is the *beau idéal* of a philosopher, a man whose life is dedicated to the advancement of knowledge for its own sake, and not for the sake of money or fame, or of professional position or advancement. He undertakes scientific investigations exclusively or mainly because he loves the work itself, and not with any reference to the probable utility of the results. Such men delight in mental effort, or in the observation of natural phenomena, or in experimental work, or in historical research, in giving play to their imagination, in framing hypotheses and then in endeavoring to verify or disprove them, but always the main incentive is their own personal satisfaction (with which may be mingled some desire for personal fame), and not the pleasure or the good of others. Carried to an extreme, the eulogy of such men and their work is expressed in the toast of the Mathematical Society of England: "Pure mathematics; may it never be of use to any man!" Now, it is one thing to seek one's own pleasure, and quite another thing to pride one's self upon doing so. The men who do their scientific work for the love of it do some of the best work, and, as a rule, do not pride themselves on it, or feel or express contempt for those who seek their pleasure and amusement in other directions. It is only from a certain class of eulogists of pure science, so called, that we get such specimens of scientific "dudeism" as the toast just quoted, opposed to which may be cited the Arab saying that "A wise man without works is like a cloud without water."

There are other men who devote themselves to scientific work, but who prefer to seek information that may be useful; who try to advance our knowledge of Nature's laws in order that man may know how to adapt himself and his surroundings to those laws, and thus be healthier and happier. They make investigations, like the men of pure science— investigations in which they may or may not take pleasure, but which they make, even if tedious and disagreeable, for the sake of solving some problem of practical importance. These are the men who receive from the public the most honor, for it is seen that their work benefits others. After all, this is not peculiar to the votaries of science. In all countries and all times, and among all sorts and conditions of men, it has always been agreed that the best life, that which most deserves praise, is that which is devoted to the helping of others, which is unselfish, not stained by envy or jealousy, and which has as its main pleasure and spring of action the desire of making other lives more pleasant, of bringing light into the dark places, of helping humanity.

But, on the other hand, the man who makes a profession of doing this, and who makes a living by so doing, the professional philanthropist, whether he be scientist or emotionalist, is by no means to be judged by his own assertions. Some wise German long ago remarked that *"Esel singen schlecht, weil sie zu hoch anstimmen"*—that is, "asses sing badly because they pitch their voices too high," and it is a criticism which it is well to bear in mind.

In one of the sermons of Kin O[1] the preacher tells the story of a powerful clam who laughed at the fears of other fish, saying that when he shut himself up he felt no anxiety; but on trying this method on one occasion when he again opened his shell he found himself in a fish-monger's shop. And to rely on one's own talents, on the services one may have rendered, on cleverness, judgments strength, or official position, and to feel secure in these, is to court the fate of the clam.

There are not very many men of science, and there are no satisfactory means of increasing the number; it is just as useless to exhort men to love science, or to sneer at them because they do not, as it is to advise them to be six feet three inches high or to condemn a man because his hair is not red.

While the ideal man of science must have a "clear, cold, keen intellect, as inevitable and as merciless in its conclusions as a logic engine," it would seem that, in the opinion of some, his greatness and superiority consists not so much in the amount of knowledge he possesses, or in what he does with it, as in the intensity and purity of his desire for knowledge.

This so-called thirst for knowledge must be closely analogous to an instinctive desire for exercise of an organ or faculty, such as that which leads a rat to gnaw, or a man of fine physique to delight in exercise. Such instincts should not be neglected. If the rat does not gnaw, his teeth will become inconvenient or injurious to himself, but it is not clear that he deserves any special eulogium merely because he gnaws.

It will be observed that the definition of a scientific man or man of science, says nothing about his manners or morals. We may infer that a man devoted to science would have neither time nor inclination for dissipation or vice; that he would be virtuous either because of being passionless or because of his clear foresight of the consequences of yielding to temptation.

My own experience, however, would indicate that either this inference is not correct or that some supposed scientific men have been wrongly classified as such. How far the possession of a scientific mind and of scientific knowledge compensates, or atones for, ill-breeding or immoral-

---

[1] Cornhill Magazine, August, 1869, p. 196.

ity, for surliness, vanity, and petty jealousy, for neglect of wife or children, for uncleanliness, physical and mental, is a question which can only be answered in each individual case; but the mere fact that a man desires knowledge for its own sake appears to me to have little to do with such questions. I would prefer to know whether the man's knowledge and work is of any use to his fellow-men, whether he is the cause of some happiness in others which would not exist without him. And it may be noted that while utility is of small account in the eyes of some eulogist, of the man of science they almost invariably base their claims for his honor and support upon his usefulness.

The precise limit beyond which a scientist should not make money has not yet been precisely determined, but in this vicinity there are some reasons for thinking that the maximum limit is about $5,000 per annum. If there are any members of the Philosophical Society of Washington who are making more than this, or who, as the result of careful and scientific introspection, discover in themselves the dawning of a desire to make more than this, they may console themselves with the reflection that the precise ethics and etiquette which should govern their action under such painful circumstances have not yet been formulated. The more they demonstrate their indifference to mere pecuniary considerations the more creditable it is to them; so much all are agreed upon; but this is nothing new, nor is it specially applicable to scientists. Yet while each may and must settle such questions as regards himself for himself, let him be very cautious and chary about trying to settle them for other people. Denunciations of other men engaged in scientific pursuits on the ground that their motives are not the proper ones are often based on insufficient or inaccurate knowledge, and seldom, I think, do good.

This is a country and an age of hurry, and there seems to be a desire to rush scientific work as well as other things. One might suppose, from some of the literature on the subject, that the great object is to make discoveries as fast as possible; to get all the mathematical problems worked out; all the chemical combinations made; all the insects and plants properly labeled; all the bones and muscles of every animal figured and described. From the point of view of the man of science there does not seem to be occasion for such haste. Suppose that every living thing were known, figured, and described. Would the naturalist be any happier? Those who wish to make use of the results of scientific investigation of course desire to hasten the work, and when they furnish the means we cannot object to their urgency. Moreover, there is certainly no occasion to fear that our stock of that peculiar form of bliss known as ignorance will be soon materially diminished.

From my individual point of view, one of the prominent features in the scientific procession is that part of it which is connected with Government work. Our Society brings together a large number of scientific men connected with the various Departments; some of them original investigators; most of them men whose chief, though not only, pleasure is study. A few of them have important administrative duties, and are brought into close relations with the heads of Departments and with Congress. Upon men in such positions a double demand is made, and they are subject to criticism from two very different standpoints. On the one hand are the scientists, calling for investigations which shall increase knowledge without special reference to utility, and sometimes asking that employment be given to a particular scientist on the ground that the work to which he wishes to devote himself is of no known use, and therefore will not support him. On the other hand is the demand from the business men's point of view—that they shall show practical results; that in demands for appropriations from the public funds they shall demonstrate that the use to be made of such appropriations is for the public good, and that their accounts shall show that the money has been properly expended—"properly," not merely in the sense of usefully, but also in the legal sense—in the sense which was meant by Congress in granting the funds. Nay, more, they must consider not only the intentions of Congress but the opinions of the accounting officers of the Treasury, the comptroller and auditor, and their clerks, and not rely solely on their own interpretation of the statutes, if they would work to the best advantage, and not have life made a perpetual burden and vexation of spirit.

There is a tendency on the part of business men and lawyers to the belief that scientific men are not good organizers or administrators, and should be kept in leading strings; that it is unwise to trust them with the expenditure of, or the accounting for, money, and that the precise direction in which they are to investigate should be pointed out to them. In other words, that they should be made problem-solving machines as far as possible.

When we reflect on the number of persons who, like Mark Twain's cat, feel that they are "nearly lightning on superintending;" on the desire for power and authority, which is almost universal, the tendency to this opinion is not to be wondered at. Moreover, as regards the man of science, there is some reason for it in the very terms by which he is defined, the characteristics for which he is chiefly eulogized.

The typical man of science is, in fact, in many cases an abnormity, just as a great poet, a great painter, or a great musician is apt to be, and this not only in an unusual development of one part of the brain, but in an inferior development in others. True, there are exceptions to this rule

—great and illustrious exceptions; but I think we must admit that the man of science often lacks tact, and is indifferent to and careless about matters which do not concern his special work, and especially about matters of accounts and pecuniary details. If such a man is at the head of a bureau, whose work requires many subordinates and the disbursement of large sums of money, he may consider the business management of his office as a nuisance, and delegate as much of it as possible to some subordinate official, who, after a time, becomes the real head and director of the bureau. Evil results have, however, been very rare, and the recognition of the possibility of their occurrence is by no means an admission that they are a necessity, and still less of the proposition that administrative officers should not be scientific men.

I feel very sure that there are always available scientific men, thoroughly well informed in their several departments, who are also thoroughly good business men, and are as well qualified for administrative work as any. When such men are really wanted they can always be found, and, as a matter of fact, a goodly number of them have been found, and are now in the Government service.

The head of a bureau has great responsibilities; and while his position is, in many respects, a desirable one, it would not be eagerly sought for by most scientific men if its duties were fully understood.

In the first place the bureau chief must give up a great part of his time to routine hack work. During his business, or office, hours he can do little else than this routine work, partly because of its amount, and partly because of the frequent interruptions to which he is subjected. His visitors are of all kinds and come from all sorts of motives—some to pass away half an hour, some to get information, some seeking office. It will not work well if he takes the ground that his time is too important to be wasted on casual callers and refers them to some assistant.

In the second place he must, to a great extent at least, give up the pleasure of personal investigation of questions that specially interest him, and turn them over to others. It rarely happens that he can carry out his own plans in his own way, and perhaps it is well that this should be the case. The general character of his work is usually determined for him either by his predecessors, or by Congress, or by the general consensus of opinion of scientific men interested in the particular subject or subjects to which it relates. This last has very properly much weight; in fact, it has much more weight than one might suppose, if he judged from some criticisms made upon the work of some of our bureaus whose work is more or less scientific. In these criticisms it is urged that the work has not been properly planned and correlated; that it should not be left within the power of one man to say what should be done; that the plans for work should be prepared by disinterested scientific men—as, for instance, by a committee of the National Academy—and that the function of the bureau official should be executive only.

I have seen a good deal of this kind of literature within the last ten or twelve years, and some of the authors of it are very distinguished men in scientific work; yet I venture to question the wisdom of such suggestions. As a rule, the plans for any extended scientific work to be undertaken by a Government department are the result of very extended consultations with specialists, and meet with the approval of the majority of them. Were it otherwise the difficulties in obtaining regular annual appropriations for such work would be great and cumulative, for in a short time the disapproval of the majority of the scientific public would make itself felt in Congress. It is true that the *vis inertiæ* of an established bureau is very great. The heads of Departments change with each new administration, but the heads of bureaus remain; and if an unfit man succeeds in obtaining one of these positions, it is a matter of great difficulty to displace him; but it seems to me to be wiser to direct the main effort to getting right men in right places rather than to attempt to elaborate a system which shall give good results with inferior men as the executive agents, which attempt is a waste of energy.

You are all familiar with the results of the inquiry which has been made by a Congressional committee into the organization and work of certain bureaus which are especially connected with scientific interests, and with the different opinions which this inquiry has brought out from scientific men. I think that the conclusion of the majority of the committee, that the work is, on the whole, being well done, and that the people are getting the worth of their money, is generally assented to. True, some mistakes have been made, some force has been wasted, some officials have not given satisfaction; but is it probable that any other system would give so much better results that it is wise to run the risks of change?

This question brings us to the only definite proposition which has been made in the direction, namely, the proposed Department of Science, to which all the bureaus whose work is mainly scientific, such as the Coast Survey, the Geological Survey, the Signal Service, the Naval Observatory, etc., shall be transferred.

The arguments in favor of this are familiar to you, and, as regards one or two of the bureaus, it is probable that the proposed change would effect an improvement; but as to the desirability of centralization and consolidation of scientific interests and scientific work into one department under a single head, I confess that I have serious doubts.

One of the strongest arguments in favor of such consolidation that I have seen is the address of the late president of the Chemical Society of Washington, Professor Clarke, "On the Relations of the Government to

Chemistry," delivered about a year ago. Professor Clarke advises the creation of a large, completely-equipped laboratory, planned by chemists and managed by chemists, in which all the chemical researches required by any department of the Government shall be made, and the abandonment of individual laboratories in the several bureaus on the ground that these last are small, imperfectly equipped, and not properly specialized; that each chemist in them has too broad a range of duty and receives too small a salary to command the best professional ability. He would have a national laboratory, in which one specialist shall deal only with metals, another with food products, a third with drugs, etc., while over the whole, directing and correlating their work, shall preside the ideal chemist, the all-round man, recognized as the leader of the chemists of the United States. And so should the country get better and cheaper results. It is an enticing plan and one which might be extended to many other fields of work. Granting the premises that we shall have the best possible equipment, with the best possible man at the head of it, and a sufficient corps of trained specialists, each of whom will contentedly do his own work as directed and be satisfied, so that there shall be no jealousies, or strikes, or boycotting, and we have made a long stride toward Utopia. But before we centralize in this way we must settle the question of classification. Just as in arranging a large library there are many books which belong in several different sections, so it is in applied science. Is it certain that the examination of food product or of drugs should be made under the direction of the national chemist rather than under that of the Departments which are most interested in the composition and quality of these articles? This does not seem to me to be a self-evident proposition by any means.

The opinion of a scientific man as to whether the Government should or should not undertake to carry out any particular branch of scientific research and publish the results, whether it should attempt to do such work through officers of the Army and Navy, or more or less exclusively through persons specially employed for the purpose, whether the scientific work shall be done under the direction of those who wish to use, and care only for, the practical results, or whether the scientific man shall himself be the administrative head and direct the manner in which his results shall be applied; the opinion of a scientific man on such points, I say, will differ according to the part he expects or desires to take in the work, according to the nature of the work, according to whether he is an Army or Navy officer or not, according to whether he takes more pleasure in scientific investigations than in administrative problems and so forth.

It is necessary, therefore, to apply a correction for personal equation to each individual set of opinions before its true weight and value can be estimated, and, unfortunately, no general formula for this purpose has yet been worked out.

I can only indicate my own opinions, which are those of an Army officer, who has all he wants to do, who does not covet any of his neighbors' work or goods, and who does not care to have any more masters than those whom he is at present trying to serve. You see that I give you some of the data for the formula by which you are to correct my statements, but this is all I can do.

I am not inclined at present to urge the creation of a department of science as an independent department of the Government having at its head a Cabinet officer. Whether such an organization may become expedient in the future seems to me doubtful; but at all events I think the time has not yet come for it.

I do not believe that Government should undertake scientific work merely or mainly because it is scientific, or because some useful results may possibly be obtained from it. It should do, or cause to be done, such scientific work as is needful for its own information and guidance when such work cannot be done, or cannot be done so cheaply or conveniently, by private enterprise. Some kinds of work it can best have done by private contract, and not by officials; others, by its own officers. To this last class belong those branches of scientific investigation, or the means for promoting them, which require long-continued labor and expenditure on a uniform plan—such as the work of the Government Observatory, of the Government surveys, of the collection of the statistics which are so much needed for legislative guidance, and in which we are at present so deficient, the formation of museums and libraries, and so forth.

Considering the plans and operations of these Government institutions from the point of view of the scientific public, it is highly desirable that they should contribute to the advancement of abstract science, as well as to the special practical ends for which they have been instituted; but from the point of view of the legislator, who has the responsibility of granting the funds for their support, the practical results should receive the chief consideration, and therefore they should be the chief consideration on the part of those who are to administer these trusts. It must be borne in mind that while the average legislator is, in many cases, not qualified to judge *a priori* as to what practical results may be expected from a given plan for scientific work, he is, nevertheless, the court which is to decide the question according to the best evidence which he can get, or, rather, which is brought before him, and it is no unimportant part of the duty of those who are experts in these matters to furnish such evidence.

But in saying that practical results should be the chief consideration of the Government and of its legislative and administrative agents it is not meant that these should be the only considerations. In the carrying out of any extensive piece of work which involves the collection of data, experimental inquiry, or the application of scientific results under new conditions there is more or less opportunity to increase knowledge at the same time and with comparatively little increased cost. Such opportunity should be taken advantage of, and is also a proper subsidiary reason for adopting one plan of work in preference to another, or for selecting for appointment persons qualified not only to do the particular work which is the main object, but also for other allied work of a more purely scientific character.

On the same principle it seems to me proper and expedient that when permanent Government employees have at times not enough to do in their own departments, and can be usefully employed in scientific work, it is quite legitimate and proper to thus make use of them. For example, it is desirable that this country should have such an organization of its Army and Navy as will permit of rapid expansion when the necessity arises, and this requires that more officers shall be educated and kept in the service than are needed for military and naval duty in time of peace. It has been the policy of the Government to employ some of these officers in work connected with other departments, and especially in work which requires such special training, scientific or administrative, or both, as such officers possess. To this objections are raised, which may be summed up as follows:

First, that such officers ought not to be given positions which would otherwise be filled by civilian scientists, because these places are more needed by the civilians as a means of earning subsistence, and because it tends to increase the competition for places and to lower salaries. Put in other words, the argument is that it is injurious to the interests of scientific men, taken as a body, that the Government should employ in investigations or work requiring special knowledge and skill men who have been educated and trained at its expense, and who are permanently employed and paid by it. This is analogous to the trades union and the anti-convict labor platforms.

The second objection is that Army and Navy officers do not, as a rule, possess the scientific and technical knowledge to properly perform duties lying outside of the sphere of the work for which they have been educated, and that they employ as subordinates really skilled scientific men, who make the plans and do most of the work, but do not receive proper credit for it. The reply to this is that it is a question of fact in each particular case, and that if the officer is able to select and employ good men to prepare the plans and to do the work, this in itself is a very good reason for giving him the duty of such selection and employment.

A third objection is that when an officer of the Army or Navy is detailed for scientific or other special work the interests of this work and of the public are too often made subordinate to the interests of the naval or military service, more especially in the matter of change of station. For example, civil engineers object to the policy of placing river and harbor improvements in the hands of Army engineers, because one of the objects kept in view by the War Department in making details for this purpose is to vary the duty of the individual officer from time to time so as to give him a wider experience. Hence it may happen that an officer placed on duty in connection with the improvement of certain harbors on the Great Lakes shall, after three or four years, and just as he has gained sufficient experience of the peculiarities of lake work to make his supervision there peculiarly valuable, be transferred to work on the improvement of the Lower Mississippi with which he may be quite unfamiliar.

In like manner Professor Clarke objects to having a laboratory connected with the medical department of the Navy on the ground that the officer in charge is changed every three years; consequently science suffers in order that naval routine may be preserved.

There is force in this class of objections, but the moral I should draw from them is, not that Army and Navy officers should not be allowed to do work outside their own departments or in science, but that when they are put upon such duty, the ordinary routine of change of station every three or four years should not be enforced upon them without careful consideration of the circumstances of the case, and satisfactory evidence that the work on which they are engaged will not suffer by the change. And, as a matter of fact, I believe this has been the policy pursued, and instances could be given where an officer has been kept twenty years at one station for this very reason.

I pass over a number of objections that I have heard made to the employment of Army and Navy officers as administrators, on the ground that they are too "bumptious," or "domineering," or "supercilious," or "finicky," because every one knows what these mean and their force. An Army officer is not necessarily a polished gentleman; neither is a civilian; and a good organizer and administrator, whether officer or civilian, will at times, and especially to some people, appear arbitrary and dictatorial.

There is another objection to special details of Army or Navy officers for scientific duties which comes not so much from outside persons as from the War Department and the officers themselves, and it is this: Among such officers there are always a certain number who not only prefer special details to routine duty, but who actively seek for such details, who are perpetual candidates for them.

The proportion of men whose ideas as to their own scientific acquirements, merits, and claims to attention are excessive as compared with
the ideas of their acquaintances on the same points is not greater in the
Army than elsewhere, but when an Army officer is afflicted in this way
the attack is sometimes very severe, and the so-called influence which he
brings to bear may cause a good deal of annoyance to the Department,
even if it be not sufficient to obtain his ends. I have heard officers of high
rank, in a fit of impatience under such circumstances, express a most
hearty and emphatic wish that no special details were possible, so that
lobbying for them should be useless. This, however, seems to me to be
too heroic a remedy for the disease, which, after all, only produces comparatively trifling irritation and discomfort.

The same evil exists, to a much greater extent, in the civil branches
of the Government. Few persons can fully appreciate the loss of time,
the worry, and the annoyance to which the responsible heads of some of
our bureaus for scientific work are subjected through the desire of people
for official position and for maintenance by the Government. They have
to stand always at the bat and protect their wickets from the balls which
are bowled at them in every direction, even from behind by some of
their own subordinates.

It is true that a great majority of the balls go wide and cause little
trouble, and a majority of the bowlers soon get tired and leave the field,
but there are generally a few persistent ones who gradually acquire
no small degree of skill in discovering the weak or unguarded points, and
succeed in making things lively for a time. Considered from the point
of view of the public interests, such men are useful, for although they
cause some loss of valuable time, and occasionally do a little damage by
promoting hostile legislation, yet their criticisms are often worth taking
into account; they tend to prevent the machine from getting into a rut,
and they promote activity and attention to business on the part of administrative chiefs. It is a saying among dog fanciers that a few fleas on
a dog are good for him rather than otherwise, as they compel him to
take some exercise under any circumstances.

At all events I think it very doubtful whether the jealousies and desire
for position for one's self or one's friends which exist under present circumstances would be materially diminished under any other form of
organization, even under a departmenf of science.

Some conflict of interests now exists it is true; some work is duplicated;
but neither the conflict nor the duplication are necessarily wholly evil
in themselves, nor in so far as they are evil are they necessary parts of
the present system. This system is of the nature of a growth; it is organic
and not a mere pudding-stone aggregation of heterogeneous materials,

and the wise course is to correct improper bendings and twistings gradually, prune judiciously, and go slow in trying to secure radical changes lest death or permanent deformity result.

It will be seen that in what I have said I have not attempted to eulogize science or scientists in the abstract. I should be very sorry, however, to have given any one the impression that I think they should not be eulogized. Having read a number of eloquent tributes to their importance by way of inducing a proper frame of mind in which to prepare this address, it is possible that I overdid it a little, and was in a sort of reaction stage when I began to write. But the more I have thought on the subject, and the more carefully I have sought to analyze the motives and character of those of my acquaintances who are either engaged in scientific work or who wish to be considered as so doing, and to compare them with those who have no pretensions to science, and who make none, the more I have been convinced that upon the whole the eulogium is the proper thing to give, and that it is not wise to be critical as to the true inwardness of all that we see or hear.

At least nine-tenths of the praises which have been heaped upon scientific men as a body are thoroughly well deserved. Among them are to be found a very large proportion of true gentlemen, larger, I think, than is to be found in any other class of men—men characterized by modesty, unselfishness, scrupulous honesty, and truthfulness, and by the full performance of their family and social duties.

Even their foibles may be likable. A little vanity of thirst for publicity, zeal in claiming priority of discovery, or undue wrath over the other scientist's theory, does not and should not detract from the esteem in which we hold them. A very good way of viewing characteristics which we do not like is to bear in mind that different parts of the brain have different functions; that all of them cannot act at once, and that their tendencies are sometimes contradictory.

There are times when a scientific man does not think scientifically, when he does not want to so think, and possibly when it is best that he should not so think. There is wisdom in Sam. Lawson's remark that "Folks that are always telling you what they don't believe are sort o' stringy and dry. There ain't no 'sorption got out o' not believing nothing." At one time the emotional, at another the intellectual, side of the scientific man has the ascendency, and one must appeal from one state to the other. Were scientific thinking rigorously carried out to practical results in every-day life there would be some very remarkable social changes, and perhaps some very disagreeable ones.

That scientific pursuits give great pleasure without reference to their utility, or to the fame or profit to be derived from them; that they tend to make a man good company to himself and to bring him into pleasant associations is certain; and that a man's own pleasure and happiness are things to be sought for in his work and companionship is also certain. If in this address I have ventured to hint that this may not be the only, nor even the most important, object in life, that one may be a scientific man, or even a man of science, and yet not be worthy of special reverence; because he may be at the same time an intensely selfish man, and even a vicious man, I hope that it is clearly understood that it is with no intention of depreciating the glory of science or the honor which is due to the large number of scientific gentlemen whom I see around me.

A scientific gentleman—all praise to him who merits this title—it is the blue ribbon of our day.

We live in a fortunate time and place; in the early manhood of a mighty nation, and in its capital city, which every year makes more beautiful, and richer in the treasures of science, literature, and art which all the keels of the sea and the iron roads of the land are bringing to it. Life implies death; growth presages decay; but we have good reasons for hoping that for our country and our people the evil days are yet far off. Yet we may not rest and eat lotus; we may not devote our lives to our own pleasure, even though it be pleasure derived from scientific investigation. No man lives for himself alone; the scientific man should do so least of all. There never was a time when the world had more need of him, and there never was a time when more care was needful lest his torch should prove a firebrand and destroy more than it illuminates.

The old creeds are quivering; shifting; changing like the colored flames on the surface of the Bessemer crucible. They are being analyzed, and accounted for, and toned down, and explained, until many are doubting whether there is any solid substratum beneath; but the instinct which gave those creeds their influence is unchanged.

The religions and philosophies of the Orient seem to have little in common with modern science. The sage of the east did not try to climb the ladder of knowledge step by step. He sought a wisdom which he supposed far superior to all knowledge of earthly phenomena obtainable through the senses. The man of science of the west seeks knowledge by gradual accumulation, striving by comparison and experiment to elimi- nate the errors of individual observations, and doubting the possibility of attaining wisdom in any other way. The knowledge which he has, or seeks, is knowledge which may be acquired partly by individual effort and partly by co-operation, which requires material resources for its development, the search for which may be organized and pursued through the help of others, which is analogous in some respects to property which may be used for power or pleasure. The theologian and the poet claim that there is a wisdom which is not acquired but attained to, which cannot be communicated or received at pleasure, which comes in a way vaguely expressed by the words intuition or inspiration, which acts through and upon the emotional rather than the intellectual faculties, and which, thus acting, is sometimes of irresistible power in exciting and directing the actions of individuals and of communities.

The answer of the modern biologist to the old Hebrew question, *viz.*, "Why are children born with their hands clenched while men die with their hands wide open?" would not in the least resemble that given by the Rabbis, yet this last it is well that the scientist should also remember: "Because on entering the world men would grasp everything, but on leaving it all slips away." There exist in men certain mental phenomena, the study of which is included in what is known as ethics, and which are usually assumed to depend upon what is called moral law. Whether there is such a law and whether, if it exists, it can be logically deduced from observed facts in nature or is only known as a special revelation, are questions upon which scientific men in their present stage of development are not agreed. There is not yet any satisfactory scientific basis for what is recognized as sound ethics and morality throughout the civilized world; these rest upon another foundation.

This procession, bearing its lights of all kinds, smoky torches, clear-burning lamps, farthing rush-lights, and sputtering brimstone matches, passes through the few centuries of which we have a record, illuminating an area which varies, but which has been growing steadily larger. The individual members of the procession come from, and pass into, shadow and darkness, but the light of the stream remains. Yet it does not seem so much darkness, an infinite night, whence we come and whither we go, as a fog which at a little distance obscures or hides all things, but which, nevertheless, gives the impression that there is light beyond and above it. In this fog we are living and groping, stumbling down blind alleys, only to find that there is no thoroughfare, getting lost and circling about on our own tracks as on a jumbie prairie; but slowly and irregularly we do seem to be getting on, and to be establishing some points in the survey of the continent of our own ignorance.

In some directions the man of science claims to lead the way; in others the artist, the poet, the devotee. Far reaching as the speculations of the man of science may be, ranging from the constitution and nature of a universal protyle, through the building of a universe to its resolution again into primal matter or modes of motion, he can frame no hypothesis which shall explain consciousness, nor has he any data for a formula which shall tell what becomes of the individual when he disappears in the all-surrounding mist. Does he go on seeking and learning in other ways or other worlds? The great mass of mankind think that they have some information bearing on these questions; but, if so, it is a part of the wisdom of the Orient, and not of the physical or natural science of the Occident. Whether after death there shall come increase of knowledge, with increase of desires and of means of satisfying them, or whether there shall be freedom from all desire, and an end of coming and going, we do not know; nor is there any reason to suppose that it is a part of the plan of the universe that we should know. We do know that the great majority of men think that there are such things as right and duty—God and a future life—and that to each man there comes the opportunity of doing something which he and others recognize to be his duty. The scientific explanation of a part of the process by which this has been brought about, as by natural selection, heredity, education, progressive changes in this or that particular mass of brain matter, has not much bearing on the practical question of "What to do about it?" But it does, nevertheless, indicate that it is not a characteristic to be denounced, or opposed, or neglected, since, even in the "struggle-for-existence" theory, it has been, and still is, of immense importance in human social development.

"Four men," says the Talmud, "entered Paradise. One beheld and died. One beheld and lost his senses. One destroyed the young plants. One only entered in peace and came out in peace." Many are the mystic and cabalistic interpretations which have been given of this saying; and if for "Paradise" we read the "world of knowledge" each of you can no doubt best interpret the parable for himself. Speaking to a body of scientific men, each of whom has, I hope, also certain unscientific beliefs, desires, hopes, and longings, I will only say: "Be strong and of a good courage." As scientific men, let us try to increase and diffuse knowledge; as men and citizens, let us try to be useful; and, in each capacity, let us do the work that comes to us honestly and thoroughly, and fear not the unknown future.

When we examine that wonderful series of wave marks which we call the spectrum we find, as we go downwards, that the vibrations become slower, the dark bands wider, until as last we reach a point where there seems to be no more movements; the blackness is continuous, the ray seems dead. Yet within this year Langley has found that a very long way lower down the pulsations again appear, and form, as it were, another spectrum; they never really ceased, but only changed in rhythm, requiring new apparatus or new senses to appreciate them. And it may well be that our human life is only a kind of lower spectrum, and that, beyond and above the broad black band which we call death, there are other modes of impulses—another spectrum—which registers the ceaseless beats of waves from the great central fountain of force, the heart of the universe, in modes of existence of which we can but dimly dream.

Medicine in the United States, and Its Relations To Co-operative Investigation

(Excerpts)

* * * *

There is a class of medical schools in the United States whose object is to give the minimum amount of instruction which will enable a man to commence the practice of medicine without much danger of making such serious and glaring blunders as will be readily detected by the public. There are other schools whose aim and object is to make fairly well trained practitioners; the general character of the instruction given in these being substantially the same as that given in your English hospital medical schools. The results of such a three years' graded course of instruction in medicine as these schools furnish, depend upon the character of the material upon which they work; that is to say, upon the general preliminary education possessed by the student at the time of his matriculation. This is evidently too often defective, and only a few schools have thus far ventured to establish any standard of preliminary examination which at all approaches in its demands that which is required in England.

The proverb that it does not pay to give a 5,000 dollar education to a 5 dollar boy is clearly of American origin, and sums up a great deal of experience.

You have nineteen portals of entrance to the profession, and have not found it easy to keep them all up to the standard. In America we have over eighty gates, a number of turnstiles, and a good deal of the ground is unenclosed common. Many of our physicians are more or less dissatisfied with this state of things, and with the results thereof; and every year in some States efforts are made to secure legislation, which it is supposed will protect the interests of the profession, though those who advocate such legislation are usually prudent enough to claim as their only motive a desire for the protection of the public.

Now, how does this free trade in medicine and the low standard of qualification, or no standard at all, required by law, affect practitioners as individuals? To answer this, we must divide the profession into sev-

The annual address in medicine delivered before the British Medical Association, August 11, 1886. *British Medical Journal* 2: 299–307 (14 Aug 1886). Excerpts are from pp. 300–3, 304, 304–5, 305, and 307.

eral classes. In the first place, in all our cities, great and small, there is a large class of physicians who are as well educated and as thoroughly competent to practise their art, as can be found in the world. They have studied both at home and abroad, have had extensive clinical training, are always supplied with the latest and best medical literature and the most improved instruments, and many of them are connected with hospitals and medical schools. Among them are found the majority of our writers and teachers, and the successful men are the survivors of a struggle in which there has been keen and incessant competition. These physicians, whose positions are fairly assured, and who, as a rule, have all the practice they desire, are not usually active leaders in movements to secure medical legislation, although they passively assent to such efforts, or at least do not oppose them; and their names may sometimes be found appended to memorials urging such legislation. They are clear-headed, shrewd, "practical" men, who know that their business interests are not specially injured by quacks and ignoramuses, rather the contrary in fact, for they are called on to repair the damage done by the quack to people who have more money than brains; and they are not inclined to risk the fate of the Mexican donkey who died of *congejos agenas*, that is, "of other people's troubles."

Then there is another large class of honest, hard-working practitioners, who rely more on what they call experience and common sense than on book learning. Many of these have obtained assured positions of respectability and usefulness, and are comparatively indifferent to medical legislation so far as their own interests are concerned. Others, however, who are not so successful, feel the competition of the local herb-doctor or of the travelling quack more keenly, and have more decided views about the importance of diplomas. Among these are the young men who have not yet acquired local fame, and who are apt to become very indignant over the doings of some charlatan in the neighbourhood, or of some druggist who prescribes over his counter. These last are usually quite clear in their minds that the State ought to interfere and prevent injury to the health of the people.

I have known two unsuccessful physicians who finally abandoned practice, and who gave as a reason for their failure—one that "he did not know enough" and the other that "he had not the manners and tact which would inspire confidence in his patients;" but such frank-speaking men are rare.

* * * *

The relations of the United States Government to medical education and to the practice of medicine are indirect only, the regulation of these matters by law being part of the police power which, under the constitution, is reserved exclusively to the individual States. The United States employs physicians in its Indian Department, in the Pension Department, in the Marine Hospital Service, and in the medical departments of the army and navy, and it has power to regulate the practice of medicine in those territories which are not yet organised into States, and also in the District of Columbia; but thus far it has made no use of such power. The qualifications of physicians employed in the army and navy, and in the Marine Hospital Service, are determined by examinations made by boards of medical officers belonging to those services. The possession of a diploma from a respectable medical college is a prerequisite for such examination, but beyond this it does not count; that is to say, the examination is the same for the holders of all diplomas, and covers all branches of medicine. But while the relations of the general government to medical education are thus indirect, they have of late years become of very considerable practical importance, and are now exerting much influence upon medical investigations and literature. This is being effected by the museums and libraries, which are now being formed under the auspices of the government at Washington, and also, to some extent, by certain special investigations undertaken by the government in the interests of preventive medicine. Of these various agencies, one of the most important is the library which has been formed at Washington, under the auspices of the medical department of the army in connection with the Army Medical Museum; both of these institutions being a part of the results of the late civil war. The museum was at first formed to illustrate military medicine and surgery, giving the results, primary and secondary, of injuries inflicted by modern weapons of warfare, and of the diseases of armies in the field; in which direction the collection is unrivalled in extent and completeness. Gradually its scope has been enlarged to include illustrations of anatomy, development, and all branches of pathology and therapeutics, so that it is fast covering the whole field of medical science. In like manner the library, which commenced in a collection of those books relating solely or especially to military medicine and surgery, which were required in the compilation of the *Medical and Surgical History of the War*, has expanded into a great medical library, which is now one of the best practical working collections of the kind in the world. These collections, then, no longer appertain exclusively, or chiefly, to the business of one department, but belong to the whole profession of the United States as a body; and the department which has charge of them is managing them from this point of view. The influence of the library in stimulating research, and upon the quality of medical literature, is already very perceptible, and is destined to increase with advancing years. I think I may also venture to claim that the utility of these collections, and especially of the library, is by no means confined to the medical profession of the United States, for the catalogues and indices, which are being issued in connection with them, are of service to medical writers and teachers all over the world.

*   *   *   *

As to the condition of medical science and art in America, it partakes of the general progress, for the press now makes all discoveries the common property of the civilised world. The marked feature of the present epoch is the recent advance in knowledge as to the relations between micro-organisms and certain diseases, and the strong stimulus which this has given to preventive medicine. Sanitation is becoming fashionable, and if we may believe some of its votaries, it is a very simple matter to prolong the average lifetime to the scriptural "three-score years and ten." All that is necessary is that everything shall be clean, and every person virtuous.

Having learned to distinguish those diseases which can be prevented much more easily and certainly than they can be cured, we may turn them over to the sanitarian, who has his own battles to fight with ignorance and prejudice. If he succeeds, and so far as he succeeds, he will change, in certain respects, the work of the practitioner.

The lives which are saved from cholera and typhoid, from consumption and diphtheria, and from the acute specific diseases, will, at last, be weakened and destroyed in other ways. The work of the physician will not be lessened by preventive medicine; it will simply be required more for older persons, and for another class of diseases. As sanitarians must depend upon practitioners for much of the information which is essential for their work, it follows that if preventive medicine is to become a working power, it will bring the mass of the profession into closer relations with the State than its members have held heretofore. What these relations shall be is one of the most interesting, and, at the same time, one of the most difficult, of the many problems with which we, or our successors, must deal. I have referred to some experiments on this subject which are now being tried in America, where it is much easier to make such trials than it is in an older country hampered with vested interests. Just at present, in this, as in a number of other things, our tendency is toward centralisation, both in the several States and for the whole country, and it is not improbable that we may go far on this road in the future.

*   *   *   *

A marked feature of the present day, in medicine as in other things, is the tendency to specialisation in study and in practice. But this very development of specialties, of increasing minuteness in the division of labour, increases the necessity for co-operation, and, in fact, tends to create what we may call the specialty of co-operation. Formerly, a rifle, or a watch, was made by a single workman. No two instruments were exactly alike, each piece had its own individuality and was not interchangeable, and the cost of the whole was such as to put it beyond the reach of the multitude. Now, the work on these things is greatly subdivided; one man makes only one small wheel, or spring, or pinion, and another another, each doing his work according to a uniform pattern, rapidly, perfectly, and at comparatively small cost.

But, in addition to the workmen who make the individual parts, it is now necessary to have one person specially skilled in making drawings and preparing patterns, another to assemble the completed parts, and a third to test the whole after it has been put together. As the centrifugal force increases, the centripetal power must also increase.

In one sense medicine, as we have it to-day, is the result of co-operation, not of deliberate centrally planned and direct co-operation, but of natural selection from results produced by many men, often working at cross purposes and, therefore, wasting much energy, but nevertheless working, though blindly, to a common end. And it is safe to predict that in the future much of the best work will be done in the same way, by individual effort inspired by the love of science, by personal ambition, etc. But the results obtained in this way come slowly, and some things that we want can hardly be obtained by individual effort, even if we were willing to wait; hence we must look to organisation for help.

This is an age of machinery, of exchanges, of corporations, for all these correspond to one and the same fundamental idea. Men make machines to do what the individual cannot do, and they make them not only of brass and iron, but of men, for such an obvious source of power to the man or men who can master the combination is not likely to be overlooked. One result of such organisation is seen in our encyclopaedic works on medicine, whether these be called dictionaries or handbooks; another in the great medical journals; another in associations which seek to wield political influence; another in the comparatively recent attempt at collective investigation of disease. With these may be classed also the attempts of government departments to make scientific investigations, to form libraries and museums, to do things which require long continuity of effort on a definite plan in order to produce the best results. And it is by the combination of all these, with the efforts of individual workers, that substantial advance and improvement are to be effected.

In this broader view of co-operation, it is interesting to consider those fields of labour to which comparatively few physicians can devote themselves, because of want of time and opportunity, but whose proper working is, nevertheless, of the greatest importance to the practitioner.

One of these is experimental laboratory-work; and in this direction the prospect of valuable contributions from America is now exceedingly good. Some of the wisest of our most wealthy men have shown their appreciation of the responsibilities which riches entail on their possessors, by seeking new channels through which to benefit their fellow-men. While the old and well known methods of endowing hospitals and charitable institutions are not neglected, there is apparent an increasing tendency to endeavour to promote the advancement of knowledge, and especially of such knowledge as tends to the mitigation of suffering and the improvement of the race, to furnish means for the investigation of disease, to provide laboratories, and to endow medical schools, and thus place them beyond the reach of the temptations and difficulties which must always exist when such schools are dependent upon the fees of students, and are, therefore, practically commercial manufacturing establishments.

As illustrations of this tendency, I may mention the bequest of £1,400,000 by Johns Hopkins to endow, in the city of Baltimore, a university and a hospital of which the medical department is to be a special feature, to be provided with the best laboratory and other facilities for original investigation as well as for teaching; the gift of Mr. Carnegie to the Bellevue Hospital Medical School of New York, in the shape of a well-equipped pathological laboratory; the presentation by Mr. Vanderbilt, and members of his family, to the College of Physicians of New York, of £200,000, to provide for that school new buildings and clinics having the best means of teaching and research; and the endowment by an unknown donor, of a laboratory for the University Medical College of New York, with the sum of £20,000.

Last year, in his retiring address as President of the New York Academy of Medicine, Dr. Fordyce Barker referred to this tendency to regard wealth as a trust to be used for the benefit of humanity, and, after sketching the requirements of the Academy on a scale which would require an endowment of at least a million of dollars, predicted that such an endowment would be furnished by wealthy citizens of the city. I believe that he was right, and that his prediction will become history.

As the class of men who have wealth, leisure, and knowledge becomes greater, there comes an ever increasing demand, not only for the best medical skill, for the most expert practitioner, but also for exhaustive research in every direction which promises to furnish new means for the prevention or relief of suffering, and for warding off, as long as possible, the inevitable end; and hence there is little reason to doubt that the examples I have named will be followed by others in the near future. With such opportunities, and under such conditions and influences, the stimulus to the young and ambitious worker is strong; we have abundance of material of this kind upon which the process of natural selection can operate, and there is little reason to doubt that the result will be substantial and valuable contributions to physiology, pathology, and therapeutics.

* * * *

I have spoken to little purpose if I have failed to show you that there is a great deal of human nature in American physicians, and that it is a kind of human nature with which you are tolerably familiar. It should be so, for we are of the same race—a race which, perhaps, as Emerson says, "sets a higher value on wealth, victory, and material superiority than other men, has less tranquility, is less easily contented." Our ancestors were restless, fighters, freebooters and from these ancestors we have the common inheritance of energy of what we call "firmness", and our opponents unreasonable, pigheaded, stubbornness; of liking to manage our own affairs, and, at the same time, to exercise a little judicious supervision over those of our neighbours; of hatred of humbug and lying; and, in spite of our discontent, of a firm belief that our wives and children, habits, houses, modes of business, and of treating disease are, on the whole, better than those of any other people under the sun.

Privately, and between ourselves, we grumble and declare that the country and profession are going to the dogs—nay, we must do so, or we should not be of true English blood; but there is no need for me to tell you that these are only "growing pains," and not symptoms of progressive ataxy.

While we must consider the difficulties in the way of the improvement of the science and art of medicine, difficulties due to ignorance, to indolence, to conflict of interests, and to the eternal fitness of things, the existence of such difficulties is not a matter to be bemoaned and lamented over. These obstacles are the spice of life, the incentives to action, the source of some of the greatest pleasures which it is given to man to experience.

The child, spending a happy hour with its new puzzle, is a type of the scientific investigator. The naturalist who objected to the statement that this is a miserable world which it is well to be soon done with, on the ground that there are still many species of rhizopods which he had not examined and classified, is another type. On the ethical and sociological side, the matter is summed up in Ruskin's aphorism, that "Fools were made that wise men may take care of them."

It is surely not without cause that there has been given to us this restless spirit of inquisitiveness, this desire to compass the heavens and the earth, this raging infinite thirst for knowledge: it is the outcome of brain-training and natural selection for thousands and tens of thousands of years.

We are in a period of the world's history characterised by material prosperity, by increase of populations, by tendencies to uniformity, to the making of individuals of small account. According to the Swiss philosopher, Alphonse de Candolle, this is to last a thousand years or so, after which the pendulum will swing the other way, and there will follow a long period of diminution and separation of peoples, and of decadence.

Against that decay of nations we know of but one remedy, and that is increase of knowledge and of wisdom. And this increase must be in our knowledge, in the world's wisdom, and not merely in that of John, of Fritz, or Claude.

As each man has special opportunities and duties, if he can only recognise them, so it is with guilds, with professions, and with nations.

I have tried to indicate to you some of these opportunities which are presenting themselves to my colleagues, your brothers, in the lands beyond the sea, and I hope that I shall not be considered rash or vainglorious in saying that I believe they will so use those opportunities as to return compound interest for what they have received from the storehouse of our common inheritance. Force changes form and place, the stored energy of the soil of our plains and valleys has been coming here in the form of meat and grain, has appeared in muscle and brain, and in a hundred other shapes, but none has been destroyed; our loss has been your gain, and in our turn we have received full and fair exchange.

It is our part now to remember that there are not two springs in the year, there are not two periods of youth abounding in energy and desire, or of manhood's strength and self-poise, in the life of any man or of any nation, and for us, as for those who have been before us, the Kanuri proverb holds true, "*Kabu datsia, kargum bago*"—The days being finished, there is no more medicine.

Methods of Research in Medical Literature

When I promised to speak briefly at this meeting on medical bibliography, it was not because I had anything new to say on this subject, but because it seemed possible that a few remarks might start a discussion by the medical writers and teachers of this Association as to the methods which they have found useful, and as to what they think can and should be done here to facilitate this kind of research. From the days of Galen to the middle of the seventeenth century, bibliographical work was the most important business of the medical teacher. The great majority of the writers of the Middle Ages busied themselves, not so much with observation of facts, or with experimental inquiry, as with seeking to find out what Hippocrates, Galen, Avicenna, and other old masters had said about the matter. When the discovery was made that, in order to determine the precise anatomy of a part, the function of an organ, or the results produced by a disease, it was best to look for one's self, instead of consulting the fathers, and when this discovery had become popularized, bibliographical and historical research fell for a time into neglect. Within the last fifty years, however, there has been a revival in interest in the collection of medical libraries and in historical research, which last has become a necessity in many cases, if one would avoid doing useless work. Attempts to learn what has been done, or said, or thought, by our predecessors are due to widely different needs, and may be pursued by widely different methods.

As specimens of subjects with regard to which bibliographical work is most frequently called for, I give the following:

(1) To gather and compare the records of all reported cases of particular forms of abnormity, disease, or injury. The rarer and more anomalous the abnormity or the disease, the more important it is to find the widely-scattered records.

(2) To obtain statistical data with regard to the circumstances affecting the prevalence of a certain disease, the relative frequency of particular symptoms, and the comparative merits of different modes of treatment, or the results of special operations.

(3) To obtain information as to details of methods which have been tried in experimental physiology, pathology, or pharmacology, and as to

Delivered before the Association of American Physicians, Washington, June 2, 1887.
Transactions of the Association of American Psyicians 2: 57–67 (1887).

the results; in order to avoid waste of time in devising apparatus, or in trying methods, which have been already found worthless, or to obtain suggestions as to new modes of experimentation.

(4) To trace the origin and development of medical organization in a particular city or country, or to gather materials for a biographical sketch of some celebrated physician, or for the history of a medical society.

(5) To obtain data for a comparison of the laws and customs of different countries affecting medical education, or the right to practice, or the care of the insane, or public hygiene, etc.

In literary research for biographical purposes, or to trace the development of theories or institutions, the work must be done mainly by the writer himself; and, while at the commencement he may be greatly helped by systematic works of medical bibliography, he will soon find himself wandering off into all sorts of curious by-paths and out-of-the-way corners, into which he is led by obeying the golden rule for this kind of work, namely, to "verify your references." In the first book which he consults he will probably find two or three references, which will indicate to him as many different books or articles which he will wish to consult. When he gets these, each of them will probably give a few more references, to be hunted up in like manner.

Meantime, it will not be an unprecedented or very remarkable occurrence if, in the course of his reading, he stumbles over several interesting points not precisely connected with his original quest, but still having some relation to it, and which it seems a pity not to look up while he is about it, so he makes note of these, and of the references connected with them, and sends for a fresh lot of books. He finds, also, that some of his quotations are erroneous, that "some one has blundered or plagiarized," and proceeds with a sense of refreshment and satisfaction to hunt down the culprit. And so the work expands, for, as Teufelsdröckh remarks, "any road will lead you to the end of the world." To those who like this sort of literary work it has a great fascination, and there are few educated men who do not enjoy a short hunt of this kind, if they have time and facilities for it. From a strictly utilitarian and merely pecuniary point of view, the results of such bibliographical excursions are not usually very remunerative, but they afford capital mental exercise, and occasionally result in the production of some really interesting and valuable additions to medical literature.

Men engaged in this line of research do not usually, except just at first, care much about subject catalogues or indexes. They know what books they want to see, and the catalogue which interests them most frequently is a catalogue of authors in alphabetical order. The questions which they ask of the librarian are something like the following: Have you got such a book in the library? Who is the author of a book having such a title? John Smith published a book about such a date—what is its title? I want to see all the books that Peter Brown wrote or edited. How many editions were published of "Jones's Surgery," and what translations were made of it? When did the *Ohio Medical Repository* begin and end, and who were its editors? These are all simple questions, which almost any physician can answer for himself by the aid of good, ordinary author-catalogues.

If the question is as to a collection of laws regulating medical practice in Brussels, or the number of supplements to the "Catalogue of the New York Hospital," some physicians might be troubled a little to find the desired information in an author catalogue, not knowing the rule that a government or corporation is considered to be the author of its laws, reports, etc., and that, therefore, Belgium is the author of the first book, and the New York Hospital of the second.

But while a simple alphabetical catalogue of authors will serve many purposes in bibliographical research, and is, perhaps, the one most used by the librarian, there are many points on which it fails to give the desired information, and for which bibliographical lists or subject-catalogues are desirable; and just here a few definitions may be useful. By a bibliography I mean a list of titles of books, and of references to articles or paragraphs which relate to the subject in hand. By a critical bibliography I mean a list in which shall be indicated those books or articles which are of real value, as containing some addition to knowledge. In many, perhaps most, cases, such lists are best published in chronological form, thus indicating the successive dates on which new information was given; but, in making them, the use of separate slips or cards, arranged in alphabetical order, is the most convenient. The more complete such lists can be made, the more valuable they are, but often too much time is wasted in attempts to make them absolutely perfect. The great thing to be kept in view is to make them accurate as far as they go, and one of the best means of doing this is to indicate distinctly for each title quoted as to whether you yourself have or have not seen and examined the book. It should be constantly borne in mind that the proper object in giving bibliographical lists is not to impress the reader with the extent and variety of the author's research, but to give him the means of verifying the author's statements, and of pushing the research further. It is analogous to giving details of methods used in an experiment in physiology. Hence the references given should not be too condensed. They should be so clear, that from them it shall be easy to find the books, and for this reason I ask your attention to the desirability of using a uniform system of abbreviations of titles of journals and transactions in referring to them, and venture to suggest that the set of such abbreviations given at the beginning of Vol. VII of the Index Catalogue may be found useful for this purpose.

I have elsewhere called attention to the essential differences between medical bibliography, properly so called, and subject-catalogues of particular libraries. No matter how large and complete a medical library may be, its subject-catalogue can never form anything like a satisfactory medical bibliography; it only makes a good foundation for one.

On the other hand, when you wish to use bibliographical lists prepared by others, you have usually much difficulty in finding some of the books referred to, while the references which you do find in a subject-catalogue of a given library, can at all events be verified by visiting that library. The labor of preparing bibliographical lists, and of research, after one has been furnished with such a list, is in many cases very considerable, and such work can usually only be carried on to advantage in a large library. As this is preëminently an age of division of labor, it is natural to apply this principle also to bibliographical research. There are many cases in which what may be called mechanical bibliography and literary research may be used to excellent advantage, and the field for this kind of work will expand in the future. It is especially applicable in those cases, indicated in a preceding part of this paper, in which it is desired to compare the records of cases and operations, and to prepare statistics. It is often much better for the busy practitioner to have this work done for him than to attempt to do it himself, and especially is this the case if he does not easily read other languages besides his own. It is true that by employing others to do such work, he loses both pleasure and instruction, but the field of professional work and study is now so wide that it is impossible for any one man to cover it all, and he must be content with coöperative effort. It is also true that such work is not only sometimes expensive, but that it is often difficult to tell beforehand what it will cost. There are several physicians in Washington who are willing to undertake work of this kind in the library of the Surgeon-General's Office, for physicians at a distance who cannot conveniently visit this city, and their charge for such work, hunting up references, making abstracts, translations, etc., is one dollar per hour. You can readily see that there can be no very definite relation between the time occupied and results produced: a half-page abstract may require two hours to prepare, or it may be done in ten minutes, and sometimes it may cost less to purchase a pamphlet than to obtain an abstract of it in this way. Nevertheless the demand for this kind of work is steadily increasing, and a supply will arise to meet the demand.

In order to obtain satisfactory results from bibliographical work done in this way it is necessary that the points to be looked up shall be stated as concisely, and as precisely, as possible; in other words that the person who requests the search shall know clearly what he wants. I have elsewhere called attention to this by quoting the warning which is printed on the title-page of the Washington City Directory, namely, "If you want to find a name in this directory, you must know how to spell it," which is the same as the old Latin proverb, "qui nihil affert, nihil refert." When I receive a letter stating that the writer is about to prepare a paper for his county medical society; that he has selected for his subject, tumors of the liver, or locomotor ataxy, or the causes of insanity in modern times; and that he would be glad to have as complete a list of references as possible to all articles, reports of cases, or statistics connected with these subjects,—and that his paper must be prepared in two weeks,—I know of course that what he wants is one of the recent encyclopædias of medicine, and advise accordingly. The problem is not always so simple, however, and I must confess that I am sometimes very much puzzled as to what to reply to some of the queries which I receive. Nevertheless, we are all learning gradually how to use medical libraries, and in a few years more I predict that the wonder will be how we ever got on without them.

I have here a few of the books which are most used in this library for subject-references, a list of which is appended to this paper. I include in this list the catalogues of certain libraries for reasons already given. For other valuable works consult in the Index-Catalogue the headings, Bibliography Medical, Biography Medical, and Medicine, History of. With regard to the Index-Catalogue of this library, with which you are all more or less familiar, I may say that its most important defects are those of omission, that is, the failure to give under subject-headings all the references to books and articles actually in the library which really belong there, and it requires a little practice to enable one to get the best results from it.

There are many books and journal articles which different men would classify under different heads, and in most cases when one consults the index for a particular subject he finds more references than he cares to be bothered with, although the list is almost always incomplete owing to the fact that we have not yet obtained all the medical books which have been printed. We are, however, making fair progress in this direction; I think we now have over three-fourths of all medical books which have any special value or interest, and at least two-thirds of all the medical literature which has been printed.

In consulting the index on any given subject it will usually be found possible to select from the rather formidably large mass of titles those which are most likely to be of interest by giving a little attention to author's names, to the place and date of publication and to the number of pages and plates, if it is a journal article. The cross-references should be consulted, and under the headings to which these will guide you will often be found new cross-references which should also be looked up.

Since the year 1800, about one-half of the medical literature which has been published, consists of medical journals and transactions. Nine-tenths of the demands made on this library are based on references to this class of literature, and it is therefore of the greatest importance in medical bibliography. The number of medical journals and transactions now received by this library, excluding those devoted to pharmacy and dentistry, is over seven hundred, and it has been steadily increasing for the last five years.

If we take Ploucquet's *Literatura medica digesta* to be as complete an index of the medical literature in existence at the beginning of this century as the Index Catalogue is of the medical literature now in existence, it is evident that the number of references has more than quadrupled during the present century. Nine-tenths at least, of it, becomes worthless, and of no interest within ten years after the date of its publication, and much of it is so when it first appears. Of that which is really new and good a large part is pretty promptly made use of by systematizers and compilers, but there is also a considerable portion which we cannot use in our present state of knowledge but which become valuable building material hereafter. To get this roughly sorted out, classified and labelled, so that it can be found when wanted, is the object of indexing; to bring it into use is the object of bibliography.

One of the most useful pieces of work which could now be undertaken for the benefit of medical writers and investigators would be the preparation of a dictionary of critical bibliography of medical bibliography, in which should be indicated for each subject in alphabetical order a reference to where the best bibliography relating to that subject can be found. This could only be well done by a coöperation of a number of writers, each taking a special field.

I have not attempted in this brief paper to eulogize bibliography or to comment on the desirability that there should always be a few men interested in the study of the history and literature of medicine. I think that you will all agree with me that they may be sources of much pleasure, and that this alone is a fairly good reason for giving them some attention, and for exerting the influence of the profession to make it possible in at least one place in this country to carry out such studies with a full supply of material.

And while the librarian is in one respect only a sort of hod-carrier, who brings together the bricks made by one set of men in order that another

set of men may build therewith—he is apt to take quite as much pride
and satisfaction in the resulting structure, provided it be a good one, as
if he had built it himself; and he has constantly unrolling before him a
panorama which, though at times a little monotonous, contains as much
wisdom, humor, and pathos, as any other product of the human intellect
with which I am acquainted.

List of Books Most Useful for Reference

Haller (Albertus). Bibliotheca botanica, qua scripta ad rem herbariam facientia a
rerum initiis recensentur. 2 v. 4°. Figuri, apud Orell, Gessner, Fuessli, et soc., 1751.

Heffter (Joh. Carolus). Museum disputatorium physico-medicum tripartitum. Ed. nova.
4 pts in 2 v. 4°. Zittaviæ Lusatorum, sumt. Schœpsianis, 1763–4.

Haller (Albertus). Bibliotheca chirurgica, qua scripta ad artem chirurgicam facientia
a rerum initiis recensentur. 2 v. 8°. Bernæ et Basileæ, Haller et Schweighauser,
1774–5.

Haller (Albertus). Bibliotheca anatomica qua scripta ad anatomen et physiologiam
facientia a rerum initiis recensentur. 2 v. 4°. Figuri, apud Orell, Gessner, Fuessli
et soc. 1774–7.

Haller (Albertus). Bibliotheca medicinæ practicæ qua scripta ad partem medicinæ
practicam facientia a rerum initiis ad a. 1775 recensentur. 4 v. 4°. Basileæ, Joh.
Schweighauser; Bernæ, apud Em. Haller, 1776–8. Tome IV. Ex ejus schedis
restituit auxit et edidit Joachim Diterich Brandis ab anno 1686 ad a. 1707.

de Ploucquet (Guilielmus Godofredus). Literatura medica digesta sive repertorium
medicinæ practicæ, chirurgiæ atque rei obstetriciæ. 4 v. in 2. 4°. Tubingæ,
J. G. Cotta, 1808–9.

Watt (Robert). Bibliotheca Britannica; or a general index to British and foreign literature. 4 v. 4°. Edinburgh, A. Constable & Co., 1824.

Jourdan (A. J. L) Dictionnaire des sciences médicales. Biographie médicale. 7 v. 8°.
Paris, Panckoucke, 1820–25.

Dezeimeris (J. E.) Ollivier et Raige-Delorme. Dictionnaire historique de la médicine
ancienne et moderne, ou précis de l'histoire générale, technologique et littéraire
de la médicine, suivi de la bibliographie médicale de dix-neuvième siècle, et
d'un répertoire bibliographique par ordre de matières. 4 v. in 7. 8°. Paris, Béchet
jeune, 1828–39.

á Roy (Cornelius Henricus). Catalogus bibliothecæ medicæ. 5 v. 8°. Amstelodami, L.
van Es, 1830.

Forbes (John). A manual of select medical bibliography in which the books are arranged chronologically according to the subjects, etc. 8°. London, Sherwood,
Gilbert & Piper, 1835.

Callisen (A. C. P.) Medicinisches Schriftsteller-Lexicon der jetzt lebenden Aerzte,
Wundärzte, Geburtshülfer, Apotheker und Naturforscher aller gebildeten Völker.
33 v. 8°. Copenhagen u. Altona, 1830–45.

Choulant (Ludwig). Handbuch der Bücherkunde für die ältere Medicin zur Kenntniss
der griechischen, lateinischen und arabischen Schriften im ärztlichen Fache und
zur bibliographischen Unterscheidung ihrer verscheidenen Ausgaben, Ueber-
setzungen und Erläuterungen. 2. aufl. 8°. Leipzig, L. Voss, 1841.

Bibliotheca medico-historica sive catalogus librorum historicorum de re medica et
scientia naturali systematicus. 8°. Lipsiæ, sumpt. G. Engelmann, 1842.

Holtrop (Leonardus Stephanus Augustus). Bibliotheca medico-chirurgica et pharmaceutico-chemica, sive catalogus alphabeticus omnium librorum, dissertationum, etc., ad anatomiam, artem medicam chirurgicam, obstetriciam, pharmaceuticam, chemicam, botanicam, physico-medicam et veterinariam pertinentium, et in Belgio ab anno 1790, ad annum 1840 editoram. Hagæ-Comitis. C. Fuhr, 1842.

Royal College of Surgeons in London. A classed catalogue of the books contained in the library of the, 8°. London, J. Scott, 1843.

Jahrbücher der in und ausländischen gesammten Medicin. v. 1–40, 1834–43. roy. 8°. Leipzig, O. Wigand. Continued as: Schmidt's Jahrbücher. v. 41–213, 1844–87. roy. 8°. Leipzig.

Bibliotheca medico-chirurgica pharmaceutico-chemica et veterinaria oder geordnete Uebersicht aller in Deutschland neu erchienenen medicinisch-chirurgisch-geburts-hülflichen pharmaceutisch-chemischen und veterinär-wissenschaftlichen Bücher. 8°. Göttingen, 1847–86.

Engelmann (W.) Bibliotheca medico-chirurgica et anatomico-physiologica. Alphabetisches Verzeichniss der medicinischen, chirurgischen, geburtshülflichen, anatomischen und physiologischen Bücher, welche vom Jahre 1750 bis zu Ende des Jahres 1867 in Deutschland erschienen sind. 2 v. 8°. Leipzig, W. Engelmann, 1848–68.

Fischer, (Emil). Catalogue raisonné of the Medical Library of the Pennsylvania Hospital. 8°. Philadelphia, T. K. & P. G. Collins, 1857.

Bibliothèque nationale. Départment des imprimés. Catalogue des sciences médicales. 2 v. 4°. Paris, Didot frères, 1857, 1873.

Dictionnaire encyclopédique des sciences médicales. Directeur: A. Dechambre. Collaborateurs: MM. les docteurs Archambault, Arnould (J), Axenfeld, Baillarger [et al.] 1 s., v. 1–34; 2. s., v. 1–22; 3. s., v. 1–16; 4. s., v. 1–12; 5. s., v. 1. Paris, 1864–87.

Royal Society of London. Catalogue of scientific papers compiled and published by the, 8 v. 8°. London, G. E. Eyre & W. Spottiswoode, 1867–79.

Catalogue of the Library of the Royal College of Physicians of Edinburgh. 4°. Edinburgh, R. and R. Clark. 1863. Supplement, 1863–70. 4°. Edinburgh, Crawford and McCabe, 1870.

Nouveau dictionnaire de médicine et de chirurgie pratique. Rédigé par Anger, Bailly [et al.] Directeur de la rédaction, le docteur Jaccoud. 40 v. and suppl. 8°. Paris, 1864–86.

Jahresbericht über die Leistungen und Fortschritte der gesammten Medicin (Fortsetzung von Canstatt's Jahresbericht). Unter Mitwirkung zahlreicher Gelehrten hrsg. von Rud. Virchow und Aug. Hirsch. Jahrg. 1–20, 1866–85. 39 v. 8°. Berlin A. Hirschwald, 1867–86.

Manchester Medical Society. Alphabetical Catalogue of the Library of the, 8°. Manchester, W. Alcock, 1866. Supplementary Catalogue of the Library of, 8°. Manchester, W. Alcock, 1872.

Papily (Alphonse). Bibliographie des sciences médicales: bibliographie, biographie, histoire, épidémies, topographies, endémies. 8°. Paris, Tross, 187[2–]4.

Jahresbericht über die Leistungen und Fortschritte in der Anatomié und Physiologie. 10 v. 8°. Berlin, A. Hirschwald, 1874–85.

Waring (Edward John). Bibliotheca therapeutica, or bibliography of therapeutics, chiefly in reference to articles of the materia medica, with numerous critical, historical and therapeutical annotations, and an appendix containing the bibliography of British mineral waters. 2 v. 8°. London, New Sydenham Soc., 1878.

Haeser (Heinrich). Lehrbuch der Geschichte der Medicin und der epidemischèn Krankheiten. 3. Aufl. 3 v. 8°. Jena, H. Dufft, 1875–82.

Royal Medical and Chirurgical Society of London. Catalogue of the Library of the, 3 v. 8°. London, 1879.

Index Medicus. A monthly classified record of the current medical literature of the world. v. 1–9. 8°. New York, Boston, Mass., and Detroit, Mich., 1879–87.

Bibliotheca medica Davidsoniana. Catalogue de la bibliothèque précieuse médicale de feu. M. le docteur Davidson. 8°. Breslau, G. Paetz, 1880.

United States. War Department. Surgeon-General's Office. Index-Catalogue of the Library of the Surgeon-General's Office, United States Army. I–VIII. A-Medicine (Naval) 8 v. roy. 8°. Washington, 1880–87.

Neale (Richard). The medical digest, or busy practitioner's vade-mecum. Being a means of readily acquiring information upon the principal contributions to medical science during the last thirty-five years. 2 ed. 8°. London, Ledger, Smith & Co., 1882.

Hirsch (A.) Biographisches Lexikon der hervorragenden Aerzte aller zeiten und Völker. Unter Mitwirkung der Herren A. Anagnostakis. E. Albert [et al.] und unter Special-Redaction von A. Wernich, und E. Gurlt. 8°. Wien u. Leipzig. Urban & Schwarzenberg, 1884–87.

Faculty of Physicians and Surgeons of Glasgow. Alphabetical catalogue of the Library of the ... 4°. Glasgow, R. Maclehose, 1885.

Neale (Richard). The first appendix to the medical digest, including the years 1882–3-4-5, and early part of 1886. 8°. London, Ledger, Smith & Co., 1886.

Hollerith Cards

For all cities having a population of 200,000 and upwards, and for all states which have a registration of deaths sufficiently complete to make it worth while to compile the statistics, I recommend that the data for each individual death be recorded, as fast as reported, upon cards by punching out holes. Several members of this Association have seen the system of cards, and the machine for counting any desired combination of data from these cards, which has been devised by Mr. Herman Hollerith, and which is now in Washington. It is comparatively simple, not liable to get out of order, and does its work rapidly and accurately. I have watched with great interest the progress in developing and perfecting this machine, because seven years ago I became satisfied that some such system was possible and desirable, and advised Mr. Hollerith, who was then engaged on census work, to take the matter up and devise such a machine as is needed for counting various combinations of large numbers of data, as in census work or in vital statistics. I think that he has succeeded, and that the compilers of demographical data will be glad to know of this system.

Excerpted from "On some forms of tables of vital statistics, with special reference to the needs of the health department of a city." Pp. 204–5 of *Public Health Papers and Reports, American Public Health Association* 13: 203–23 (1887).

Ideals of Medical Education

When the medical faculty of an ancient, famous, and progressive university honors a physician by the request that he will deliver an address to it, and to its friends, upon such an occasion as this, the subject of that address must be sought within certain limits. It should have some relation to the special work of the Faculty—to medical education as it was, or is, or should be. The fact that you have already had three addresses bearing on this subject by distinguished medical teachers, who are more familiar with its practical bearings and needs than I can be, does not authorize me to try another field, although it greatly increases my difficulty in selecting reflections and suggestions which are suited to the occasion and to the audience, and which, at the same time, will not be a wearisome repetition of what is already familiar to you. I know, however, that discourses of this kind are soon forgotten; were it otherwise, this would indeed be a hard world for address givers.

Of course the Medical Department of Yale is organized in the best possible manner, and is doing the best possible work,—under the circumstances. I do not know precisely what its organization is, or what work it is doing, or the exact circumstances which govern it, but I have no doubt it is safe to assume this. There is one circumstance, however, which very commonly affects medical schools and universities—and which, therefore, may possibly affect you—and that is the want of means to do everything that anybody may consider desirable. Perhaps, then, some remarks upon certain modern ideals of medical education, and upon first class medical schools and their cost based upon data derived from other schools, may be of some interest—especially in the light of Rochefoucauld's aphorism that there is something in the misfortunes of our best friends which is not displeasing to us.

The great mass of the public—the majority of the voters of all parties, and of the women who are not voters, know little and care less about the details of professional education, or about the standard of qualification attained to by those to whom they entrust more or less of the care of their souls, their property, or their bodies. The popular feeling is, that in a free country every one should have the right to follow any occupation he likes, and employ for any purpose any one whom he selects, and that each party must take the consequences.

It is noteworthy, however, that each individual professing to hold this

Address delivered before the Medical Faculty of Yale University, June 23, 1891. *Boston Medical and Surgical Journal* 124: 619–23; 125: 1–4 (1891).

opinion, almost always makes an exception as to his own occupation if it is one involving skilled labor,—he is in favor of free trade in the abstract—and of limitations with regards to his own particular trade, either as to number of apprentices, as to time of study, or as to some form of trust which will, as far as possible, prevent competition in that special business. In one of its aspects, medicine is a trade, carried on for the purpose of making money in order to support the physician and his family, and to the majority of practitioners this is a very important aspect, although to very few of them is it the only one. Hence it is that medical faculties must consider schemes of medical education from this point of view also, not exclusively so by any means, but, nevertheless, with reference to the questions—what do we propose to offer?—how much will it cost us?—how much shall we charge for it? With reference to the first question, it is obvious that there are several quite different kinds of education which a medical faculty may offer to its students. It is by no means easy to decide as to the quality and quantity of the article offered by consulting only the advertisements, circulars, and prospectuses of the hundred and more medical schools in the United States, but even from these it can be seen that one can get a diploma of Doctor of Medicine in much less time, and at much less expense, from some schools than from others, and we all know that the diplomas of these different schools are guarantees of very different education and qualifications.

There are also several different ideals as to what is desirable in medical education. For instance, there is the ideal of the literary man, of the clergyman—of the laborer, and of other classes of the general public. There is the ideal of the man who wants to obtain a medical degree as soon and as cheaply as possible in order that he may commence practice; the ideal of the same man after he has obtained such a degree and has been for two or three years trying to get practice; and the ideal of the middle aged successful practitioner who has learned several things by experience since he graduated. Then we have the ideal of the Army and Navy Examining Boards; the ideal of the man of means who wants to become a specialist without ever going into general practice—and the ideal of the man who wishes to be an investigator and a teacher either from the love of science or from the desire for fame. Let us consider some of these ideals briefly. The chief demand of the great mass of the non-professional public is for general practitioners,—and the qualifications which these should possess may be summed up in the statement that they should be competent to recognize the forms of disease and injury which are common in the community in which they practice,—and should know, and be able to apply, the remedies which are most frequently used and found efficacious in such cases. They are expected, for the most part, to follow and not to lead—it is not necessary that they should be skilled in the refinements of modern pathology—or be thoroughly trained in minute anatomy or experimental physiology, or be great surgeons, or be well up in all the specialties. Observe that I say it is not *necessary*—it may be desirable, but in the majority of cases it is not practicable.

In their brief journey of life through this world, the great majority of people must travel on the routes and by the vehicles provided for them by others, and, fortunately, they are usually content to do so. They move in groups which are "personally conducted," see the things they are told to see, try, with more or less success, to admire the things which they are told to admire, and their chief discomfort occurs when their conductors are either silent, or give contradictory orders, when it comes to the parting of the ways. Most travelers on an Atlantic steamer accept without murmuring the edict that "Passengers are not allowed on the bridge."

The information which those who propose to earn their living by the general practice of medicine stand most in need of, is that which will enable them to recognize the ordinary emergencies of practice and to deal with them in the ordinary way. As students, their time, money, and zeal for study and investigation, are all usually more or less limited, and there are many things in a course in what is called the "higher medical education" which are of comparatively little use to them. The clinical instruction which they can get at a school in the region of country in which they intend to practice will often be more valuable to them than that which they could get at a distant school of greater repute, simply from the difference in the class of cases presenting themselves for treatment. "Good local pilots are in demand, although we have a Superintendent of the Coast Survey." In some respects, the old fashioned system of medical apprenticeships, in which the student spent from one to three years in the office of a physician in general practice before he went to a medical school to hear lectures, was a good one for producing these general practitioners. To learn to do such work easily and properly one must live among the sick, learn how they look, how they talk, how they are to be talked to and handled; and must do this at close quarters, and not by looking on from the top bench of an amphitheatre, or from the outer ring of a group of thirty or forty men standing around a bed. Moreover, it is the common everyday ailments and their effects and treatment that the student wants to become familiar with at first, rather than the rare cases. Cases of colic, of effects of over eating or drinking, of sore throats, croup or diphtheria, or scarlet fever or mumps, or the ordinary fevers, of simple fractures and dislocations, of bad cuts of the palm of the hand—are far more important to him from a business point of view than brain tumors or ligations of the innominate artery.

And these comparatively simple, every-day cases are just what the young man reading in the office of his preceptor may become familiar with. How many of the men without such experience, who graduate this year at our great medical schools, have ever seen closely a case of measles, or scarlet fever, or incipient small-pox—or have actually looked into the throat of a child suffering from diphtheria, or have ever assisted in adjusting and dressing a fractured thigh bone, or in getting the clothing off from a case of extensive burn or scald? I have no doubt most of them could repeat the descriptions of these things which they have heard or read, but they are not as well prepared to deal with such cases in that unhesitating way which commands confidence, as is the man who has seen and touched one or two such cases in his preceptor's office, and has observed what that preceptor said and did. On the other hand, the number of practising physicians who are qualified to act as preceptors, and who are willing to give the requisite time and attention to students, is very limited,—and with any other kind of preceptor, the student wastes much time, is apt to lose interest, and becomes idle and unfit for continuous mental effort.

If the student spent his apprentice year, or two years, in a preceptor's office either at the end of his first or second year's medical lectures, or after obtaining his degree, it would be much better for him,—but the latter course is open to the objection that he would probably think that he knew more than his preceptor. The Scotch medical schools prefer that the year spent as an articled pupil shall come after the first two years of education in a medical school. The decision of the British Medical Council has been that a five years' course of study shall be compulsory, and that the last year shall be spent in practical work.

Theoretically there is still a considerable amount of preliminary reading with a preceptor done in this country, but practially, this method of beginning the study of medicine is fast disappearing. Through the kindness of the officers of some of our large medical schools, I have obtained some data on this point from which I infer that in the eastern schools the proportion of students who claim to have read with a preceptor for one year before commencing lectures, is from 1.5 to 30 per cent., and in western and southern schools, from 25 to 60 per cent., but no doubt such reading, in the majority of cases, was merely nominal, and the student had seen little or nothing of practice. In most schools the certificate of the preceptor is not required.

The ideal of the average student who is in a hurry to begin practice needs no special description. What he wants is to pass the examinations with the least possible labor,—the less he is compelled to take for his money the better he is pleased. The ideal of the majority of the medical profession as to what should be the minimum course of study for the degree of M. D. appears to be that the student should first obtain at least such a preliminary education as is furnished by our ordinary high schools, and then should study medicine four years, the first of which may be with a preceptor, and three of which are to be occupied in attending a graded course of lectures, the last two years being largely devoted to clinical and hospital instruction. About one-third of our medical schools have expressed their intention of carrying out this programme. As regards the time, it is not sufficient, according to European standards, but is perhaps the best general standard which can be fixed at present for the education of the general practitioner for this country. Its success depends upon whether the student has had the needed preliminary education. It is the want of this last which is the chief deficiency.

The ideal of the Army and Navy Examining Boards is that a Surgeon in the Government service should have received either the literary, classical, and mathematical training of the ordinary college course for the degree of Bachelor of Arts, or the training leading to a degree in scientific studies—and that after that he should have spent five years in medical studies, the last year as resident in a hospital.

This ideal cannot yet be enforced in either service, for the reason that they could not get enough men who come up to this standard to fill the vacancies, so that the actual standard is somewhat lower than this, although it is higher than the minimum standard of any medical school or of any State Board of Examiners. Through the courtesy of the Surgeon Generals of the Army and Navy, I am able to give you the following results of the work of their Examining Boards for the last ten years.

Before the Army Boards 348 candidates presented themselves during this period, of whom 76, or 22.3 per cent. were approved and passed; 31 were rejected for physical disqualifications; 90 failed to pass the preliminary examination; and the remainder failed to pass the medical examination. The rejections for physical defects are for the last three years only.

Before the Navy Boards 237 candidates presented themselves, of whom 55, or 23.1 per cent. were approved and passed; 75 were rejected for physical disqualifications; and the remainder either withdrew or failed to pass.

Evidently the standards of the two Boards are about the same. The proportion of those rejected for physical defects is noteworthy. In a general way we may say that about one-fourth of the candidates before such boards are approved—and one-fourth fail on the preliminary examination as to general education. Putting aside those rejected for physical causes, and making the necessary corrections for a certain number who come before the Boards more than once, we find that of 429 examined, 129 or 30.2 per cent. were successful.

Of those candidates who had a college degree, 34 per cent. succeeded, and of those who had no such degree, 28.9 per cent. succeeded. Of those candidates who had had one year's residence in hospital, 40 per cent. passed, while of those who had not been residents, only 21 per cent. were successful. The percentage of successful candidates from different schools varies greatly, ranging from 9 to 56 per cent. for those schools from which more than ten candidates presented themselves. I cannot go into details on this point, but may say that taking the Medical Schools of Harvard, Yale, the College of Physicians, and Bellevue Hospital of New York, the University of Pennsylvania, and the University of Virginia together, of 141 candidates, 65 or 46.1 per cent. succeeded, while for all the rest of the schools in a body, of 286 candidates, 64 or 22.3 per cent. succeeded.

The figures from Yale alone, are too small to draw accurate conclusions from, but in strict confidence I will tell you that of the five graduates of the Yale Medical School who come before the Army and Navy Boards during the last ten years, three, or 66.6 per cent. have passed. The greatest percentage of successful candidates comes from those who were between 24 and 25 years of age when they graduated, being 31.7 per cent. as against 27.9 per cent. for those who were under 22, and 26.2 per cent. for those who were over 25 on graduation.

Admitting it to be a fact that different schools have different minimum standards for graduating Doctors of Medicine, to what extent are these differences necessary, or desirable? There is at present a very general demand that those schools which have the lower standards shall raise them to the ideal of the medical profession just stated. It seems as if the supply of physicians is now, in most parts of the country, in excess of the demand, the number of medical men being from two to three times as great among us, in proportion to the population, as it is in France or Germany, while the annual number of graduates also greatly exceeds the number of places to be filled.

Under these circumstances, there is necessarily a struggle for existence in which the men of inferior qualifications usually, though not always, fail. The schools, however, will not shape their course so much with reference to the real or supposed interests of the profession or of the public, as with reference to the demands of their immediate customers, the students, and many of these, as has been said, do not want any more education than is absolutely necessary to enable them to begin practice.

The ability and inclination to pay for professional services differs greatly in different localities, and among different classes of people. Attempts to enforce a minimum time for the course, and a minimum for the number of lectures in certain specified branches, will not result in fixing an uniform minimum of results obtained, for this can only be assured and maintained by some system of inspection and testing of results which is independent of the schools, or, at all events, of each individual school. When, as Professor Sumner says: "A and B put their heads together to see what C ought to be made to do for D," there is small prospect of result so long as C is free to do as he likes.

In the Russian myth, when the raven brought the water of life and the water of death to the gray wolf, the first thing that the wolf did was to test their powers on the raven himself to determine whether his task was properly done. The public do not have an opportunity of seeing the effect of such a test as this upon those who come to them from the schools professing to have obtained the knowledge of healing; if they had, the complaints of overcrowding in the profession would probably cease.

From a commercial point of view it seems plain that there are too many medical schools in this country, that the education which many of them are giving is a very poor one, and that the students who are attracted to these last by offers of a cheap and short course, waste their time and their money.

The only really efficient remedy for this state of affairs is a system of State examinations with minimum standards. This also has its evils, since it must lead to cramming, but it is the best we can do at present. It is urged by some that this minimum standard should be uniform throughout the United States—but in that case, it would be unnecessarily low in some parts of the country. The precise nature of the requirements in different regions depend on the density of population, and on the ability of the great mass of the people to pay enough to induce highly educated physicians to settle among them. It would be better if it were otherwise, and if everyone could have the benefit of the best professional skill, but matters are adjusted in this world largely by conflict of interests. Certainly no one who intends to practice medicine should be content with the least amount of knowledge which will enable him to pass the required examinations, whatever the standard of those examinations may be. Putting aside now this matter of a minimum standard, let us consider briefly an ideal of a medical education of a higher type.

In addition to the incipient family practitioner of ordinary qualifications—the beginners in the profession—there is need of, and employment for, highly skilled, thoroughly trained physicians and surgeons as family physicians, as consultants, as specialists, and as investigators and teachers.

There are two ways in which these needed men may be educated and developed. The first is by their commencing with the ordinary course of instruction for general practice in the manner just spoken of, and then going on, after graduation and commencing practice, to study and perfect themselves in details—according to individual tastes and opportunities; and this has been the course pursued by a large number of our most distinguished American consultants and specialists. The other is to lay a broad and sound foundation of preliminary education before giving any attention to clinical study or practice. This means an education at least equivalent to that required of candidates for the degree of Bachelor of Arts from our leading universities, including Latin, French, and German, and mathematics to include trigonometry, and the elements of analytics. It should also include one year's work in a physical laboratory, two years' work in chemistry, two years' work in biology,—at least one year's work in practical anatomy—and one year's course in materia medica.

In other words, it requires that the youth of sixteen, having obtained a good high school education, shall go on to spend at least five years in additional study before he commences to see anything of practice. He should then spend at least three years more in special medical and clinical studies, during one year of which he should, if possible, reside in a hospital. If then his purpose is to become a specialist, an original investigator and a teacher, it is desirable that he should spend two years more in clinics and laboratories devoted to his special subject—and at least half of this time should, at present, be spent abroad. These are the broad outlines of what I suppose most physicians of the present day would consider a desirable scheme of medical education for an intelligent boy with a fair amount of liking for study, good health, and sufficient means to enable him to go through with it without making undue demands upon his parents or guardians.

You will observe that there are several qualifying clauses in that last sentence. The aphorism that it does not pay to give a five thousand dollar education to a five dollar boy, must be constantly borne in mind in considering these questions. On the other hand, it is also to be noted that in the preparation of educational schemes, it is not necessary to provide for the demands of youths of extraordinary ability and industry —for men of genius. Beds suitable for giants are not required as part of the stock of an ordinary furniture store, especially if it require giants to make them. Some cases of disease will recover without treatment, though the cure may be hastened by proper management, some will die under any treatment, the result of some depends on the treatment.

It is much the same in education. Some will acquire knowledge and power without special training,—others will never acquire those things under any training, but the career of many depends, to a large extent, on the training which they receive. The recent announcement of a compulsory four years course of medical studies by Harvard and the University of Pennsylvania, soon to be followed by a similar announcement from Columbia, looks towards this ideal.

The number of those who are obtaining a college education as a preparation for medical study has increased, and will still more increase as the competition among an excessive number of physicians becomes fiercer.

From information received from some of our leading medical schools for the present year, it appears that the proportion of students who have taken preliminary degrees before commencing the study of medicine varies from 14 to 43 per cent. in eastern schools, from 3 to 12 per cent. in western schools, and from 15 to 20 per cent. in southern schools.

Just here comes in a very difficult point. When shall general education cease and special training begin? The answer to this must depend largely on the individual, but it seems to me that the present tendency is to begin to specialize too soon. This early specialization of study and work may lead to more prompt pecuniary success, but not, I think, to so much ultimate happiness and usefulness as the longer continuance of study on broader lines. "For it is in knowledge as it is in plants: if you mean to use the plant it is no matter for the roots; but if you mean to remove it to grow, then it is more assured to rest upon root than slips; so the delivery of knowledge as it is now used, is of fair bodies of trees without the roots— good for the carpenter but not for the planter. But if you will have science grow, it is less matter for the shaft of body of the tree, so you look well to the taking up of the roots." [1]

In discussions on medical education and the duties of medical schools, we are too apt to lose sight of the fact that the best that the student can do in them is to begin to learn. If he does not study much longer and harder after he graduates than he does before, he will not become a successful physician. Moreover, the great majority of men have different capacities for learning certain things at different ages. They lose receptive power as they grow older.

Permit me to use here a personal illustration, and pardon the apparent egotism of an old gentleman who refers to his youthful days. Thirty-three years ago I began the study of medicine, having obtained the degree of Bachelor of Arts after the usual classical course of those days. It so happens that the smattering of Latin and Greek which I

---

[1] Lord Bacon.

obtained has been of great use to me, and I may, therefore, be a prejudiced witness, but my acquaintance with many physicians at home and abroad has led me to believe that the ordinary college course in languages, mathematics, and literature is a very good foundation for the study of medicine, and I do not sympathize with those who demand that all who are to enter on this study shall substitute scientific studies for all the Greek and a part of the Latin of the usual course. This change is good for some but not for all. I had attended lectures in physics and chemistry but had done no laboratory work, and I could read easy French and German. Thus equipped I began to read anatomy, physiology, and the principles of medicine. Nominally I had a preceptor—but I do not think I saw him six times during the year which followed, for I was teaching school in another State. Nevertheless, he told me what books to read, and I read them. The next thing was to attend the prescribed two courses of lectures in a medical college in Cincinnati. Each course lasted about five months and was precisely the same. There was no laboratory course, and I began to attend clinical lectures the first day of the first course. One result of this was that I had to learn chemical manipulation, the practical use of the microscope, etc., at a later period when it was much more difficult. In fact I may say that I have been studying ever since to repair the deficiencies in my medical training and have never been able to catch up.

Probably a large number of physicians over fifty years of age have had much the same experience, and felt that there are certain things, such as the relation of trimethyloxyethylene-ammonium hydroxide in the body, or the causation of muscular contraction by migration of labile material between the inotagmata—the bearings and beauty of which might as well be left to younger men. Not that these things are specially difficult to understand, but they form a part of a new nomenclature which in most cases it is not worth the while of the older men to learn, because it is far more difficult for them to master it than it is for their sons. One of the most comfortable and satisfactory periods in a man's life is that when he first distinctly and clearly recognizes that in certain matters he is a hopelessly old fogy, and that he is not expected to know anything about them.

Having thus roughly sketched what is wanted in the way of medical education by different classes of students—the article for which there is market, let us next consider briefly what an university may wisely attempt to provide in this direction. Some suggestions on this point may perhaps be obtained from an examination of the condition of affairs as regards medical education in the University of Oxford.

The Corporation of Oxford has a little more than half the number of inhabitants possessed by the City of New Haven, and its relations to London are, in many respects, similar to those of New Haven with the cities of New York and Boston. For a number of years it has been urged by some physicians in England, that the University of Oxford, with her great resources, has not been doing as much for medical education as she should have done, and that it is her duty to establish and maintain a completely organized medical school of the usual pattern, using the small local hospital and dispensary facilities for the clinical side of the work.

On the other hand, other physicians, of whom my friend Sir Henry Acland may be taken as the representative, maintain that it is much better that Oxford should use her resources in giving a broad foundation of literary and scientific culture, including, for those who propose to study medicine, the means of special instruction in general biology— and comparative and human anatomy, physiology, and pathology—and that the men thus prepared should go to the great Hospital Medical Schools of London to obtain their clinical training, after which, they may return and pass their final examinations and obtain the coveted degree of Doctor of Medicine from the university.

There is no doubt that this can be done, and that a great part of the scientific foundation of a complete medical training can be furnished by a well equipped university, with little or no reference to clinical instruction at the same time and place. This, for example, is the course followed by many of the students in the medical department of the University of Virginia, and it seems to be that there is also no doubt that the men who go through such a course of training, followed by clinical training in a great city, will have a better course of instruction, a wider experience, and a better chance of seeing and appreciating the methods of great clinical teachers, than would the majority of those who obtained their clinical as well as their scientific training in the small town, or than those who obtain all their instruction in a large school devoted exclusively to medical studies. Upon this last point I need not dwell, for Dr. Welch, in his address before you in 1888, has clearly pointed out the advantages of giving to a medical school an university atmosphere, and of making the union of the school and the university close and intimate. It should be noted, however, that the more true this is, the more it is the duty of an university to maintain such a school, because educational work which cannot be, or is not, done so well elsewhere, has superior claims upon university aid. The chief thing which can be said in favor of the attempt to attract a large number of medical students of average qualifications to an institution having the means to give the higher education are, first, that it brings in more money—and, second, that it enables those professors who desire advanced workers, to select these from a somewhat wider field. Also it should be remembered that the small hospitals of from 50 to 100 beds should be fully utilized for clinical teaching, even if they cannot furnish all the clinical material that is desirable for a complete course of instruction.

It must be confessed that nearly all our great American universities are unwilling to apply their funds to the creation and maintenance of a well equipped medical department. They are willing to have such a department no doubt, but they want the money for establishing and maintaining it to be provided in addition to the money which has been, or is to be, provided for the general purposes of the university. The ideal university culture of the present day appears to be designed to fit a man to take pleasure in his own thoughts and musings, and in mental exercise in languages, literature, the higher mathematics, and the problems of physics and natural history. Incidentally his knowledge of these things may not only give him pleasure, but enable him to help others, but the studies are not to be pursued on account of any practical utility which they possess, but for the love of learning and pure science, i.e. for personal gratification of a particular kind. Those who hold these views are apt to consider medicine as a technological matter, which should be left altogether to special schools, because, being practically useful in a commercial sense, the means of teaching it are sure to be provided through commercial interests, just as they are sure to be provided for the teaching of practical engineering. This is far from the old university idea as embodied in the three faculties and four nations of the University of Paris. So far as the interests of the public are concerned, it is only the possession and control of a large amount and variety of clinical material, or of unusually qualified clinical teachers, which makes it the positive duty to use it, or them, for purposes of medical instruction in order to train ordinary general practitioners of medicine. There is no present deficiency in the number of such practitioners, and we certainly have plenty of schools for producing them, so that there is no fear of failure in the supply.

But in medicine as in every other profession, art, or trade, the supply of the best is never too great, and the demand for something better than that which already exists never ceases.

What then does an university, or its medical school, need in order that it may be able to supply the demand for this higher medical education? First,—competent teachers. Second,—suitable buildings, collections, books, and apparatus. Third,—clinical material. To secure and retain these things requires money, and brains to use it. First as to the competent teachers. There are many teachers available—but the number of

these who have shown that they are competent for and suited to positions in a medical school which is to supply the best and something
better, is limited—much more so than one who had not tried to find
them would suppose, and these few are not seeking engagements. How
many anatomists, or physiologists, or pathologists, of the first class,
thoroughly trained, authorities in their special fields, capable of increasing knowledge, and with the peculiar gift of ability to teach—do you
suppose there are in this country? It is a liberal estimate to say that a
dozen of each have thus far given evidence that they exist. And the
great clinical teachers in medicine and surgery,—the men who are up
to the times in matters of diagnosis, pathology, and therapeutics, and
who are also successful teachers both by the spoken and written word—
how many such have we—and especially how many such have we who
are not fixed and established, so that they may be induced to go to a
school which needs them? Such men are either men of genius, and even
this boasted nineteenth century has produced them rarely, or they are
men of talent made the most of by unflagging industry with special opportunities, and they are also rare. Yet these are the men whom a great
university should seek to obtain, and retain, for her faculties. To do
this, and to get the best work from such men, is by no means a mere
matter of salary, although sufficient salaries must be paid. We have also
to consider the buildings, collections, books, and apparatus required,
and this is largely a question of money. How much money? What would
be the cost of establishing and maintaining a first-class medical school
in this country at the present time? Let us suppose that 150 students are
to be provided for—that the course of instruction for those coming with
a good high school education is to occupy four years, and for those coming with the degree of Bachelor of Arts, and having done at least one
year's work in a chemical laboratory and one year's work in a biological
laboratory, the course shall occupy three years, that the last year's studies
shall be almost exclusively clinical, and that provision is to be made for
advanced post-graduate work.

We shall want then, practical anatomy rooms for 50 students, a physiological laboratory, a pathological laboratory, a pharmacological laboratory, a laboratory of hygiene, and the means of clinical teaching, a library
and a museum. The days have long gone by when one or two amphi-
theatres or lecture rooms and a small museum, were all the outfit required for medical teaching. The little amphitheatre of the University of
Bologna was sufficient for almost every purpose of medical teaching as
that was carried on three hundred years ago, but now the lecture room
is the smallest part of the outfit required. In his evidence before the Royal
Commission, Professor Lankester stated that to establish such a Medical

School at Oxford as he thought desirable, about $225,000 would be required for buildings in addition to those already existing, and that about $100,000 a year would be required for running expenses. Professor Billroth estimates that about $400,000 would be required for buildings for the medical department of a univeristy, exclusive of the building for clinical teaching, which he thinks would cost about as much more,—and that the annual expense would be about $105,000. He says that these estimates are based on an average standard of efficiency—not the highest —and concludes by saying, "let us hope that a rich man may some day give three millions of dollars to found a school to be devoted to medicine and natural science."

Perhaps these figures may seem high to you. Yet building is cheaper, and salaries lower in England and in Germany than with us—if only first-class work and first-class men are accepted. To build and equip a laboratory which shall give work room for 75 men, will cost here between $75,000 and $100,000. At least four such laboratories are needed by the ideal medical department, besides a building for general lectures, library, etc., which would cost about $50,000.

It is of course possible to consolidate all these into a single three or four story building and thus save money, especially in cost of ground— but the results are not so good. I am not speaking now of temporary makeshift buildings, but of permanent structures—which, though plain, should not be hideous, and should be thoroughly well built. Where land is abundant and not too dear, it is usually better to construct these laboratories one at a time and endeavor to secure for each, a proper endowment and equipment. The average expenses of each laboratory may be put at $15,000 per annum. In other words, it requires about $400,000 to build, equip, and endow a physiological, pathological, or hygienic laboratory such as is suited to the needs of a first-class university in this country. By paring down in various directions, this sum can be reduced to $300,000, but not lower without seriously impairing the efficiency of the plan. And in all this I have said nothing of the cost of the means for clinical instruction—which should be borne, in part, at least, by the school, for the simple reason that only by doing this can the school have that control of hospital appointments which is so necessary for its proper work.

Of course every professor who is skilled and energetic, and who is imbued with the true university spirit, has innumerable wants and suggestions which require money to supply and carry out. He wants the new books and journals relating to his specialty, specimens, apparatus, models and illustrations, and if he is at the head of one of the laboratories which I have named, the sum of $15,000 per annum will be required to pay him and his assistants, and to provide for their needs. All this means that the educating of physicians on this plan will cost the medical department between four and five thousand dollars for each graduate. It will receive from them $800 to $1,000 each, and the balance must be made up from subscriptions, appropriations, or endowments. Practically endowment is the only resource.

The student himself has to give four or five years time and labor and four or five thousand dollars to obtain his medical education. For some, this expenditure of time and money will be an excellent investment—for others not, even if they have enough of both to spare for this purpose. After all, the most that the university can do is to afford opportunities for learning, and a certain kind and amount of stimulus to mental work. The professor may declare that he will teach certain branches, but there are some sent to him for instruction who are not teachable, and the only thing he can do is to return them as little damaged as possible.

The number of men for whom it is specially desirable to provide laboratory and other special facilities for original work in physiology, pathology, pharmacology, and hygiene, is limited. There are not a great number of men who have the desire and the qualifications necessary for this sort of work, and the number of positions in which they can find remunerative employment in devoting themselves to such investigations, is still more limited.

The laboratory facilities in Germany are, as a whole, at present in excess of the number of properly qualified men who can be found to make use of them, although a few are overcrowded.

Advanced work and original investigations cannot, as a rule, be made by undergraduates, if for no other reason than that of lack of time.

Is it advisable that the same medical school shall undertake to furnish such different courses as to provide for all wants—to offer to meet the minimum requirements for the Degree of Doctor of Medicine, as well as the wants of those who demand more advanced and detailed instruction? The answer to this depends largely on the location of the school, and on the means which it can command, especially as regards facilities for hospital and clinical instruction. In any case, its diploma of Doctor of Medicine should have an uniform value, and if it does undertake the double function, the higher education must be largely post-graduate work. It must also be, to a great extent, a voluntary matter on the part of both schools and students.

As indicated at the beginning, this address is not intended to criticize existing medical institutions, or to give specific advice to any college or university. I have simply tried to formulate roughly what seems to be the present ideal of a course of medical education in the minds of many physicians, and then to show what the carrying out of this ideal involves to the schools and to the students.

I believe in ideals—that is in their beauty, and in their utility when they do not dominate a man so as to make him a visionary, or a dangerous crank or fanatic,—but one ideal is often more or less incompatible with another, and all of them must be held subject to the possibilities afforded by surrounding circumstances. But we must not be too skeptical about these possibilities. And we are all directly interested in this matter —every one of us. Every one of this audience will probably see the time when the knowledge and skill of the physician called in to advise in the calamity which has fallen on him, or his wife, or child, will seem to him of vast importance.

Sometimes he can select his physician—often he cannot—but must rely on the first one who can be found. Hence these discussions about medical education, although chiefly carried on by physicians, because they are most familiar with the difficulties of the subject, should be considered by those who are not physicians quite as much as by those who are, or intend to be. It is a dangerous business, however, for a doctor to discuss other doctors in public. He can make more trouble for himself in less time in this way, than by almost any other method that I know of. Nevertheless, it is my duty to tell you that there is little probability that the ideal facilities for higher medical education, either here or elsewhere, will be furnished by the doctors themselves. There are several reasons for this, but one is sufficient, and that is they have not got the money which I have shown you is necessary to provide and maintain these facilities. Hence, if these ideals are to be realized, the means must be furnished by those who are not members of the medical profession, and it seems to me that this is what will be done.

What is the best way for a university, a real university, to begin this line of work? In most cases I should say by establishing one department at a time on a proper basis. Which departments should be the first to be thus established? Just here is where many of the doctors will begin to differ.

I should say that the first of these departments to be provided for are two which will form the main links in the university bond between the medical and other departments,—covering two branches of knowledge which every university graduate should study somewhat, namely, biology, and hygiene. For the clergyman, the teacher, the journalist, and the sociologist, systematic instruction in these two branches is as desirable as it is for the physician—for the lawyer it will be useful—only the philologist would I excuse entirely from these departments.

Of course, in specifying that they are to teach,—and to teach undergraduates, I do not mean that teaching is to be their sole function. This is not the modern idea of a scientific department of a true university. It is to increase knowledge as well—to provide for the needs of special investigators and seekers who have obtained their elementary training elsewhere.

Let the plans for such a department be well thought out, the expenses carefully estimated—and then bring the matter to the attention of those who have the means to realize this ideal, and sooner or later, it certainly will be realized. I have elsewhere ventured to express my sympathy for two classes of men who have in all ages and in all countries received much disapprobation from philosophers, essayists, and reformers,—namely, rich men, and those who want to be rich.

So far as the wealthy are concerned, there seem to be a good many of them in these latter days who use their stored force to endow universities and professorships, to build libraries and laboratories, and to such let us give due praise and honor.

They may or may not be scientific men, but at all events they make scientific men possible. The unscientific mind has been defined as one which is willing to accept and give opinions without subjecting them to rigid tests. "This is the kind of mind which most of us share with our neighbors. It is because we give and accept opinions without subjecting them to rigid tests" that the sermons of clergymen, the advice of lawyers, and the prescriptions of physicians have a market value.[2] The unscientific public has its uses, and one of its characteristics is a liking for ideals, some of which it occasionally helps to realize. I can only hope that whenever an American university approves the ideal which I have roughly sketched, this public will see that the means are provided for carrying it out. It may be objected by some that it would be better to help to raise the average standard by endowing chairs in the medical schools in large cities, than to provide special facilities for the use of a limited number. It is quite true that all medical schools should be endowed—and this is coming;—for voluntary associations of physicians—who are not a wealthy class—cannot afford to compete with endowed schools, when State laws shall come to enforce a higher standard of acquirements. Nevertheless, we need universities properly so-called, as well as colleges and higher schools, and we need university men in the medical profession as well as elsewhere.

I have no fears as to the creation of a medical aristocracy by giving facilities for higher education to those who have the means to avail themselves of them. It is quite true that only a fraction of those who have the means will use these facilities properly—and that there will be a number who have not the means who would make good use of such

---

[2] Scientific Men and their Duties, by J. S. Billings, Washington, 1886.

facilities if they could get them—but these last will not be helped by the total absence of such facilities for anybody. Let us try to give the best minds a chance to obtain the best training—let us try to discover these best minds wherever they may be—and if their owners have not the means to avail themselves of training, let us try to furnish the means—but to do this, one of the first and most essential steps is to provide somewhere the teachers, and the buildings, and apparatus necessary for giving such instruction, and where is a better place to do this than in connection with an university?—or, if you please, in connection with this University?

The Conditions and Prospects of the Library of the Surgeon-General's Office, and of its Index Catalogue

Of late years those physicians in this country who make use of medical literature in connection with their investigations or writings, have, for the most part, become acquainted with the resources of the "Library of the Surgeon-General's Office," as it is officially designated, and many of them are much interested in its progress and prospects. I am often asked how the collection is progressing, how near it is to completion, what it is most in need of, when the *Index Catalogue* will be done, whether it will be followed by a supplement, whether there is danger that the work of the Library may be checked in the future through changes in administration, and so on. These manifestations of interest are, of course, very gratifying, and when the Chairman of your Programme Committee demanded a ten-minute paper from me on this occasion it occurred to me that I would try to answer some of the foregoing questions so far as I am able to do so.

The present condition of the Library is fairly satisfactory. It now contains 102,000 volumes and 152,000 pamphlets, counting as pamphlets all octavos and smaller sizes having less than 100 pages, and all quartos of less than 50 pages. During the last five years, *i.e.*, from July 1, 1886, to June 30, 1891, the additions to it have included 25,237 volumes and 55,900 pamphlets, or an average of 5000 volumes and nearly 12,000 pamphlets yearly. Of this annual increase, about 2000 volumes and 4000 pamphlets have been of new or current literature, and the remainder have been publications of previous years or centuries. About one-fifth of these accessions, of both new and old literature, have been presented, the remainder have been purchased. So far as mere size goes, it is the largest collection of medical literature in the world, and for the last five years has been increasing more rapidly than any other similar library containing 25,000 volumes and upward. It is especially rich in medical periodicals and transactions of societies, of which classes it now contains about 34,350 volumes. The American, English, French and German literature in all branches of medicine which has appeared during the

Read before the Association of American Physicians, at its Sixth Annual Session, Washington, September 25, 1891. *Transactions of the Association of American Physicians* 6: 251–7 (1891).

present century is very fully represented, and over 90 per cent. of all the medical literature of the world for the last ten years is in the library. The whole is conveniently arranged in a fire-proof building, and is catalogued.

So much for the favorable side of the situation; now for a statement of some of the principal defects and deficiencies. Of medical incunabula, it contains 140 volumes, or about one-eighth of the medical works published prior to 1500. Of the published works of the ancient Greek, Roman, Arab and Hebrew medical authors, it has one or more editions of nearly all, but these editions are not in every instance the best. Of the early Spanish and Portuguese medical literature, it has almost nothing; of French medical works of the sixteenth century, but little; of French medical theses prior to 1800, very few. Of the English, French and German medical books of the 16th, 17th, and 18th centuries, which are of any importance historically or practically, it has about 75 per cent.; of the Italian, about 50 per cent.; and of the Spanish, about 25 per cent. In its periodical literature it is especially deficient in the Spanish and Italian prior to about 1850, in the French prior to 1780, and in the Russian prior to 1860. If I could add to it about ten thousand volumes of my own selection, it would, I think, contain at least one edition of every medical work of any practical use or importance which has ever been published, although it would still not possess some fifty thousand pamphlets and theses, each of which might be of some historical interest.

These deficiencies in the Library are being gradually supplied, but the acquisition of the older books and pamphlets which are still wanted is becoming every year a slower, more difficult, and more costly process. This is due to the fact that the books still wanted are many of them rare, and only appear in the market at intervals of from five to fifty years; to the fact that the number of competitors for such books is increasing, and, above all, to the fact that the expenditure of time required for the examination of the numerous catalogues and lists received at the Library, in order to select those books which are still wanted, is becoming very great in proportion to the results obtained. To check off a catalogue of a thousand medical books with the result of finding about four which are really desirable, a dozen which may be accepted as filling gaps, and about twenty small theses which are not in the collection, involves an amount of clerical work which costs as much as, if not more than, the books thus obtained. In one sense, it is true that this is a satisfactory condition for a library to be in, but, nevertheless, the time spent in such checking is to be regretted.

With regard to current medical literature, the amount increases each year, but the rate of increase is becoming slower. Comparing the period of 1890 with that of 1880, we find that the number of medical writers increased from 11,600 to about 14,200, or a little over 22 per cent. There were published in 1890 about 2000 volumes and 4000 theses, pamphlets, and reports in medical literature. Of the volumes, about 930, or not quite half, were furnished by medical journals and transactions, as against 864 of the same kind in 1880—being an increase of about 7½ per cent. Excluding the journals, transactions, and theses, the number of medical books and pamphlets published in 1890 was about 1,850 as against 1,600 in 1880—being an increase of about 15½ per cent. This indicates that the increase in the number of medical writers, and in the quantity of medical literature which they have produced, has not been proportionally as great as the increase in population and in the number of physicians in civilized countries during the decade, which confirms the statement which I made ten years ago, that the rate of increase is becoming smaller.

In the United States the proportion of periodical literature to the whole is much greater than it is in other countries—for in 1890 it produced about 250 volumes of medical periodicals, 60 volumes of new medical books, 20 volumes of later editions, and 28 volumes of reprints of English books and transactions; while France produced about 160 volumes of medical periodicals, 250 volumes of new medical books, 20 volumes of later editions, and 15 volumes of transactions; Great Britain about 85 volumes of periodicals, 140 new books, 45 volumes of later editions, and 12 volumes of transactions; and Germany about 175 volumes of medical periodicals, 175 volumes of new books, 80 volumes of later editions, and a dozen volumes of transactions. All this is exclusive of pamphlets. Of course, quantity in medical literature has no definite relations with quality or value, but I am speaking now merely with reference to the number of separate pieces which are to be obtained, catalogued, and cared for, and you will see that including journals, transactions, reports, books, pamphlets, reprints, and theses, we shall have at least 6000 new pieces to provide for this year. The indexing of articles in journals and transactions will involve the writing and classifying of about 25,000 titles in addition.

Of the *Index Catalogue* of the Library, twelve volumes have now been printed—carrying the work to S. The thirteenth volume is nearly ready for the press, and the manuscript for the rest of the work—at least two volumes more—has been prepared, but has not yet been finally corrected and arranged. As we can print but one volume a year, it is evident that during the twelve years which have elapsed since the publication was commenced a large number of titles of books and articles received too late to be placed in their proper places must have accumulated, and this accumulation becomes more rapid every year as we get further down the alphabet in the course of printing the work. At present the number of unprinted titles thus accumulated under authors and subjects down to S, probably amounts to about 70,000 author and 240,000 subject titles, the latter of course including the titles of indexed journal articles. If these were now printed they would make about four volumes of the size of the volumes of the *Index Catalogue*, and three years hence, when this first series of the *Catalogue* is finished, there will probably be material on hand enough to form at least five volumes of a supplement or second series, which will no doubt expand into six volumes by the time the printing of this second series is finished—that is, if the library continues to increase as it has done for the last five years.

The twelve volumes of the *Index Catalogue* already printed contain 137,578 author titles covering 66,855 volumes and 120,000 pamphlets, 522,092 subject titles covering 128,284 titles of books and pamphlets, and 393,808 articles in journals and transactions. The titles of articles in journals and transactions are printed only under subject headings, those of books and separately paged pamphlets and reprints are printed twice —once under the name of the author and once under the name of the subject. All the cards for journal articles have been preserved, and when the printing of the *Catalogue* is completed, it is proposed to assort these by authors so as to bring under each man's name the title of all the articles he has written which have been indexed. Whether this will ever be printed I do not know. The chief errors in the *Index Catalogue* are those of omission. About fifty serious errors in the first twelve volumes have thus far been detected, but the main defect is the failure to include under the proper subject headings some books and journal articles which are in the collection. We have gained experience as the work has progressed, and the later volumes seem to be more full and accurate than the first.

Of main and subordinate subject headings the *Index Catalogue*, as a whole, contains about 20,000, and in placing the proper headings on the subject cards to indicate where each is to be placed, it is necessary, in order to secure good results, that the person doing this shall not only remember the general scheme of classification, but the details of between four and five thousand of the subject headings used. If he makes an error, the card goes to the wrong place and is liable to be omitted in printing; but, in the long run, it is sure to be discovered and placed where it belongs.

In connection with the *Index Catalogue* a few words with regard to the *Index Medicus* may be of interest. This, as you know, is in the main a record of the titles of new books and articles in periodicals received at the library, to which are added the titles of a few books advertised as published but not yet received. It is not published by the Government, but by Mr. George S. Davis, of Detroit, who pays all expenses connected with it, and is entitled to the thanks of all who use it for his public spirit and enterprise in maintaining its existence, since the amount received by him for subscriptions barely meets the cost of its publication. At present 482 subscriptions are made for this periodical, of which 90 come from the U. S. Army Medical Department, 224 from the rest of the United States, and 168 from other countries. Of the subscriptions from foreign countries, Australia sends 5; Belgium, 2; Brazil, 1; Canada, 2; England, 41; France, 26; Germany and Austro-Hungary, 63; India, 1; Ireland, 2; Italy, 1; Mexico, 1; Russia, 9; Scotland, 9; Sweden, 2; and Switzerland, 2. Of the home subscribers, California furnished 8; Colorado, 1; Connecticut, 3; District of Columbia, 13; Georgia, 2; Illinois, 9; Kentucky, 1; Louisiana, 3; Maine, 2; Maryland, 10; Massachusetts, 31; Michigan, 8; Missouri, 4; Nebraska, 1; New Jersey, 5; New York, 69; Ohio, 8; Pennsylvania, 33; Rhode Island, 4; South Carolina, 1; Tennessee, 1; Vermont, 1; Virginia, 1; Wisconsin, 4. For the large cities, the figures are, New York, 50; Philadelphia, 32; Boston, 24; Baltimore, 10; Cincinnati, 7; Chicago, 6; San Francisco, 4; Detroit, 4; and St. Louis, 3.

This is the last of the statistics of the Library and matters connected with it which will be inflicted on you at this time. The figures themselves may be dull, but some interesting, and even amusing, conclusions may be drawn from them, which I leave for you to do.

In conclusion, I may say that the future prospects of the Library are excellent. It is not dependent on the skill or energy, or goodwill, of any one man; it is becoming more and more known to, and more and more used by, the members of the medical profession, and so long as they are interested in it, the necessary appropriations will be made and the skilled force employed to increase, preserve, and catalogue it. The service rendered by a number of those employed in the Library is not a mere matter of money—they are deeply interested in their work and proud of the results, and they can and will carry it on and instruct others who will come after them and do likewise. They have to handle much rubbish, for the proportion of what is both new and true is not much greater in medicine than it is in theology, but in a great national collection this is unavoidable, and the best they can do is to make a first rough assortment, and then make the whole accessible to those who wish to use it. There is no doubt that the publication of the *Index Catalogue* will be completed, nor that a supplement will speedily follow.

Just at present the most unsatisfactory thing about the Library is the fact that many of its books and journals are not fully available for use owing to the fact that we cannot get them bound. Under existing laws all the binding of the Library must be done at the Government Printing

Office, which has not room nor men sufficient to do the work required for the different departments of the Government and for members for Congress. The result is that the Library now has about 10,000 unbound volumes, and this number is increasing every year. When a journal is sent to be bound it may be six months or more before it is returned. With the erection of additional accommodations for the Government Printing Office it is to be hoped that this evil will in time be abated; but there will always be more or less delay in making recent books and periodicals available for use under the present system. The most effectual remedy would be a change in the law, whereby the Library could have its own binding done in its own building and under its own control.

A Card Catalogue of Scientific Literature

EDITOR OF SCIENCE—*Dear Sir:* I presume that there is no doubt of the existence of considerable demand among workers in, and writers upon, various branches of science for an index catalogue of the books and papers relating to the subjects in which they are interested, and that an accurate card catalogue, each card to be promptly furnished as soon as the book or paper is published, will best meet this demand. It is also desired that each card should contain a brief summary of the contents of the article. A large number of investigators and writers would be glad to have their work done for them by some automatic or mechanical means, as far as possible, up to a point just short of the conclusions or results. These, of course, they prefer to prepare and state themselves. Those who like literary research would be pleased to have coöperative laboratories established in which, for a moderate annual subscription, they could have any experiments made which they might suggest, the results to be reported to them for their use. Others would prefer to do the experimenting themselves, and have someone else tell them everything that other people have done and written about the matter. And if each party is able and willing to pay for the assistance he requires, and can find persons competent to give that assistance and willing to do the work merely for the pay offered, every one will agree that it is a good thing, and will furnish new channels of employment and remuneration for experts, for which channels the need is steadily increasing.

It is, however, not clear that the benefits to science and to humanity, which would result from a complete card index of science up to date and available for every one who would like to consult it, would be so great as to make it the duty of any existing scientific body or institution to incur the great expense of taking charge of the matter or to contribute largely to its support.

Physicians meet with some cases for which it is desirable that the food should be carefully minced and partially digested before it is given, and sometimes it is necessary to push this food far back on the tongue to make sure that it will be swallowed, or even to forcibly inject it, but in most cases this benefits no one but the patient.

There is a very considerable number of men now engaged in preparing

Science 1: 406–8 (April 12, 1895).

abstracts and summaries of what is known in various branches of science, and publishing them as monographs, monthly reviews, year books, etc.; and in medicine, at all events, the supply of this kind of material is quite equal to the paying demand for it.

Moreover, it is not certain that the investigator who wishes to know everything that has been suggested with regard to the subject which he has under consideration will be much happier when he gets his card index up to date, if he has not made it himself. He will find references to articles by Smith, and Schmidt, and Smitovich; but where are the books containing these articles? Very probably, after a week's hunt and correspondence, he finds that there are one or two of them that are not in any library accessible to him, and then he is decidedly worse off than he would be if he did not know that they existed.

It is probable that such complete card catalogues with abstracts would be the means of adding largely to the bulk of scientific literature, as the Index Catalogue of the National Medical Library and the Index Medicus have done to the literature of medicine. The bibliography and the abstracts will be published over and over again in successive papers by different writers.

The expediency of having such card indexes prepared depends upon the cost, and upon whether the money could be used to better advantage in promoting the increase and diffusion of knowledge in other ways. I should suppose that $25,000 a year would be a moderate estimate for providing 25 copies of such a card index for all branches of science, and to bring the cost within this limit would require careful selection.

If each author were to make his own abstract, and every article thus abstracted is to be indexed, probably $50,000 a year would be required. Much might be done for the advancement of science with a fund of $25,000 per annum.

I do not wish to be understood as opposing the preparation and furnishing of an universal card index; the schemes proposed are beautiful in the glow and shimmer of their optimism—reminding one of Chimmie Fadden, "Up t' de limit an' strikin' er great pace t' git on de odder side of it," but they must be looked at from the practical business point of view by those who are to defray the cost, and who have, I feel sure, other important uses for their money and for the skilled brains required for such work, and more definite information is wanted with regard to the number of titles, etc., which must be indexed annually upon such a scheme before a wise decision can be made. For general Biology, Morphology, Physiology, Bacteriology and scientific Pathology, and other subjects of scientific importance connected with medicine, I think that about 10,000 cards a year would be sufficient if all second-hand matter and hash were carefully excluded.

Very truly yours,

J. S. BILLINGS

WASHINGTON

The Card Catalogue of a
Great Public Library

Every one admits that a large library must have an author catalogue, but there are some students, scholars, and librarians who are more or less doubtful about the relative importance of a subject catalogue, and as to whether it would not be wiser to use the money which such a catalogue costs in employing experts in the different departments of the library to guide and instruct readers, or in purchasing more books. In favor of this view it is urged that the great majority of readers do not want a subject catalogue, and will not use it if they can help it. They want to go directly to the shelves, or else that the attending librarian shall tell them whether a certain book is in the library, or what is the best edition of a certain book, or what are the best books on a certain subject, and become impatient when they are requested to examine the catalogue and fill out order slips for the books selected.

So far as the New York Public Library is concerned this statement is not correct for ninety per cent. of the readers, but it is true that a considerable number of the casual or occasional readers who come to a library for information on some specific point, do not know how to use a catalogue, are not acquainted with the rule on the title-page of the Washington Directory, *viz.*, "To find a name in this Directory you must know how to spell it," do not know that McCarty is classed with the "Macs" and St. Bridget with the Saints, never read the directions on the guide cards, and when they do find a card containing the title they want, cannot copy it legibly and fully on the order slip. This proves that it is necessary to have a special attendant to show such people how to use the catalogue, but it does not prove that the catalogue is useless.[1]

It is also said that the person who is making an original research upon the history of some particular place, period, theory, method, or invention, has little use for the ordinary subject catalogue, because the data he wants are for the most part contained in single chapters, or essays,

Read before the New York Library Club, May 9, 1901, *Library Journal* 26: 377–83 (1901). [Sample subject heading array here somewhat abridged.]

[1] (A reader in search of a book on "Factory legislation in Europe with special reference to the hours of labor for women and children," which was entered in our catalogue under the subjects of "Labor (Female)—Hours of" and "Labor (child) Hours of,"" gave up his search in despair when he failed to find the title under "Labor—Hours of," though the guide card for this latter subject plainly referred him to the two other related subjects.)

or periodical or newspaper articles, to which the titles of the books or periodicals give him either no guidance or very little. His ideal library is one in which he can go to the shelves and search for himself, and can also go to one of the librarians and ask him "What are the latest statistics about the birth rate in different countries as compared with the birth rate in Georgia?" or, "What were the ceremonies at the coronation of Louis Napoleon?" or, "In what cities in the United States is acetylene used for illumination?" or, "What are the opinions of scholars as to the origin of the Russian alphabet?" or, "Have you a list of the marriages and deaths in Bury St. Edmunds in the first half of the 18th century?" or, "What are the text-books on analytical geometry now used in France and Germany?" or, "Where can I find the best criticism of the theories of Karl Marx?" or, "Have you a print giving the correct costume of a Sicilian peasant woman?" and in each case receive a prompt, definite answer. In other words he wants his bibliography peptonized, and given to him condensed.

It would be perfectly possible to organize a library staff which should contain persons capable of answering at least nine-tenths of all questions of this kind in general history, early American history, Oriental history, Chemistry, Physics, Engineering, Music, Maps, etc., etc., after they had made themselves familiar with the resources of the library, each in his own department. But would their employment do away with the need for a subject catalogue? I think not—in fact most of these experts, if in a large library, would desire a subject catalogue and would make one for their own use—but even if they did not, they will occasionally be absent, and will sometimes die, and the substitute, or new professor, will not be able to fill the place for a considerable period of time.

What does the subject catalogue cost? Let us say five cents per title, which would make the cost of the present subject catalogue of the New York Public Library to be about $30,000. It has been five years in making—or has cost $6000 per year. We might have employed two or three experts for the same money during that time. Would it have been wise to do so and omit the subject cataloguing? Probably some who read this paper will be surprised at the above figures for cost and it may be of some interest to give the data on which they are based so far as the Astor collection is concerned. When this card catalogue was commenced the books in the library were located by a number indicating a tier or case of shelves, and a letter indicating the shelf in that tier— thus 416 C meant that the book ought to be found on the third shelf of case 416. This had to be changed to a relative location mark under a new system of classification. Had there been no readers, the easiest and cheapest method would have been to commence at one end of the library and catalogue every book and pamphlet by author and subject, putting on each card the new classification mark which would show its location. But there were readers, and it was desirable to increase their number, hence the new books must be catalogued and made accessible as fast as possible. The number of purchases was increased—some large collections were presented—and the total accessions from these two sources and from exchanges have averaged over 30,000 pieces per year. The system of classification adopted was in many respects a new one, which required the actual seeing of the books and pamphets in working out the details; for only a broad outline could be decided on at first.

Books and pamphlets, belonging to every department, were pouring in and these must be located—for which purpose the old system was used temporarily. The result was that when in the course of classification a section was reached which contained a number of these recent additions—the author and subject cards had to be picked out, the new marks substituted for the old ones, the books placed in the new location, and the cards returned to the catalogue. In January, 1896, the cataloguing staff of the library consisted of one cataloguer at the Lenox and two at the Astor. This force was gradually increased until for the last three years the average force has included 20 cataloguers and 18 copyists, producing about 300,000 cards yearly, or an average of about 1000 cards for each working day. This provided for one set of author cards for the official catalogue in the catalogue room, and one set each of author and subject cards for the public catalogue. In addition about 17,000 index cards for current periodicals were placed in the public catalogue each year. To file these cards in the official and public catalogues has kept three of the cataloguing force busy. The searching in the official catalogue for titles of all purchases except the newest books, and of all gifts, requires the constant work of one person—and often of two. One skilled cataloguer is constantly employed on indexing current periodicals, another on indexing public documents, and another on the manuscripts at the Lenox building.

The chief cataloguer, Mr. Meissner, and his assistant, Mr. Moth, are engaged mainly in supervision and revision work. One cataloguer is kept busy with proof-reading. There remain then 14 cataloguers and 14 copyists actually engaged in preparing catalogue cards. Each of these has one month's vacation during the year, and the cataloguing force must supply the substitutes when places in the reading department are temporarily vacated by reason of vacations or sickness, for the readers department must be kept always efficient. The average production per person has been about 35 cards per day. Many of the readers of this paper will no doubt think that this is a very slow rate of work, and that 50 cards a day per person would be nearer the proper average. I can only say that in my opinion the rate of progress has been a fair one considering the large number of anonymous pamphlets to be looked up in various bibliographical authorities, the great variety of languages, and the requirement of fairly full titles with proper collation.

The preparation of author and subject cards, and the filing them in alphabetical order in the public catalogue, does not by any means complete the proper preparation of this catalogue, and if no more is done the result will often be very unsatisfactory. The pencil headings on the subject cards have been placed there by at least half a dozen different persons acting under general instructions, such as, to use substantives instead of adjectives for the first or index word as a rule, making an exception in the case of adjectives indicating nations, races, etc., and for synonomy to follow in general the "A. L. A. list." No two of them ever would, or could, assign the same subject headings to a miscellaneous lot of 100 cards, and no one of them would give precisely the same headings this year to a lot of a thousand cards which he, or she, headed two years ago. As a rule, they give only the main index word, *e.g.*, "Banking," "Commerce," "Shakespeare"—or they will go a step farther and write "Education (History of)" "Chemistry, Organic," etc., knowing that these headings are to be revised, furnished with cross-references, and added to by the librarian in charge of the public catalogue, Miss Henderson. This final revision, with the preparation of guide cards and references, can properly only be done by one person, and up to the present that person has had little time to give to this part of her work. The result is that if the inquirer is looking for references to the history of education in Pennsylvania, he may find a thousand or more cards under the heading "Education (History of)" but not classified further. There is also the possibility that half a dozen cards have gone in under "Pennsylvania, Education in." Many important sections have been arranged, and supplied with guide cards and cross-references—and the work is going on—but it will probably be about three years before it will be fairly complete. Absolutely complete it will never be, for such a catalogue in a large growing library will always have some cards wrongly headed, out of place, or obsolete. This last word "obsolete" applies mainly to cards containing references to journal articles. When a new subject of public interest comes up, such as the Spanish-American war, or liquid air, or the Boers, a considerable number of journal articles are indexed for the immediate information of readers. In a year or two, many of these have lost most of their interest, and when the new supplement to Poole's "Index" appears containing them, they are not worth the space they occupy in the card catalogue, and should be removed.

The question, "What shall be done in the way of analytical work?" is one that is always under discussion in the catalogue department. The numerous general and special encyclopædias, year-books, directories, almanacs, etc., which are essential in the reference department of a large library often contain special articles, statistical tables, etc., which are worth an index card, but the general rule is to rely on those in charge at the readers' desk to point out these sources of information. So long as there are a considerable number of books and pamphlets on hand uncatalogued the decision usually is to defer analytical card making until the separate works have been catalogued, if for no other reason than to prevent the addition of duplicates, yet there are exceptions to this rule, the chief being the indexing of periodicals. As an exception, take Schaff's "The creeds of Christendom," a valuable reference book to be found in most libraries. The subject is so distinct that it seems hardly worth while to make any analyticals for the card catalogue, and yet the reader who wants to see the text of the Heidelberg catechism, or the "original confession" of the Society of Friends, or the Savoy declaration of the Congregational churches may be very glad to find in the catalogue a card telling him that what he wants is in Schaff's "Creeds," and hence we have placed such cards there. The same argument, however, would apply to the list of "Churches in Manhattan and the Bronx," the "Strength of the militia in the several states," the "Population of the largest cities of the earth," the "Statistics of American college fraternities," and "The forty Immortals of the French Academy," all of which are given in the *World Almanac* for 1901, but which we do not index. The question as to whether analytical or index cards shall be made is not usually "Are they worth making?" but "Are they more worth making for this than for something else?" Every number of a daily newspaper contains something that would be of interest to some reader of the next century, even if it be only an obituary notice, but it does not follow that every number of a newspaper should be indexed or even preserved.

Some of the questions which arise in preparing the subject catalogue may be indicated by the subdivisions which have been made for the subject "Commerce," and the cross-references in connection therewith. The first question is, Should the main subject word be "Commerce" or "Trade"? "Trade" is the word used by Mr. Fortescue in his subject index for the British Museum, probably because he considers it a more comprehensive term than "Commerce," which is usually understood to refer to trade on a large scale, as between nations or communities, rather than to what is called retail trade. We use the word "Commerce" because 95 per cent. of our readers would search first under that heading, and we place under "Business" the references to retail trade. The second question is, Should works on the commerce of a country or state be indicated under the name of that country primarily, as is done by Cutter, Fortescue, and others, or under *Commerce, History of, regional* or under *Commerce, regional,* by countries?

Another series of questions relates to cross-references, and especially as to when a cross-reference is to be used in place of duplicating a card for two subjects.

A book on the condition of the agricultural and commercial interests of the United States might properly be referred to under both Agriculture and Commerce, and also, perhaps, still more properly, under Free Trade, but it will usually be sufficient to catalogue it under one subject only, relying on cross-references from the others.

In this library a book is catalogued as to both author and subject before it is accessioned and receives a class mark. The result is that the person who assigns the class mark has the benefit of the cataloguer's opinion as to what the book is about, but sometimes he differs from this opinion, and this may become a subject for discussion.

The following lists of headings used on the guide cards under "Ireland" and "Shakespeare" will give a general idea of the subdivisions and cross-references adopted:

Fenianism, Ireland. *See also* Ireland,—History
Folk lore (Irish). *See also* Ireland,—Manners, Customs, etc.
Home rule, Ireland. *See* Ireland.—History 1873–1900
            IRELAND *as author:*
Government publications. (Public documents)
            IRELAND *as subject:*
Ireland.
    —Bibliography (dated)
    —Archæology and antiquities. *See also* Ireland.—History, (Ancient); Lake dwellings,
        —Ireland. Dolmans; Round towers; Wells (Holy)
    Refer from Archæology; Antiquities
    —Census. (dated). *See also* Ireland,—Statistics; Statistics (Vital), Ireland
    —Charities. *See* Charities,—Ireland; Poor laws,—Ireland (dated); Poor,—Ireland
    —Commerce. *See* Commerce,—Ireland
    —Description,—Scenery,—Travels, etc. (dated). *See also* Ireland,—Geography and
        Guides; Ireland,—History (arranged chronologically)
    Refer from Geography,—Ireland; Travels,—Ireland
    —Economics. *See* Economics,—History, Ireland
    —Ethnology. *See* Ethnology,—Ireland
    —Finance. *See* Finance,—Ireland (dated); Money,—Ireland (dated)
    —Gilds. *See* Gilds,—Ireland

—Geography and Guides. *See also* Ireland,—Maps, (in Lenox)
  Refer from Geography,—Ireland
—Government. *See* Ireland,—History arranged chronologically

* * * *

—Social life. *See* Ireland,—Manners,— Customs, etc.
—Statistics. *See also* Statistics (Vital),—Ireland
  Refer from Statistics,—Census
—Taxation. *See* Taxation,—Ireland
—Topography. *See* Ireland,—Descriptions, etc.
—Travels. *See* Ireland,—Descriptions, etc.
—University question
—Vital Statistics. *See* Ireland, Census; Vital Statistics,—Ireland
SHAKESPEARE (William)
  Bibliography.
  [Works by him]
    Collected works, dated
    Single plays
    Doubtful plays
    Poems
    Sonnets
    Selections
  [Works about him]
    Shakespeare, William
      as an archer
      Bacon question
      and the Bible
      Biography and Personalia. *See also* Shakespeare (Portraits of)
      (Botany in)
      Celebrations
      (Comedies of)
      Commentaries and criticism. (Commentaries and criticism on a single play
        follow its text.)
      Concordances
      (Contemporaries of)
      as a dramatist
      (Emblems in)
      (England of)
      (Ethics of)
      (Euphuisms in)
      (Folklore in)
      in France
      in Germany
      (Ghosts in)
      (Grammar of)
      (History in)
      (Home of) *See also* Shakespeare—Biography and Personalia; Shakespeare—
        (England of)

* * * *

The subdivision of labor which is necessary in a large library gives
to some extent the usual unsatisfactory result of such subdivision in

that most members of the staff become thoroughly familiar with only a part of the work. Those engaged at the readers' desk rely more on their knowledge of the books than on the catalogue, to which they resort only in case of necessity, and require some time to become familiar with it. They see all the new books as they go through to the shelves, but not all the old ones. On the other hand those who assign subject headings to the cards are not always as familiar with the form in which readers' queries are put as they should be. We try to remedy this by having the classifiers take turns at the readers' desk, and by carefully noting the complaints of readers about the catalogue, and trying to do away with the causes for such complaints, and no doubt with time many of the difficulties will be minimized or entirely removed.

The space occupied by a large card catalogue is a matter that requires careful consideration and sufficient provision. In the new library building on Fifth avenue the public catalogue will be in a room 78 x 85, through which it is necessary to pass to enter the main reading rooms. In this room provision will be made at first for cases to contain two and one half millions of cards, and there will be space for cases for two and one half millions more. These cases have corresponding tables on which the single drawers of cards can be placed when in use. These will provide for a catalogue of about 1,500,000 books—and when this limit is reached an extension of the building will be urgently needed.

When the libraries are moved into the new building there will probably be 800,000 books and pamphlets to be stored in it, requiring a public catalogue of about two million cards. I do not venture to prophesy much about the details of arrangement of this catalogue, but these are some of my hopes:

1. That it will contain an author card for every book and pamphlet in the building, showing its location. This includes the books in the lending part of the library.

2. That it will contain one or more subject cards for every book in the reference library not catalogued by subject in the special catalogues connected with the special collections having separate rooms, such as of maps, music, manuscripts, incunabula, public documents, sociology, Jewish collection, Oriental Collection, Bibles, genealogy, etc., and also for the most important books in these special libraries.

3. That it will also contain subject cards giving references to important articles in periodicals and transactions for the last ten years so far as these are not obsolete or contained in special card catalogues in other parts of the building.

4. That in this room, or near it, will be a collection of catalogues of

other libraries, including that of the British Museum and of the Bibilo-thèque Nationale of Paris (printed) and a card catalogue of authors of the books in the Library or Congress.

5. That near the center of this catalogue room there will be an information desk at which a librarian with assistant will be ready to assist readers, show them how to use the catalogue and see that their order slips are correct before they go to the delivery desk. The latest accessions to the library may be at this information desk.

6. There will also be in this room tables and seats for about 25 readers, and about 5000 volumes of reference books on open shelves.

7. That in the special reading rooms in the building, devoted to special subjects, there will be special card catalogues and bibliograph-ical works related to those subjects, that in most of these rooms the books will be on open shelves and freely accessible to the readers, and there will also be a person in charge of the room competent to assist students in that particular branch.

Supposing that all this is accomplished with not more than the average proportion of errors and shortcomings, how will the result compare— from the reader's point of view—with such a card catalogue as the "repertory" at the International Institute of Bibliography at Brussels (described by Mr. Bowker in the LIBRARY JOURNAL for June, 1900, p. 273), which already contains over 3,000,000 titles?

It is probable that about 99 per cent. of those who consult the New York Public Library would never use such a "repertory" so long as the library catalogue was available. The reason is that in the great majority of cases the library catalogue would indicate enough sources of informa-tion to satisfy the wants of the inquirer, and he would know that all these sources of information are in the library, and know by what marks to call for them. If he were to consult the "repertory" his work of search would only be begun after he had copied the titles he desired, for he would then have to find out whether they are in any accessible library.

If a bibliography is a critical or annotated one, showing for each title given whether the book has any special value, or contains anything not to be found in other books, the search might give results worth the trouble, but without such notes or indication of location a long list of titles of books, pamphlets, and journal articles is simply dis-couraging to the average reader. Fancy being confronted with six thousand titles about Aristotle, or ten thousand titles about ordination sermons, or two thousand titles on the duties of parents, or eleven thousand titles on labor and capital, from which to select more or less blindly those which may have some interest in connection with the question at issue, and then to be compelled to find out where they are! The bibliography of New York colonial history, recently published by the New York State Library, has its value greatly increased by the fact that it indicates where the books may be found.

The most important objection to an alphabetical index catalogue such as that described, is, that it often separates widely the lists pertaining to closely allied subjects, as for example, food, butter, cookery, milk, etc., and while the guide cards for the general subjects will give references to other subjects for details, the student who wishes to find all that the library contains on some rather general subject would prefer to have the catalogue arranged by classes as far as possible.

This objection will be obviated to some extent by the shelf lists which will be prepared in accordance with the new classification, and which will be available for the use of readers, but these shelf lists will not be made until we move into the new building, and the books now divided between the Astor and Lenox buildings can be arranged together. Moreover a shelf list can never take the place of a subject list, because for every subject there are important pamphlets and articles in transactions and periodicals to which the shelf list gives no clue.

One of the questions which arises in the arrangement of the subject cards in a large catalogue like this, is, as to whether in certain subjects, and especially in historical groups, the arrangement should be chronological or alphabetical. Some readers prefer the first, others the second. The alphabetical arrangement is more convenient for the librarian in checking off lists of books on a certain subject in order to see what the library has, or has not, and it is also usually preferred by the casual reader, who is more accustomed to it, while the chronological order is preferred by the systematic student, and by the reader who wishes to refer to the latest work, or to the oldest work, with the least possible delay. At present we are arranging the cards of titles relating to the history of countries in chronological order, and the same plan has been followed in some of the sciences, such as mathematics, but as yet in many subjects the cards are in alphabetical order, which is easiest for the filers. The general tendency is to use the chronological arrangement for those subjects which are most likely to be studied historically, either as regards their own origin and development, or as throwing side lights on general history as, for example, Banking, Commerce, Finance, Taxation, Poor laws, etc., but for nearly all such subjects the chronological arrangement is subordinate to that by country.

In conclusion I would say that twenty-five years ago I held much more definite and positive opinions as to how an index catalogue like that of the New York Public Library should be arranged than I do at present.

Address at the Dedication of the New Building of the Boston Medical Library, January 12, 1901

No doubt we have all heard "platform figureheads"—of advanced years and much experience—commence their remarks on occasions like this by saying that one of the privileges of old age is the perspective, restrospective view which it gives of institutions, society and the world in general. I used to suppose that this was an excuse for, and explanation of, the attitude of sage and prophet assumed by the speaker, and that he enjoyed solid comfort in giving advice; but I am now beginning to appreciate how those old gentlemen really felt when they announced this important discovery. Most of them, I think, did not feel as wise as they looked, nor as certain and free from doubt as they did in their youth, but circumstance compelled them to speak, and this was a way to begin.

As I look back to the ceremonies of opening the then new building for this library in Boylston Place in 1878, I find that of the speakers on that occasion, I am the only one now present. President Eliot is still very much alive, although not here tonight; but Holmes, Ellis, Lyman, Smith, Henry I. Bowditch and Justin Winsor have passed away, and their biographies have been written. Fortunately, the results of their work remain and are enlarging, and one of these results we have before us tonight.

The medical prospect has changed somewhat within the last twenty-two years; there is a new literature, a new pathology, a new surgery, and new names for some very old things,—Christian Science, for example, —but the old records have not lost all interest, and the special value of the library is that it contains both the old and the new. In his memorable address twenty-two years ago, Dr. Holmes rightly insisted that a library like this must exercise the largest hospitality, but this applies to gifts rather than to purchases. The funds for conducting a library, medical or other, are always insufficient, and the librarian, or library committee, must therefore exclude from the purchase lists many works which might be welcome additions if obtainable from other sources. The selection is sometimes difficult, and in making it, the work of other reference libraries in the vicinity, such as the public library, the

Boston Medical and Surgical Journal 144: 61–3 (1901).

university library, and some special libraries, must be considered. Even gifts must be scrutinized with reference to available space, and to their relative utility in other neighboring institutions. This library does not want a set of United States public documents, or of Massachusetts documents, although in each of these series there are a few things which it should secure. Curious things may be found in public documents. How many of you, I wonder, have ever heard of Herkimer Sternberg, and his great medical discovery, which is vaguely indicated in the following extract from Document No. 15 of the Assembly of the State of New York, dated January 15, 1859, being a report of the Committee on Medical Societies and Colleges, relative to the petition of Herkimer Sternberg for aid in publishing his manuscript of a proposed work. The committee reports "that they have had under their serious consideration the subject referred to them and have become satisfied if the prayer of the petitioner be granted, that the result of the scheme proposed by this Herkimer Sternberg, if successful, will be the annihilation of the medical profession, and thus the five or six thousand doctors of our State will be turned out upon the cold charities of an unfeeling world; that it will introduce the millennium several years before its proper advent in the regular order of business; that it will dislocate every joint in the system of the moral universe ... and, therefore, the committee ask to be discharged from its further consideration."

In cities where there is no medical library, it is clearly the duty of the public library to provide some of the best medical books and periodicals for the use of the physicians of the city, as well as for the direct benefit of the public. It, is however, a matter of common experience that some lay readers are rather injured than benefited by reading medicine, and that it is best to restrict the use of certain classes of medical books. It simplifies the problems of the librarian of the public library when he knows that there is in the city a special medical library available for the use of physicians, and that he need only obtain those books which, if not exactly suitable for public use, are not calculated to do much harm. He will usually be glad to send to such a medical library the medical books of the eighteenth and most of the nineteenth century, old medical journals, miscellaneous medical pamphlets, theses, reports, etc., and to retain in the public library only those which have some interest in local history, or in other subjects besides medicine.

There are certain duties and responsibilities which rest upon a few large reference libraries which do not pertain to the great majority of city public libraries. For example, the average city library should collect and preserve all the reports of hospitals in its own city as a matter of local history, but it should not waste time or energy over the reports of hospitals in other cities, but should send those that come in either to a medical library or to one of the great reference libraries of the country like the Boston Public, the New York Public, or the Congressional Library. These great libraries must collect and preserve such reports as a part of their collections relating to charities—private and public— an important branch of sociology, but they are only useful in this way when the collections are very large and permit of comparisons of methods and results from a wide area and for considerable periods of time.

The field of medicine is very broad, and the special medical library might properly include not only general biology with its general subdivisions of morphology, physiology, psychology and anthropology, but also much of the literature of botany, zoölogy, chemistry, physics, municipal engineering, building and other applied sciences—and in fact the great medical libraries of London, Paris, Berlin, St. Petersburg and Washington do include many of these subjects. But this requires more space and money than most medical libraries can afford to give, and hence it is usually best to leave most of these subjects to other special libraries.

The department of first importance in a library like this is that which contains its files of periodicals, not only because they contain the original records from which textbooks and monographs are made up, but they represent the feelings, views and wants of the great mass of the profession, and are the great sources for the medical history of the nineteenth century. Medicine is now the most cosmopolitan and inter-national of all the arts and professions, and this is largely due to its periodicals. Moreover, its periodical literature is now more accessible than that of any other profession because of the indexes upon which Dr. Holmes so much insisted. All this has been fully recognized by your librarian, and you are very rich in this class of literature. Thanks to the efforts of the medical profession of Boston (aided by those of some other parts of the country), Congress was induced to order the printing of the Index Catalogue of the Washington Collection which was under consideration twenty-two years ago, and which I then thought might make six volumes. This Index Catalogue is not yet finished, only twenty volumes having been published; but it can give considerable employment to the bibliographical student even now, and has probably added to the practical utility of this library, but perhaps not always to the perfect joy and content of its readers.

The fact that the physicians of Boston have another library besides this one to care for, as shown by their action with regard to the Index Catalogue, is one that I venture to remind you of because the needs of your National Medical Library are liable to be overlooked. Just now it is in urgent need of shelving for its additions, some of which are being stored in window sills or on the floor, which is bad for the books and for the readers.

Requests for funds to provide this shelving have been presented at the last two sessions of Congress, but received no attention. An estimate is before the present Congress for $9,000 to supply this shelving, and if the Massachusetts representatives and senators hear from their medical constituents that this is a matter in which they are interested, there is no doubt that it will be done. Your Washington Medical Library now contains 136,000 volumes and 230,000 pamphlets—decidedly the largest and best library of its kind in the world—and ought to be kept up to date in good shape.

When I tried to say something on the occasion of the opening of this library in the Boylston Place Building, I well remember that I was very much embarrassed and not a little afraid, and would have been very glad to have been merely a listener.

On the present occasion, while I am in trouble to find the right words in which to express my thoughts and feelings, I am very glad indeed to have the opportunity to congratulate you upon the result of the work of the Boston Medical Library Association during the last twenty-five years, and I do congratulate you most heartily and sincerely. The collection of books, of portraits, of medals, the building in its plan, structure and furnishings, are all things of which you have good right to be proud, and with which you may rest satisfied for several weeks to come.

As you all know, these results are largely due to the fact that one man having abundance of energy and public spirit, with much knowledge and an insatiable thirst for more, and with a fairly definite idea of what he wanted, has been working incessantly for the last quarter of a century towards this end. I congratulate you upon your wisdom in letting him thus work, and in helping him to carry out this plan. His power for good has not been limited to Boston, for by way of recreation he has devoted some of his time to stirring up and stimulating other librarians like myself, when he thought they needed it, or when he had some superfluous energy to dispose of, which was often. In this and other ways, he has given material and valuable assistance to other libraries, more than any of you are aware of, and it is not my personal affection for him, great as that is, but a sense of what is just and right, which leads me to say to you that, while the Boston Medical Library has been his special pet, for which no trouble was too great to take, and no sacrifice too great to make, all other medical libraries in this country are more or less indebted for their progress and prosperity to your librarian, Dr. James R. Chadwick.

Some Library Problems of To-Morrow

When the American Library Association was organized its object was declared to be "to promote the library interests of the country by exchanging views, reaching conclusions, and inducing co-operation in all departments of bibliothecal science and economy; by disposing the public mind to the founding and improving of libraries, and by cultivating good will among its members." When the Constitution was revised in 1900, the object of the Association was declared to be "to promote the welfare of libraries in America."

This change is significant, not of a change in the purposes of the Association, but of a general opinion that verbose details of its purposes are now unnecessary. At first the Association undertook much direct missionary work, but this has gradually been taken in charge by state and local associations to such an extent that our work in this direction is now mainly to obtain records of the methods which have been found most successful, and to bring these to the attention of those directly engaged in interesting the people at large, and legislators and tax-payers in particular, in the establishment and support of free public libraries.

It is the welfare of the free public library, and especially the library intended mainly for the circulation of books for home use among the people, and supported from public funds, to which we have given the most attention. This is especially an American institution and it has seemed more important that its uses and needs should be understood and appreciated by the general public than those of purely reference libraries, since these last are fairly well understood by those who most need and use them.

The main argument in favor of the free public library is that it is an essential part of a system of free public instruction which is a necessary foundation of a satisfactory system of self government. It is not true, however, that any and every system of education tends to produce a stable democracy, and there are great differences of opinion among professional educators, and still greater differences of opinion among other thinking men who know something of the methods and results of our public schools, as to whether our present system is the best one. If the main object of the school and of the teacher is to furnish informa tion and cultivate the memory, there is good ground for objecting tc both the quantity and quality of some of the kinds of information

Presidents's address to the American Library Association, June 17, 1902. *Library Journal* 27, no. 7: 1–9 (1902).

supplied. If the object of education is to develop the intellect, to teach the student how to judge as to what is true and to know where to look for it, to recognize wise thought, and to distinguish the man who is qualified to lead from the incompetent man who wants to lead, then our public school system is not well suited to its purpose.

The relations which should exist between the system of public libraries and the system of public schools in a State or city are not yet generally agreed upon by both librarians and teachers. In a general way it may be said that the librarian's view is that the public library should be entirely independent of the public school system as regards its funds and management, that special school libraries are apt to be badly managed, and inefficient for the purpose of interesting and instructing the children, that the librarian knows more about books than the teacher, and can supplement and broaden the teacher's work: —and that teachers should recognize these facts, should be willing and anxious to receive instruction and advice from librarians by listening to lectures and talks at the library and repeating to their classes what they have been taught, and urging the children to make use of the library.

A few enthusiasts claim that the librarian ought to know more than any teacher, and should supplement the defects and ignorance of each instructor in his own branch, but treat them all kindly and tactfully, recognizing that it is not their fault that they do not know as much as librarians. Some librarians admit that some teachers may know more than they do as to the reading most desirable to supplement the particular instruction which a class is receiving, and will be glad to receive lists of books wanted. All librarians think it very important that the child should learn to use the public library and become acquainted with its attractions, methods, and resources, so that after leaving school he will continue to use it, and they do not consider that any mere school or class library can be a satisfactory substitute for the public library. Moreover, they want the children to come to the public library and use it because this is a means of bringing their parents and friends under the same influence.

Superintendents of schools, as a rule, take a somewhat different view of the matter, that is, if they have given any thought to it, but I am bound to say that many of them reply to questions on the subject, that they have never given it any special consideration. Some of those who have considered the matter say that, of course, the public library is a useful institution, that its chief use is educational, that it should be managed so as to help the public school as much as possible, but that it should not interfere with school methods. They believe that the school should have a library of its own, under its own management, selected with reference to the needs of the different classes and grades, that the teachers should see that the children use these books, and have a record of such use as a guide to dealing in the best way with the individual child. They say that the public library, in its recent arrangements for attracting children and especially those in the lower grades, tends to interfere with the school plans for reading, that the children find in the library much that is more attractive than the books which they can find in the school library, but which is also less useful; that they acquire the habit of desultory reading, and are led off from the proper course. The junior teachers in the schools in our larger cities stand in somewhat the same relation to the superintendents that the junior assistants in the public library stand to the librarian, and the opinions of each, while interesting, are not conclusive. At present the majority of teachers in the lower grades know and care very little about the public libraries; they may use them to obtain current fiction, but it seldom occurs to them to take their classes to them or to tell the children what they can find there.

At present it appears that the librarians are more aggressive, energetic, and filled with the missionary and proselytizing spirit than are the teachers, possibly because the work of the latter is more monotonous and fatiguing.

I have several times been asked by legislators and jurists whether the public schools and the public libraries could not wisely be consolidated under one central management and thus be made to work harmoniously.

It is theoretically possible, but I think that the result would be that the libraries would lose much, the schools gain very little, and the public at large be profoundly dissatisfied.

The Library Association has a special committee on co-operation with the Library Department of the National Educational Association, and it is to be hoped that this committee will find a satisfactory solution to the problems connected with the relationship of the library to the school. No hard and fast rules can be established, but it would seem that the library, supported by public funds, should not interfere with the work of the public school. On the other hand, one of the most important functions of the school is to train the children to use books and libraries, and at the present time the chief obstacle to the proper performance of this function is that the teachers themselves are in great need of instruction about public libraries and how to use them. For the great majority of children story books and works on general literature of the right kind are not only more interesting but more important means of education than the average textbooks.

The class which, at present, far outnumbers all other classes in this country is, as Professor Bryce says, the group of "thinly educated persons whose book knowledge is drawn from dry manuals in mechanically taught elementary schools, and who in after life read nothing but newspapers or cheap novels." [1]

Those who have had practical experience in free circulating libraries know the truth of this characterization, and are trying to get the children interested in the library as early as possible; if the library proves more attractive than the school it is quite possible that the school methods should be changed. But whatever may be thought of elective studies in the high school and college course, the public library system of instruction must necessarily be largely elective; and mere amusement should not be the leading elective, as seems to be too often the case.

In recent years the subject of co-operation between libraries and librarians has been one to which much thought has been given and for which a great number of plans have been proposed. To secure the most useful co-operation, it is desirable to bring into the work many libraries which are not intended for the circulation of books, except, perhaps, among a limited class and some of which are not supported by public funds. These include the libraries belonging to the general government and to the states, university libraries, and the larger libraries belonging to and managed by private corporations, either as reference libraries only, but for the use of the general public, or as reference and lending libraries for the use of members, stockholders, or subscribers only. Among these are many scientific, historical, and technical libraries.

The problems of these reference libraries have been receiving increasing attention in the Association in recent years, as is shown by the organization of a section devoted more especially to their work, and the subject of co-operation will come up for discussion at this meeting in several ways, and will, no doubt, be considered from several different points of view. The question, as it appears to most libraries, is, What can the greater libraries do for us in the way of cataloguing, bibliography, lending of books, etc., with the tacit assumption that whatever they can do, they ought to do.

It does not seem necessary to produce arguments in favor of this view, but perhaps a suggestion that the smaller libraries should, on their side, assist the larger ones so far as they can, may not be out of place.

The public library in this country, which now stands, or should stand, second, if not first, in interest to every librarian is the Library of Congress. I feel it to be a duty as well as a pleasure to report to you that the work of this library is being well done, and that Congress has

---

[1] James Bryce, Studies in history and jurisprudence. N.Y., 1901, p. 200.

recognized the wisdom and tact of its librarian by increased appropriations for books and for service. You are all familiar with the work being done by this central library for other libraries throughout the country by furnishing catalogue cards, bibliographical data, etc. I think it well, however, to remind you of your duties to this your National Library, and especially that the librarian of every city, town, or village in the country, should make it his or her business to see that one copy of every local, noncopyrighted imprint, including all municipal reports and documents, all reports of local institutions, and all addresses, accounts of ceremonies, etc., which are not copyrighted and do not come into the book trade, is promptly sent to our National Library.

I cannot speak so positively and definitely about the state libraries or the great reference libraries of the country, but most of them will be glad to receive such local publications as I have indicated, and the New York Public Library especially desires assistance of this kind.

The controversy between the individualists and the collectivists which is going on in many fields of human activity exists also among those interested in library organization and management and is taking much the same course there as in commerce and manufactures. The tendency is towards organization and division of labor, at first by co-operation, later by consolidation. The free public library is tending to become a special industry by unification of methods for the purpose of securing the greatest product with the least expenditure. The general public, and many librarians, think that the measure of greatest product is the number of books circulated. This is the argument used with city officials to secure increased appropriations, and the kind of books which will circulate most rapidly and the methods of advertising which will increase the numbers of readers are matters of much interest to library trustees and managers. From this commercial point of view much remains to be done in the way of co-operation. It is probable that the co-operative cataloguing now under way could be much facilitated, and a considerable saving to individual libraries effected if one small committee of experts selected all the books to be purchased for each and every library. These books could then be catalogued, with annotations on the most elaborate plan, classed, marked, and delivered to the several libraries, where, in course, they would go on open shelves and be advertised by co-operative short lists. The libraries could then discharge most of their cataloguers and experts. One-half the money now used for salaries could be devoted to buying books, the circulation would increase and the business would flourish.

Moreover, this committee of experts for the selection of books to be

purchased would naturally be consulted by publishers as to what particular varieties of literature are most in demand. It would suggest subjects and writers, read MSS. and indicate the pictures which would stimulate the circulation of the volume, and not be objectionable to any
one. From this, it would be an easy step to undertake the publication of books for free public libraries and thus effect a wonderful
reduction in cost; and if the librarians take up the business of book-
selling the scheme will be still more neat and compact.

I need not go into further details, or show what might be effected
for the world's progress by simply extending this scheme to an international system; no doubt you can all readily imagine the results which
might be obtained by a great cosmopolitan free circulating library trust
with the latest attachments and improvements. We should then have
accomplished an important part, what some consider the most important part, of the original object of the Association, which, you will
remember, was declared to be the "reaching conclusions and inducing
co-operation in all departments of bibliothecal science and economy."
Of course, in the formation of the expert Board of Managers, the demand for representation which will be made by the leaders and managers of different religious, political, and sociological sects and parties
would require consideration, and there are some other important
details to be considered by the Committee on Co-operation when it takes
up this part of its work.

I do not think there is any immediate prospect of the formation of
such a free public library trust as I have indicated, or that the cheapen-
ing of library service in this way is desirable, even if it were possible,
but there are many things in the mechanical details of library economy
in which co-operative work may be of service without checking or
interfering with individual development.

Circulating libraries supported from public funds will naturally tend
to greater uniformity in methods and scope than reference libraries
supported by corporations, but each has something to learn from the
other.

There are some men—and women—who have a great desire for
uniformity, who think there is only one best way; they want codes,
and rules, and creeds; they want all schools and high schools and universities to have one system, even to the periods of their vacations;
they want a rule about fiction, and about classification, and about salaries
for all libraries, and they want resolutions passed about all these things.

Concentration has its evils as well as its advantages. Some excellent
library work in our large cities is done by institutions or societies which
use the library as a means to secure attention to their special end,

which may be religious, sectarian, humanitarian, or sociological. The friendly rivalry of different libraries in the same city often has good results, though perhaps it may be a little wasteful of money. To secure the use of a library, the energy and enthusiasm of a propagandist are very useful, but the propagandist does not work to the best advantage in a systematic hierarchy. It is the old question of the individual worker or dealer versus the co-operative, or the consolidated establishment, and while the ultimate answer may be in favor of the latter as giving the greatest amount of useful results with the least expenditure of force, we can understand the feelings of the individual worker who fears that he will be crowded out, and who says that "the lion and the lamb *may* lie down together, but the same lamb don't do it again."

It must be remembered that almost every change in the manner of doing things is injurious to some individuals. Evolution affects not only the fittest, but also the unfit. If it be true that the public library is injuring the business of the bookseller, that the hustling administrator is crowding out the scholar in library positions, and that old-fashioned readers find their old resorts in the libraries less comfortable because of the crowd which now frequents them, it may still be true that the general result is satisfactory.

The question as to whether the public library shall undertake to do other work for the public benefit besides the supplying of literature has occasionally been raised, but has not been seriously discussed as a general proposition. When Mr. Carnegie's offer to provide branch library buildings for the city of New York was made public, many suggestions were made as to the desirability of making these buildings something more than libraries. For example, it was advised that they should be made social centres and substitutes for the saloon, that they should have lecture rooms, rooms for playing various kinds of games, smoking rooms, and billiard rooms, and even public baths in the basement were recommended. At the present time, in a large and crowded city, the need and demand for public library facilities is so great that it has seemed best to confine the work of these buildings to library work proper, but in more scattered communities, where sites are not so costly, and meeting-rooms less easy to be obtained, some of these suggestions are worthy of careful consideration, and it might be well to collect the experience of the members of the Association bearing on this question, and make it a subject for discussion at a future meeting.

As usual, during the past year, there have been some public expressions of doubt as to the utility or expediency of circulating libraries.

Mr. Howells suggests that we may be in danger of reading too much, "reading to stupidity." Lord Rosebery also warns us to beware lest much reading should destroy independence of thought, referring to the "immense fens of stagnant literature which can produce nothing but intellectual malaria." Of course, in some particular cases reading does produce bad results. It would, no doubt, be better for the public in general, and for their own families in particular, if some men and some women had never learned to read. "On a barren rock weeds do not grow—but neither does grass." It might also be better for the world if some sickly, deformed, degenerate children did not live, and the jail fevers of the eighteenth century probably disposed of some criminals to the best advantage; nevertheless it has been found to be wise economy to spend considerable sums of money in lessening the mortality of infants, and of jails, in the inspection and regulation of tenement houses, and in the compulsory restraint of contagious diseases, because the majority of the lives thus saved are worth saving, and they cannot be saved without preserving some others who from the mere utilitarian point of view may not be worth the cost.

The expenditure of public funds upon free libraries is in like manner justified by the general belief that it will do more good than harm. We cannot yet furnish satisfactory statistical evidence as to the results of the free public library experiments which we are trying on a large scale; there does not yet seem to be any marked decrease in crime or increase in contentment among the people who have had most use of such libraries, and, while the physical welfare of the great mass of the people has been advanced during the last fifty years, it would be difficult to trace this to the free public library because we do not know what use of such libraries has been made by the few hundred inventors and captains of industry to whom this progress is mainly due.

It does seem, however, that the free public library has lessened the power of the demagogue and unscrupulous politician to control votes, and that in public life the steadily increasing influence of educated men is, in part, due to the reading facilities which the people now enjoy.

When the author of Ecclesiasticus[2] declared that he that holdeth the plow, the carpenter and the workmaster, the smith also sitting by the anvil and considering the iron work, and the potter turning the wheel about, all these trust to their hands, without them cannot a city be inhabited,—they shall not be sought for in public counsel, they shall not sit on the judge's seat, and they shall not be found where parables are

---

[2] Ecclesiasticus, xxxviii, 25–34.

spoken, but they will maintain the state of the world, he did not foresee the effect of a system of public education including free public libraries, in a democratic government.

As regards Mr. Howells' suggestion about "reading to stupidity," that is precisely the object of many of the readers of current fiction. They are tired and worried, and they read to forget or to get asleep. The average novel will give this result in from six to ten minutes, and the after effects are not nearly so bad as those of chloral or sulfonal. The novels of five or six years ago will answer this purpose just as well, and twelve new novels a year is an ample allowance for the average free public library. But five-sixths of the other books which are produced—not because the author had anything to say, but because the publisher thought that a book on the beauties of brooks, or on the birds' nests of the Bronx, or on the homes of historical stepmothers or on the lieutenant colonels of the Revolution, would sell well—are usually of little more value in the free public library than the novel; they count for circulation, but they are not read, but merely glanced over—mainly for the pictures.

At the present time public opinion in this country tolerates expressions of great differences of opinion with regard to religion and particular creeds. Recently a few Catholics have made objections to the free public library, upon much the same grounds as those upon which the Church objects to public schools, and demand that in both the school and the library the books provided shall be subject, directly or indirectly, to their censorship. Somewhat similar demands, although not so definite and systematic, are occasionally made in behalf of other sects, and they would no doubt come from a number of other religious and political organizations if it was supposed that there was any chance of their success. The question will usually be decided for each locality by political party requirements, which vary much at short intervals, and there is no immediate danger to the free public library system from this particular form of opposition, except possibly for a short time in some limited locality. It is necessary to bear in mind, however, that public opinion is much less tolerant in matters of morals and manners than it is in matters of religion, and that in selecting books for circulation this opinion should be considered and respected.

The librarian of the free public library has, as a citizen, the same rights and duties as any other citizen, including the right to express his opinions on religious or political questions, but as a general rule, his influence for good will be greatest when he is not a partisan of any particular policy of either church or state.

As regards the large reference libraries, the selection of books must be made much broader in scope, for even the most ardent propogandist of a particular creed or shade of opinion occasionally wants to see what his opponents are saying in order that he may specify their errors, and does not object to find their publications in the reference library, provided they are carefully put away for the use of experts like himself and are not placed on open shelves consulted by the general public.

The duties and problems of our great reference libraries are in many respects peculiar, but the limits of this address permit of only a brief reference to some of them. One of their duties is to preserve the literature of the day for the use of future scholars and students. Part of the business of the circulating library is to have its books worn out and destroyed in actual service, but the reference library has also another purpose, and the books which give it the greatest value and importance should be carefully preserved.

The relations which should exist between our great reference libraries located in large cities and the rapidly multiplying smaller libraries scattered all over the country merit careful consideration. The amount of public funds which can and should be devoted to public libraries is limited, and these funds should not be employed in doing comparatively unnecessary work. Many of the smaller libraries are now, or soon will be, complaining of want of shelf room, and are at the same time accepting and trying to preserve and catalogue everything that comes to them. All of them are preserving books that will not be used by any reader once in five years, and two or three copies of which in the large central reference libraries will be quite sufficient for the needs of the whole country. The remark of President Eliot in his last annual report that "the increasing rate at which large collections of books grow suggests strongly that some new policy is needed concerning the storage of these immense masses of printed matter" is very suggestive; and his idea that if the Congressional Library and the great reference libraries in a few of our largest cities would undertake to store any and all books turned over to them and make them accessible to scholars in all parts of the country, the functions of the other libraries might be considerably amplified, is no doubt a true one.

Whether the great reference libraries could undertake the work thus indicated would depend upon the construction placed on the requirement that all books should be made accessible to scholars in all parts of the country. Whether the other libraries would be disposed to accept the suggestion to turn over their old books not in immediate use, merely because it might seem for the public good so to do, is much more doubtful, and the selection of the useless books involves some questions which would be good topics for discussion in the trustees' section of this association.

It is always possible to show that any book or pamphlet, in any edition, might be called for by some reader, student, or professor if he knew it existed, and the difficulties in selecting books to be discarded are very considerable. Mrs. Toodles' state of mind about things that it might be handy to have in the house is one that librarians well understand. It is no doubt true that in the great majority of libraries of one hundred thousand volumes and upwards, one-fifth of the books are so little used that it would be wiser to dispose of them than to use a fund available for salaries or for the purchase of books for providing additional room. Just at present, in most communities, it seems easier to obtain funds for library buildings than it is to get the means to ensure good service.

Closely connected with this is the question as to the acceptance of gifts of books, especially when made with the condition that they are to be kept together to form a permanent memorial for the donor. While each case must be decided on its individual merits, it may be said in general that the desire for a memorial can be fully met by book-plates and catalogues without the unfortunate and unwise requirement that a certain group of books must always be kept together. Even gifts without restrictions, consisting of one or more cartloads of miscellaneous public documents, odd numbers of periodials, imperfect files of newspapers, pamphlets of little interest, etc., involve some expense to the library, and very few libraries should try to retain and utilize more than a small part of such material.

General discussion as to what large reference libraries should do is of very little practical interest. The interesting question is, "What should this particular library do?"

Should the Library of Congress obtain and preserve complete files of every newspaper published in North and South America?

Should the Boston Public Library try to obtain complete sets of the public documents of the Southern States?

Should the New York Public Library complete its collection of first editions of American Authors by purchase at current prices?

Should the New York State Library try to make a complete collection in Genealogy?

Should the Chicago libraries attempt to make a complete collection of the reports of Insane Asylums?

There are many questions like these which require a knowledge not only of the present contents, the available funds, and the special needs of each library, but also a knowledge of what other libraries are doing, if proper answers are to be given.

The methods of co-operation between the great reference libraries, for the public good and for mutual benefit, are as yet rather local and rudimentary. Some points of agreement have been reached between the Congressional Library, the Boston Public Library, and the New York Public Library, as to the purchase of certain manuscripts and rare books; and in every large city there is more or less co-operation between the greater reference libraries, including the University library, as to pur-chases,—especially of periodicals. The chief subject thus far considered by them is that of Bibliography.

Many schemes for bibliographies, general, special, annotated, etc., have been suggested, and a few have been or are being tried. Each of these, from the universal bibliography to contain thirty millions of titles, to the bibliography of posters or of Podunk imprints, or of poems and essays condemned by their authors, has at least one admirer and advocate in the person who would like to have charge of the making of it; but when it comes to the question as to what has a com-mercial value there is great unanimity in the opinion that many of those bibliographies should be paid for, not by the makers or the users, but by government or by some philanthropic individual.

A bibliography is very instructive and useful to the person who makes it, and it is well to give the person having a taste for such work as ample facilities as possible; but mere uncritical lists of all the books and journal articles relating to a given subject, from the commence-ment of printing to the present time, and without indication as to where the older ones are to be found, are of little use to most libraries or to their readers. Like some speakers, they are too much for the occasion.

A good bibliography can, in most cases, only be made from the books themselves; the labor of its preparation is almost equal to that of writing a critical history of the subject, and therefore the first question in considering it is, Where are the books?

One session of this meeting is to be devoted to this subject of Bibliography, which is an important one, and I hope that the papers presented, and the discussion to follow, will bring out some valuable suggestions. These will be especially interesting just now in view of the fact that a Bibliographical Department has been proposed as one of the special lines of work for the recently organized Carnegie Insti-tion, and upon the scope and plan proposed for such a department will no doubt depend the action of the trustees of that corporation.

A considerable part of the bibliographies which would be most useful for reference libraries and those engaged in research work can only be prepared by experts in the different arts and sciences, and there is an increasing demand for such experts in the large reference libraries. Just now there are places for three or four well educated engineers who have the taste and the training required to enable them to do much needed work in the critical bibliography of their art. Every great reference library needs half a dozen such experts in different departments. Where are they?

In considering the questions as to the kinds of bibliographical work the results of which would be most useful to the great majority of the public libraries of this country and as to the means of doing such work, it appears to me that it is best that it should be done under the direction of the Publishing Board of this Association, which has had practical experience in this line, and will always be well informed as to the needs of such libraries.

This opinion was brought to the attention of Mr. Carnegie, with the suggestion that he should give to the American Library Association a special fund, the income of which should be applied to the preparation and publication of such reading lists, indexes, and other bibliographical and library aids as would be specially useful in the circulating libraries of this country. The main part of the income would be expended in employing competent persons to prepare the lists, indexes, etc., and to read proofs. The cost of paper and printing would be met by sales to the libraries. It was represented that such a gift would be wisely administered by the Publishing Board of the Association, and that the results would be of great value in promoting the circulation of the best books.

In response to this suggestion a check for $100,000 was sent to me as "a donation for the preparation and publication of reading lists, indexes, and other bibliographical and literary aids as per (your) letter of March 14th." I shall take great pleasure in turning over this money if the Association accepts it for the purposes and under the conditions stated. It is a unique gift from a unique man, who deserves our best thanks.

To diminish or destroy desires in the individual man is the object of one form of Oriental philosophy and of several forms of religion, the result hoped for being the doing away with anxiety, discontent, and fear, and the passive acceptance of what is and of what is to come.

Our work follows an opposite plan; the library aims to stimulate and increase desire as well as to satisfy it, and the general tendency of the free circulating library, as of public education, is to increase discontent rather than to diminish it. A competent librarian will be dissatisfied during most of his working hours,—he will want more books, or more readers, or more room, or a better location, or more assistants, or means to pay better salaries, or all these things together. Some readers also will usually be dissatisfied with the library because of its deficiencies in books, or because of some books which it has, or because the librarian is not sufficiently attentive or is too attentive, or because of the hours, or the excess or want of heat or ventilation, or because of other readers. All this is an almost necessary part of the business; if neither the librarian nor the readers are dissatisfied, the library is probably dying, or dead. But there is a discontent which is stimulating and leads to something, and there is a discontent which is merely indicative of disease, a grumbling discontent, which resembles the muscular twitchings which occur in some cases of paralysis. A pessimist has been defined as a person who, having a choice of two evils, is so anxious to be right that he takes both. Don't be a pessimist. Life is short and art is long; you can earn your halos without making your library perfect, but halos are not to be had by waiting for them, nor, as a rule, by hunting for them. It will make very little difference to you fifty years hence whether you got your halo or not, or whether it was a plain ring halo or something solid, but it may make a great deal of difference to some of the men and women of that time, who are now coming to your children's reading rooms, as to whether you have deserved one or not. Each of you and each of your libraries is a thread in the warp of the wonderful web now passing through the loom of time, but a living thread is not altogether dependent on the shuttle of circumstance. It is wise to try to know something of the pattern and to guess at some of the problems of to-morrow, but in the meantime we may not fold our hands and wait because we do not see clearly the way we are to go. We must do our best to meet the plain demands of to-day bearing in mind the warning of Ecclesiastes, "He that observeth the wind shall not sow, and he that regardeth the clouds shall not reap. . . . In the morning sow thy seed, and in the evening withhold not thine hand, for thou knowest not which shall prosper, whether this or that."

The Military Medical Officer at the Opening of the Twentieth Century

I suppose that it is entirely within the bounds of possibility that some forty or fifty years hence some member of this class will come back here to give the address to the graduating class of that date. I am not specially curious as to which one of you gentlemen will perform that duty,—but I should very much like to know what he will say—if I did, I could probably make a very interesting address myself, although I might have to make a very careful selection for fear of being thought a crank. I can hardly imagine what Dr. McLaren, the President of the Army Medical Board which examined me, would have thought if I had tried to answer some of his questions as you would probably answer them. He thought that great progress had been made since he entered the service at the beginning of the Florida War, and that we young fellows were going into the War of the Rebellion with great advantages. He had seen the introduction of anesthesia, and was enthusiastic over the comparatively new operations for excision of joints. He had just heard of the clinical thermometer, but doubted whether it would be of much use, and had also heard of the hypodermic syringe; and when he found I had one of these instruments, he went to Surgeon General Finley (this was in 1861), and had me assigned to duty at the hospital under his charge so that he might see how these new things actually worked. If, however, in answering his question as to the means of preventing malaria and typhoid fevers among troops, I had referred to bacilli, haematozoa, flies and mosquitoes, as you would probably do, I don't think I should have passed, and if I had referred to antitoxin as a means of treating malignant sore throat (his name for diphtheria), he would have advised me to take a six months' rest in an asylum. I was asked to describe laudable pus and the best means of securing healing by the second intention. Have any of you ever seen any laudable pus? Certainly my knowledge of medicine in those days before you were born was not great as compared with yours, but when I went to the army of the Potomac I found a few doctors who knew less, as appeared from the results of a certain examining board of which I was a member.

When the war was over and the armies of Grant and Sherman had

Address to the graduating class of the Army Medical School at Washington, April 14, 1903. *Journal of the Association of Military Surgeons of the United States* 12: 349–58 (1903).

made their last parade, when, thirty-eight years ago today, President
Lincoln was assassinated, and at last rested in the peace of death, and
the old Ford's Theatre was occupied by the Army Medical Museum and
Library, the younger medical officers in the museum became busy with
investigations, and it is interesting to remember some of the problems
which occupied them. One was the comparison of high power microscopic objectives as tested on Nobert's lines; another was the best way of
making photo-micrographs; a third was the best method of staining and
mounting tissues. I clearly recollect the feelings of triumph with which I
took some slides of stained sections of kidney and intestines mounted in
balsam to Dr. Woodward, who had been very incredulous as to the
possibility of making such preparations. Then Dr. Edward Curtis and
myself began the study of minute fungi and of Texas cattle fever, looked
for the malarial organisms on Analostan Island, and spent much time on
bacteria, following Pasteur's method. In the absence of the solid isolating
culture methods devised by Koch, we were groping blindly, but I have
not regretted the time spent in this groping. It is impossible for you to
appreciate the feelings with which we read Koch's first papers, or with
which we viewed the commencement and progress of antiseptic surgery.

When I graduated in medicine I had to write a thesis, and for divers
and sundry reasons, I chose to write on the surgical treatment of epilepsy.
I undertook to get the history of all reported cases of such treatment, and
in trying to do that I discovered that there was no library in the United
States which contained all the reports. There were no complete files of
medical journals in this country, and any man who really wanted to
write a scholarly book on medicine had to go to London or Paris for his
data. It seemed that that condition of things should be improved, and
when I came here in the Surgeon General's Office and was detailed to
settling the medical accounts of the war, I put in some side time in trying
to get this library together.

The work which was done in the old Ford's Theatre in the latter
sixties and the seventies, in connection with the Museum and Library
was in part merely incidental to the preparation of medical and surgical
history of the war, in part for the advancement of medicine, and in part
for the pleasure of the young men engaged in it. Its direct results on
the science and art of medicine were not great, but its indirect results
have been and are important. This Army Medical Museum and Library
are well known to physicians all over the world, and the opportunities
they have afforded and the aid which they have given to physicians in
the United States have been such as to produce in the medical profession
a strong interest in the Army Medical Department. It is desirable for all
parties that this interest should be maintained, and to this end the

younger members of the Medical Corps should know and feel that this Army Medical Museum and Library is an inheritance to be cared for and increased by them for their own and the general good. One of the good things about this Army Medical School is that it brings the Assistant Surgeons in touch with this institution, giving it some of the features of a central home club.

Thirty years ago there were considerable difficulties in obtaining funds for this Institution. I look back at my experience with Congressional appropriation committees with more amusement than I felt at the time. At present I am told that the difficulty is to obtain the funds required to provide shelving for the books, rather than to obtain the books. This is also amusing.

When I asked for suggestions as to what I should talk to you about, I was told:—"Oh, the usual thing, congratulations and advice."

As for my congratulations,—you have them,—and they are sincere. It is really a very fine thing to be a young army medi-officer, although there are, occasionally, short periods of time when he may not think so: He may have some doubts about it after he has been for a year at some small, isolated, very healthy post, or, for a month before his examination for promotion, or when he has to decide without advice as to what he will do for his first case of strangulated hernia, or of incipient melancholia, or of shot-wound of the abdomen, or of locked twins. He may even more than doubt it when he takes a stereoscopic view of his contemplated marriage on the one side and his salary and prospects on the other. These doubts will pass, but as a rule he will not know clearly what a good time he is having and what a fortunate man he is until he looks back over his career across the gulf of twenty or thirty years.

If it is true, and I think it is, that "a spice of danger and an element of chance add interest to work," then your work will have that interest. You are not coming on the stage of action at the beginning of a period of peace and content, but in the midst of a waxing tide of national struggles for commercial supremacy and of discontent among great masses of people. "That this turmoil and unrest can be dealt with wisely and justly, so as to preserve that which is most desirable in civilization and in our system of representative government, I believe, but here and there in special localities, the immediate problems must probably be solved by blood and steel, and that you will have a part to play in some of these is not at all unlikely."

You will have some epidemics to face, and no doubt some of you will have a chance to hear bullets whistle, arbitration to the contrary notwithstanding, but the increased interest which these things may give to an army surgeon's life is too uncertain and temporary to be worth consideration. The things most to be dreaded in your future lives are boredom and waiting, and the preventive and remedy is to see to it that you have something to do always,—and doing it. It may be, generally must be, routine, like a woman's knitting work; sketching or photography, Indian languages or calculus, infusoria or ascomycetes will any of them keep you busy. But suggesting subjects for work is a little like the plan of the man who told James Russell Lowell that he had discovered the way to make a fortune. "As the fine flavor of the canvass-back is due to the wild celery on which it feeds, I am going to feed tame ducks with it and supply the market." Some weeks later Lowell met him and asked him how the duck feeding plan was getting on. "Well," was the answer, "they wouldn't eat it."

Forty years ago the microscope was mainly used by physicians as a plaything, a source of occasional amusement. It was the correct thing for the young graduate to buy a thirty dollar Oberhauser, and keep it in a conspicuous place in his office, but his chief use of it was to show his admiring friends the terrible monsters contained in a drop of selected water.

To-day the microscope is one of our most important tools, and you have been taught how to use it, but it may be well to remind you that you can get a great deal of pleasure by using it in research work not directly connected with medicine.

When you obtained your diploma as Doctor of Medicine, it is possible that many of you thought you knew it all, or nearly all, and that what you did not know could be found in the latest text books, monographs and journals. Probably all of you are now aware that there are many things in regard to the causes, prevention and treatment of disease which, at present, nobody knows; or if any one does now, he has not told. There is no end to the things we don't know and ought to know, and probably will know within your lifetime.

Some of you have, perhaps, resolved that you will investigate some of these unsettled questions, and may have even selected the particular problem which you intend to solve. This is good, very good, but remember that in your life as an army medical officer the subject for investigation will usually be determined by your opportunities rather than by your wishes. I advise every young army surgeon to have some research work on hand for his own mental health and pleasure, just as I advise him to take a certain amount of physical exercise, and if he cannot make the particular research he would most like, that he try to like the research he can make. Of course his selection of a subject for study will be largely involuntary; if he feels a strong impulse towards some special line of work, it is well for him to follow it, but if this work has no relation to his military duties he must bear in mind that these duties have precedence. The fact that he is an enthusiastic botanist, ornithologist, or comparative anatomist, is no reason whatever for his neglecting to keep himself well informed as to advances in medical science, or not being interested in his patients or in the sanitary condition of his post. It is also a very poor reason why he should try to obtain posts which are specially favorable to his particular hobby, if this hobby is not connected with military medicine. If he considers his research work more important than his army duties, he should resign from the latter.

What amount of time and energy should be given to original research work by professional men employed in college and university work and in Government departments is a question which has been much discussed of late years. The exceptional man, who knows all that is known on some one subject and has the capacity and the desire to increase knowledge on that subject, and for whom many of our Universities and large manufacturing and engineering establishments are seeking, is not easily found, and when found it is not more than an even chance that he can be trusted to fulfill the ordinary every day duties of his profession, including administrative work.

If any of you feel satisfied that you are that sort of man he had better communicate with the Carnegie Institution.

Most of us hold our professional work as the first and most important object, and original research as a thing to be done as opportunity offers. We belong to the second class mentioned in Hesiod, i. e., those who can understand things when explained to them.

I shall not attempt to advise you with regard to your special medical, sanitary or surgical work, but merely ask you to remember that every army medical officer has some special opportunities for increasing knowledge, but that to enable him to recognize these opportunities and to take advantage of them usually requires long study and training. It was because of this study and training that your late teacher and friend Dr. Walter Reed, was able to recognize his opportunity and to make the discovery with regard to yellow fever which has placed his name high on the roll of the famous physicians who have been great benefactors to mankind. His work on this subject was not done under direction, rather in spite of it, yet the line of work in which he had been engaged for the previous ten years was what fitted him for the emergency.

These special opportunities always come to the physician, the naturalist, the anthropologist, they are connected with phenomena which are occasional—rarely just alike and must be secured at the time or be lost. But you must be able to recognize them if you are to use them. Remember the motto of the Washington City Directory "To find a name in this book you must know how to spell it."

Permit me to say a word about your social relations and duties, which are substantially those of the family practitioner, but with some special peculiarities. In time of war the surgeon is more intimately associated with line officers and their work than are the officers of other staff corps, and to a certain extent this is also true in time of peace, and as a general rule they are good friends. In my time there were two or three commanding officers who always had difficulties with medical officers, unless they were sick, but so they did with all other officers. There were also two or three medical officers who always had difficulties with their commanding officers, although they might be on very friendly terms with other officers. These gentlemen were sensitive on questions of rank, and rights, not so much on their own account (as they explained), as because they felt it to be their duty to uphold the dignity of the Medical Department. Now the nature of either personal or Departmental dignity, and the desire to have all of one's rights, is such that the more attention you give to them the more they seem to require, and it becomes hard to spare the time necessary to preserve them spotless and unfrayed.

Your military rank may, on rare occasions, be an important matter in dealing with the rank and file, but your medical skill and tact are more important in the ordinary routine of army life.

It is your duty to contribute your quota towards the social life of your post, and to try to make it cheerful and interesting. Of course, your personal likes and dislikes, strength or weakness, in such matters as athletics and games, shooting and whist, reading clubs and amateur theatricals, the nieces of the Major's wife, and other sources of amusement, will have much influence on your actions,—but be ready to give some of your time to things you don't care much about, if it is for the general good and pleasure. You have got to take into consideration the opinions, feelings and desires of some women as well as the men, but the only piece of advice I can give on this point is,—whenever you find yourself thinking that you thoroughly understand the ladies,—or a lady, —at your post, you had better not prophesy.

You have also certain social duties in connection with the soldiers under your charge. You should know them by sight and name, and you should be interested in their individual peculiarities. And this should be a real interest,—the soldier is quick to detect perfunctory, patronizing forms of apparent interest. Why does Smith sulk or mope and get off by himself as much as possible? Why has Brown suddenly become quarrelsome? How is Jones the new recruit getting on? "These matters are the business of the line officers," you will say. They are, but they should also interest the medical officer, who, without impertinent inquisitiveness, and with tactful sympathy, can often make the rough path smooth, and help his brother officer to form a wise judgment.

The medical officer may also have social and professional duties in connection with civilians in the vicinity of his post. At a few special places his medical services are in much demand by civilians and are paid for, wherefore these places are desired by army surgeons. If there are other physicians in the vicinity, and there are few places where there are not, they may think that the army surgeon's work should be confined to the limits of his post, and professional jealousy with a little mixture of the Code of Ethics, has in bygone years, caused trouble to the medical officer.

On the other hand you will find that such jealousy is the exception and not the rule, and that if you sympathize with what interests your professional brethren, wherever you may be, you will receive cordial sympathy and aid from them. You are "members of a world-wide guild, the oldest one, and the only one." The medical officer has thus a double comradeship, and this is one of the specially attractive features of his position.

Your attendance at this Army Medical school will have other results besides increase of professional knowledge. You have become more or less acquainted with each other's personality, more than you could otherwise have done in many years, and I hope you have formed some friendships which will endure.

Probably you will never all come together again in this life, after you have taken your different routes over the iron lines that bind this country to its Capital, but your paths will cross each other many times and in unforeseen places. At each crossing may your memory of your Washington experience aid in making the meeting a happy one.

As members of a great profession, as officers of the nation, as citizens of a great country, as men possessing special knowledge and selected from many candidates, you are coming on the stage of action to share the burden and responsibility of the world's work, to bring fresh blood and energy into the organism, to maintain and add to the dignity and honor of your corps and of your country. Enter upon your heritage modestly, but confidently. Be strong and of good courage. "Nos morituri salutamus."

Medical Reminiscences of the Civil War

In the Fall of 1861 I went to Washington to appear before the Medical Examining Board of the Regular Army. I had graduated from a medical college after a two years' course, each year having exactly the same lectures. I had had two years' hospital experience, and I had been demonstrator of anatomy for two years, so that while I had my doubts about my passing the ordeal of the Army Medical Board, from what I had heard of its severity, still I thought that probably I should get through. I came up before the Board, and at about noon of the second day I began to feel rather comfortable and thought I was getting on very well; but by noon of the third day there was a consultation between the examiners, and they began all over again, going back to anatomy and to the beginning of things. That went on for three days more and made me very uneasy. I did not learn the explanation of this until long afterward. When it was all over Dr. McLaren, the President of the Board, said to me that he hoped I would take service at once with him—that he could not get my commission for some time, but that I could be made a contract surgeon without delay. I agreed to this, was introduced to Surgeon-General Finley, got my contract and was told that I was especially detailed to go to the Union Hotel Hospital in Georgetown, which was under the direction of Surgeon McLaren.

I began service, and had three things with me that none of the other surgeons had: A set of clinical thermometers like those Dr. Keen talked about, a straight one and one with a curve; a hypodermic syringe, and a Symes staff for urethral stricturotomy. The hypodermic syringe was in constant requisition. The clinical thermometer was troublesome and was not used very much. The medical director of the army was Dr. Charles S. Tripler, who had seen me operate for stricture of the urethra the year before, and thought the results were very good. Consequently whenever any surgeon of troops about Washington applied for the discharge of one of his men for the reason that he had an impermeable stricture of the urethra, instead of granting the discharge, Dr. Tripler sent that case to me. There were quite a number of them, but I have no statistics of my cases.

One day in the Spring of 1862 I was in the hospital office when two men walked in—one a large man with an air of importance, the other a

Read April 5, 1905. *Transactions of the College of Physicians of Philadelphia* **27**: 115–21 (1905).

small man who had said very little. The large man said they would like
to see some of the cases in the hospital. They did not give their names,
but I thought it was proper to show the cases, and so took them around.
Practically I had done most of the operations in the hospital. After
spending about two hours they went down to the desk and the big man
said to me, "Dr. Billings, I wanted to see the man who beat my student
Adams." I told him I didn't know who "Adams" was. He said, "Don't
you know the results of your examination?" I said, "No." He then said,
"When you came up for examination they had finished their class, and
the report was just ready to go in, when you were sent over with an order
to be examined. They looked up your paper, found that you were born
in Indiana, and thought they would make short business of it. At the end
of the first day they concluded that probably you would pass, but hoped
it would not be necessary to change the order of precedence in the roll,
and that you could come in at the bottom. The second day they thought
they would have to put your name higher up, and on the third day they
concluded that you would be at the head of the class, but that, to be fair,
they ought to ask you the same questions that they had asked Dr. Adams,
who was previously the head of the class, and so they began all over again
with you. I then learned that my callers were Dr. Hammond, Surgeon-
General, and Dr. Letterman, Medical Director of the Army of the
Potomac. Dr. Hammond said to me: "Day after to-morrow all the surgeons in this hospital will be relieved, which will leave you in charge.
You will be sent some contract doctors, and you are to go to the cavalry
barracks at Cliffburne, on the hill back of Georgetown, turn them into a
hospital, and move this hospital out there as soon as possible."

The surgeons were relieved. I did establish the Cliffburne Hospital,
and when the wounded came in from the seven days' fighting before
Richmond I was ready for them, and had very excellent opportunities for
operative work.

I secured sixty Sisters of Charity, who took charge of the nursing side of
the work. We should not think them particularly skilled at the present
day, but they were very good for that period.

One of the difficulties at Cliffburne was that we had a large number of
Confederate as well as of Union wounded. The old residents of Georgetown and Washington were mostly in sympathy with the Confederates,
and came out bringing good things to eat and drink, with the desire that
these things should be for the exclusive use of the Confederates. On the
other hand, the ladies of the families of members of Congress and of
officers in the departments were enthusiastic for the Northern side, and
they also came with various good things, but with the specification that
none should go to the rebels. We would not receive gifts from either

party on these terms, but after a little explanation they were left to be used for those who needed them most.

I remember a member of Congress from New York City who came up and said: "You have got a lot of my boys here; I would like to do something for them, something that the papers will notice, you know. What do you think I had better give them?" I said: "They have all got more or less scurvy, and I think fresh strawberries would do them good. You might have a strawberry festival, and have a band here."

He agreed, and it was a great success, as the reporters duly proclaimed.

At the battle of Chancellorsville there was a good deal of joking among some of our line officers about the doctors not getting up to the front, that they kept in a comfortable place about a mile back, etc. This was mostly chaff, but there was a little bit of earnest in it; so I said I would go up and see. The regiment came under fire, and was then less than 200 yards from the Confederates, and I was, perhaps, 40 yards behind the firing line. I stopped behind a little frame house, giving notice to bring the wounded there. I soon found that the wounded who could walk would not stop where I was—it was entirely too close. At first the men that were more severely hit were brought back by members of the band, but very soon there were no more bandmen, and they never came back for a second load. When the men began to bring their wounded fellow soldiers in they would not stop where I was. Finally a shell went through this wooden shanty, making a deuce of a clatter, and that settled the question of the men stopping. The slightly wounded men would not stop, and the bearers of the badly wounded men would not stop, so I moved back about 200 yards and began to work there, but soon got an order from the medical director saying that I was still too close, and must go back to the Chancellor House about a mile away and establish my hospital there. The next morning the Chancellor House came under artillery fire and I had to move again. Fortunately I was able to get all the wounded out of the house and to move them back another mile or so into a little hollow without losing any of them. But one of my assistants was killed.

My experience in Chancellorsville was that of handling wounded without an ambulance corps, and getting them off when the troops were falling back. It is one thing to provide for wounded when the troops are advancing and leaving the hospital behind, and quite another thing to fall back with your wounded when the troops are retreating.

Let us take another field hospital scene—this was at the battle of Gettysburg. There I established the hospital at a farm house on the side of Round Top, perhaps half a mile behind the first firing line. In the house we found dough kneaded and nearly ready for the baking pans, which had even been greased. There was a fine fire in the stove, but nobody about the house. I got my men to separate that dough into reasonably sized lumps and slip them into the oven. Then we found a big copper boiler which we filled with water and made coffee and some soup. In about twenty minutes the wounded began to come in, and we had about 850 before 12 o'clock that night. They all got hot coffee and hot soup, but there was not enough bread to go beyond the first hundred. The seriously wounded were in the house, and near it under the trees and in the big barn. The slightly wounded picked their own places on the outskirts. About midnight Dr. Letterman came in and said that he had just learned that this particular place was going to be shelled early in the morning, and that we should have to move on at once. I found a place a mile to the rear, where there was plenty of water and shade, and we began to move early in the morning. Here I had an ambulance train and the work of moving was safely accomplished. A few shells began to drop near as the first train of ambulances moved off, but no one was injured.

As usually happens, about the second day it began to rain and rained continuously for five days, and the supplies were slow in coming. Various State auxiliary associations brought fresh bread, mutton, fruits, etc., for their State regiments, but there were none for the regular troops. Finally there came along a wagon from the Fire Department of Baltimore. They said: "This is just the kind of place we want to find, that don't belong to any State." Baltimore was rather neutral. After the wagon had been unloaded they informed me that they had packed one box for the surgeon. I got the benefit of that box, and it was most judiciously packed.

Let us take another scene:

A little later, at the battle of Spottsylvania, in 1864, the Army of the Potomac had an ambulance corps well disciplined. In that campaign I was a medical inspector of the army, and had a chance to look around and see what other people were doing. The first battle of the Wilderness lasted about three days. The wounded were taken back to Fredericksburg, the line of the Rapidan was then abandoned and another battle began. A large number of wounded soon resulted, but there were no ambulances, nor had we the conveniences which the ambulances supplied. Huts and shelters were built of cedar and pine branches, and we did the best we could until the ambulances returned the next day. The day was hot and sultry, the air was filled with clouds of dust, and the woods were on fire in various places. It was hard to find water, and when found it was warm and muddy. The medicine wagons could not be brought up, for the roads were blocked. The surgeons worked in their shirt sleeves, using such materials as were in the field cases, and they worked well—far into the night. I shall not give you any more illustrative scenes. My general observations agree with those of Dr. Keen, that there was not enough of operating in the state of knowledge we then had. A very few men performed operations which were unnecessary, amputating a few limbs which might have been saved, but the great majority were timid and anxious to shift the responsibility and to get the simplest dressings on as soon as possible.

During the first year of the war there was no good organization for collecting the wounded. In the second year they had acquired the idea that the doctor might be considered a general staff officer, and there was an ambulance corps. In the third year there was an order issued that the chief surgeon of the corps and the division surgeon should be at the Division Hospital, because there they could be more easily found. The brigade surgeons were often made the operating surgeons. The result of this was that all the chief officers were gathered together at the Division Hospital; and there was plenty of work for them, but the other surgeons and assistant surgeons were without directions, and were left to exercise their own will and pleasure, if they had any. In the case of Dr. Keen, when he didn't get orders, he acted on his good judgment, but a good many did not have that quality, and hence did little or nothing.

Looking back at the war as I remember it, it is a wonder that so many of the medical officers did as well as they did, and that the results were as good as they were. My main criticism of the surgical work which I saw was that too much resection was attempted in cases of injury of the long bones. If a ball smashed a femur some surgeons wanted to get out all of the fragments, although in doing so they made the injury much more severe.

During the first two years of the war the records of the wounded in field hospitals were often very imperfect, for comparatively few surgeons made notes of their cases. During the last two years of the war the records were much more complete, as a medical officer and a hospital steward were often detailed for the duty of making such records.

Address Given at the Opening of the New Library Building at Radcliffe College, Cambridge, April 27, 1908

Whether the pleasures and satisfaction obtained in pursuit, are greater or less than those derived from possession, is a question which has been the subject of many unreported debates. Fifty or sixty years ago it was a favorite subject for discussion in village and small college debating societies. It has also been the subject of a large amount of the printed literature belonging to the departments of Sport, Fiction, Poetry, Philosophy and Religion. Art for art's sake, and the delights of pure mathematics are closely related to it. You will soon be in a position to form an opinion about it,—seeing that you have had the pleasures of anticipation in the long and strenuous efforts which have been made to secure this new library building, and now, at last it is completed, and you can go on to realize the plans which have been the object of your imagination and desire. It seems to me to be very satisfactory both in its practical arrangement and in its architectural effect.

I am specially pleased to see that the library purpose of the building has been the only object you have had in view, in its plans and construction. Thanks to Mr. Carnegie, it has been easier in recent years to obtain a library building than almost any other sort of building for colleges in this country, and to many it has seemed quite natural and proper to provide for as many other college needs in such a building as possible, and, in fact, there are few of the intellectual needs of a college which cannot be shown, at least theoretically, to depend on, or to be closely connected with, the library.

The most important part of a library is, of course, the books, and of these you already have a good supply, which will, no doubt, be largely increased by the fact that you now have a suitable home for them. One of the best mottoes for a library is "Unto him that hath shall be given."

A common method in preparing an address for an occasion like this is to begin by saying that this new addition to your resources brings with it increased duties and responsibilities, and then proceed to give a few thousand words of advice. I could do this without great trouble, for I should not be hampered with knowledge of the conditions and modes

Radcliffe Magazine 10: 107–17 (1908).

of work in the college which affect the library. It is the bachelor who advises most freely as to how a man should treat his wife, and the spinster as to how children should be brought up.

Nearly all the eulogistic addresses about libraries which have been printed in recent years relate to public libraries, and especially circulating libraries, intended for the use and benefit of the great mass of the people, and in many respects do not apply to the scholars' library such as you have here.

It would be interesting to compare this library with other college libraries of about the same size, in order to ascertain the differences, if any, in the character of the books, and the principles which govern their selection. For example, does the library of a college for young men differ from that of a college for young women, and if so, how?

Of course, every college library differs from every other college library, depending on the character and tastes of the founders and of those who select the books for purchase, the special purposes of the institution, the nature of the gifts made to the library, etc. Of course, also, there are several thousand books that will be found in every college library of ten thousand volumes or more, including the ordinary reference books, such as encyclopaedias, dictionaries, standard histories, biographies and fiction, text books in the different branches of science, sets of certain periodicals, etc., also the so-called books of power, the sacred books, works of the great poets and dramatists, etc. But are there any considerable number of books which will usually be found in the man's college library and not in the woman's, or *vice versa?* Perhaps the college librarians who are here to-day might contribute to the world's stock of knowledge on this point. Mr. Gerould, librarian of the University of Minnesota, proposed in 1906 a plan for the compilation of comparative university and college library statistics[1] and a committee of the American Library Association was appointed to carry out this plan. This committee made a preliminary report in 1907,[2] but it gives no information on the question which I have suggested.

So far as I know there is no difference between the libraries of men's and women's colleges intended for general education only, and having no preparatory courses for special technical instruction, but I will refer to this later.

A library has often been compared to a laboratory for purposes of research work. There is one likeness between them, which is seldom referred to, but to which I would call your special attention, and that is

---

[1] Library Journal, Nov. 1906, v. 31, p. 761.

[2] Papers and Proceedings of the 29th annual meeting of the American Library Association, 1907, p. 261.

that both are liable to become overcrowded with useless material, and to have difficulties in the disposal of their waste products.

For a research in the laboratory special apparatus must often be obtained, but when this apparatus has been used for its particular purpose, it is often of no further value, except, perhaps, as for deposit in a museum as a bit of history. The great majority of books lose all their vitality in ten years, many of them never had any vitality to lose.

There is always a possibility that a book which seems useless, such as an old City Directory, or an old text book, may be useful to some future student, and the motive of Mrs. Toodles for buying a door-plate bearing the name of Brown because she (Mrs. Toodles), might have a daughter, and that daughter might marry a man named Brown "and then it would be so handy to have that door plate in the house" is one that appeals to some professors as well as to some librarians.

A public library necessarily accumulates much rubbish, flavorless, namby-pamby, tedious stuff—hash without salt, which one might suppose would never find a reader. But certain publishers know that there is a demand for this sort of thing, and the librarian must remember that he is managing a large public mental restaurant, and must be prepared to give toast water, and broth without salt, to some of his customers, although if they demand raw, trichinous pork, or excessively gamey birds, he can say that his supplies of those articles have not yet arrived. I have said that the character of a library depends on those who select the books. When young physicians prescribe a certain diet for their patients they are very apt to be influenced by their personal likes and dislikes, and even an old physician with a poor digestion, (which sometimes appears in old doctors), is sometimes too much guided by his own appetite.

Radcliffe is the only women's college I know of where all the instruction is given by men, and by men who are professors or teachers in a University for men. Its library has been for the most part selected by these men, each recommending the books considered as most desirable for the student for reference work in the branch of study which he teaches. It is, therefore, almost entirely a reference library, but is very little used by the teachers themselves and probably contains nothing that would not be found in a man's college library of the same size. It will accumulate some rubbish, but slowly, unless it comes in by gifts. There is generally a bad side to good things and this applies especially to gifts of books to libraries, if accompanied by restrictions as to their disposal.

As the Harvard University Library is available for research purposes to the teachers and students of this college, and as that library follows the plan of accumulating and preserving every book or pamphlet that comes to it and is not a duplicate, it seems clear that the policy of this library should be to transfer its dead and dying books to Harvard to be properly embalmed and registered.

A library may also be likened to a garden in which one may wander, picking the flowers and fruit which seem attractive,—or in which one may try to produce some new beauties or utilities by combinations or eliminations of certain characters of what is already there. But the garden must be kept properly weeded if it is to be a success, and what are weeds for your garden may be important plants for some other.

The old army proverb that "no amount of too short bed will make a man comfortable" applies to the library in which one cannot find the information desired, but in many cases the book or article which the research student wants has never been written, or at all events, printed. I found this to be the case in my enquiry as to the differences between the libraries of women's colleges and those of men's colleges to which I have just referred.

If you do not find in your garden the special combination of pineapple and potato which you have in mind, remember that you will probably not find it in any garden, and that you can have the pleasure of trying to produce it yourself and thus contribute to the joy of nations. Sometimes too much research gives unsatisfactory results, as when you find that the subject on which you wish to give an address has been entirely covered by others.

The library may also be likened to a gymnasium, in that it is a place where the intellectual and emotional faculties may be exercised and trained. Here one may learn how to master the parallel bars of memory, to take the long jump to conclusions, see how the world looks upside down without being giddy, to use the flying trapeze of imagination without bumping against too serious obstacles of fact. Here, also, one may train and cultivate one's sense of beauty, or one's appreciation of the funny side of life, or may compare what the wisest and best men of all countries and of all times have thought and said about obligations and duties, and about that which lies beyond the veil. In a large public library one may find the materials for a course of soul massage, but these are not needed here. As a rule they should not be used for this purpose, at all events, before one is fifty years old. Self-hypnotization is a dangerous business. Genuine emotion is a powerful force but it is not wise to waste it, or to seek for means of arousing it merely as a source of pleasure or as a means of passing the time. Emotionalism is somewhat like alcoholism, it produces weakening or loss of the normal powers of judgment and of will, and indicates an unbalanced nervous system, which at first may be only slight and temporary, but which, as a habit, may become pernicious.

For some people the library is like the flying carpet of Arabian story, with an improvement which enables it to transport you not only to other countries but to other times, and even to countries and times which have never yet existed.

The mind can travel when the body cannot, and by means of books it can face glaciers, and deserts, and savages with impunity,—it can ramble through Rome, or lounge in the Islands of the South Pacific,—it can "go afishing" with Walton, or Van Dyke,—it can look in at the new excavations in Nippur, or Egypt, or Crete, or get a view of the Mississippi from a pilot house with Mark Twain, or of the effects of the driver ants and the mysteries of fetish of West Africa with Miss Kingsley, or of the shooting experiences of the "Two Dianas in Somaliland" with Agnes Herbert. Arcady, or Atlantis, or Utopia may be viewed in an hour,—you may see the ashes sifting down on Pompeii, or the banners waving in the lists of the Field of the Cloth of Gold, or the black draped streets of Washington the morning after the assassination of Lincoln, at your will and pleasure.

When I was in college fifty years ago, the Library was not recognized as a part of the system of instruction. No professor ever referred the students to it, or suggested any use of the books in it. It contained about 8,000 volumes, and was open on Saturday mornings from 9 to 12. Each student could borrow two books, many of them did not borrow any, and I always found it easy to get half a dozen or more students to give me permission to borrow for them, so that I usually left with as many books as I could conveniently carry.

During the long summer vacations I used to make a burglarious entrance into the library, and then I had long hours of enjoyment. I had no wise librarian to guide me,—I simply tried every book on the shelves, skimming and skipping through the majority, and really reading those which interested me, and if there had been a librarian there I should have carefully kept away. Mr. Frederic Harrison declares that this sort of miscellaneous reading gorges and enfeebles the intellect so that it cannot properly develop. On the other hand, Mr. Arthur Balfour says that Mr. Harrison has no evidence to prove this.[3] "It is true no doubt that many learned people are dull; but there is no indication that they are dull because they are learned. True dullness is seldom acquired; it is a natural grace. Fill a dull man to the brim with knowledge and he will not become less dull as the enthusiasts for education vainly imagine; neither will he become duller, as Mr. Harrison appears to suppose * * * But whereas his dullness would, if left to itself, have been merely vacuous, it may have become, under careful cultivation pretentious and pedantic."

I cannot tell whether my example supports the view of Mr. Harrison or

---

[3] The pleasures of reading, by A. J. Balfour. Edinburgh, 1888, p. 14.

of Mr. Balfour, all I can say is that my experience in the college library has been very useful to me, and that I still skim more than three thousand books a year to my own pleasure, if not for others' benefit.

I give this personal note in order that you may understand, and make allowances for, the special point of view from which I am about to consider the possible uses of this library.

When we consider what this library may, or should be to the students of this college,—to the young women,—the ladies,—the girls,—if there are any girls here, it seems clear that only a very few general statements can be made.

It is intended to be a source of information on every subject in which they should be interested, but it should also be a source of pleasure in which every one, in any mood, can find something which will interest her, which will seem as if it had been expressly written for her, which will advise her when in doubt, be restful when she is tired, amuse and stimulate her when she is languid and bored.

No one student will require many books for all these purposes, but no two students will want the same books, so that the library will require a considerable stock to supply all needs.

But, the student will perhaps say, How am I to find the books I want, when I don't even know what they are or who wrote them? How am I to find in this wilderness garden the particular flower or fruit which will suit me, when I may not know it when I see it? That brings up the question of "How to use a library," a subject which ought to receive more attention than it does in schemes of university and college instruction. A graduate of Radcliffe ought to know what are the best reference books, encyclopaedias, bibliographies, anthologies, etc., and in particular those which best serve her special needs. These are books to be used as tools, not to be read. She ought to know how to begin a research in almost any branch of history, literature, philosophy, or theology, and in the special branches of science, applied science or art in which she is interested.

All these are matters in which instruction can be usefully given by methods well known, and which are not difficult to understand. The important thing in this, as in other branches of education, is to find out how the student can be made to want to learn about it.

Hesiod's classification of men, no doubt, applies also to the students in this college—there are those who understand of themselves the use and pleasure of books, there are those who can understand and appreciate these things when they are explained to them, and there are those who can neither understand them of themselves nor when they are explained to them. For the first and the last of these three classes, the librarian can do little, but for the second class it is possible to do much.

Of course, to find a name in a directory you must know how to spell it, and if you do not know the name of the author or the title of the book or its subject, the quest is a little difficult. Yet, in a certain way, this indicates a part of the information which the educated woman should have acquired in the college library. She needs to know what are the hundred or so best books *for her*, the books which she will wish to own and have always with her, the books which are to be her companions and friends. She cannot learn this from bibliographies, or from catalogues, or from professors, she must find them out by actual trial, by continued browsing among books old and new.

In talking with graduates of several of the leading women's colleges in this country, I have found that they knew little about the library beyond the particular reference and collateral reading books which they had used. They did not seem to have wandered about the library testing and tasting a book here and there. They said when they were in the library they had no time for anything but reference work, and that for their own leisure reading in their rooms, they got books from other libraries. They did not know whether the library contained any books specially intended for women, or not.

This seemed to me to indicate something lacking somewhere, but whether it was in the girl, or in the character of the books in the college library, or in the methods used to induce the students to use the library, I do not know.

I have alluded to the fact that no differences seem to exist between the libraries of colleges for men and of those for women. To use the words of a librarian of a women's college, "There is no flavor of the exclusively feminine attaching itself to the library of a women's college any more than to the curriculum." (This is not from Bryn Mawr.) So far as the literature relating to the curriculum is concerned, this may be well, but when it comes to providing browsing ground where the girls may find out what are the books which they want for their very own, it seems possible that a little flavor of the exclusively feminine might be desirable.

I should like to see in every college library a browsing corner, not arranged according to decimal, or the progressive, or any other system of classification, which should be what Mr. Balfour describes as a "peaceful desert of literature as yet unclaimed by tutors or coaches, where it might be possible for the student to wander, even perhaps to stray, at her own pleasure without finding every beauty labelled, every difficulty engineered, every nook surveyed."

This browsing corner should contain no book associated with memories of study, and no book recommended by any professor for reference or for collateral reading. I could make some suggestions for a few of these books for a man's college,—such as books on sport, or travels with a large sporting element, or life in the woods, the history of Flatland, Montaigne, the history of magic of Eliphas Levi, Lavengro and the Romany Rye, a set of Punch, and Puck, etc.

For the browsing corner of the women's college library I think it wise to make no specific suggestions, but I should place in it a few of the best illustrations of the taste of women at different times and in different countries in matters of applied art.

According to the catalogue of this library it contains no book on lace, or on tapestry, but I would admit a few books of this kind to the browsing corner, which should also contain a special selection of biographies and fiction and of the latest poetry. I should give the students an opportunity of seeing in the browsing corner, some of the newest books, and for this purpose the method adopted in some clubs seems a good one. For example, in the Century Association of New York, there are always six of the latest books on the table. These books are furnished by subscription to a circulating library, and are changed every two weeks. One of them is usually a novel, the others are books of travel, and sport, essays, biographies, etc., books that are being noticed in the daily and weekly press; they are much used but seldom read through.

A lady of great experience in library management to whom I mentioned this browsing corner idea, highly approved of it and went on to suggest that two or three rocking chairs and an upholstered window seat with plenty of sofa pillows would improve it. I think they would.

In his book on the private library[4] Mr. Humphreys has a section of "Boudoir libraries," which begins, "Women have their own way of loving books." This is probably true, just as they have their own way (in several senses) about most things. The greater part of this section is devoted to the bindings which are appropriate for a boudoir library and closes with an essay "On my lady's library," given in the Spectator. I suppose you all remember it. Elsewhere he says that every bedroom should have a bookcase, and that housemaids are seldom bibliophiles.

If I only knew what books, or what kinds of books, each of you will have in her own library twenty-five years from now, I could prepare an address which would be of great interest to historians and sociologists. But I can only say that the character of your private libraries will depend much on the manner in which you have used this library.

Owing to the wide diffusion of public library facilities, and perhaps for other reasons, men do not now accumulate books for their private use to the extent that they used to do. They do not, as a rule have as much affec-

---

[4] Humphreys, Arthur L. The Private Library. What we do know, what we don't know, what we ought to know about our books. N.Y. Post., 1897.

tion for their books, they have not given as much time, and trouble, and sacrifice to obtain certain books as their grandfathers did. Dr. Oliver Wendell Holmes used to say that there was an invisible thread connecting each book in his library with his heart and brain, and that it was cruel to ask him to part with any of his treasures merely because they would be more useful in a general library.

I have said little about the practical utilities of books or of libraries. In this library are gathered the most important records of the world's memory, of the progress of man from the days when Accad ruled the land between the rivers and the first dynasty was building in the valley of the Nile.

The dreams and hopes, the joys and sorrows, the sayings and doings of the wisest men of all times and of all countries are gathered here, and it is from these that our teachers, our legislators and our people must draw the stores and weapons with which to contend with the same ignorance, indolence, folly and vice which have led to the downfall of the kingdoms and cities of long ago. "In this library there are also suggestions as to beautiful and as to unpleasant things in this world of which it is difficult to see the use. Of such are the Aurora, and the hidden anemone which no one sees, and the grief for the loss of a dear one, mother or child. There is no unit of measure for the utility of these things," but they are necessary.

I have no doubt that you have all heard of the "Philobiblon" of Richard de Bury and some of you have read this eloquent appeal for the collection and preservation of books. He says "We must consider what pleasantness of teaching there is in books, how easy, how secret! How safely we lay bare the poverty of human ignorance to books without feeling any shame! They are masters who instruct us without rod or ferule, without angry words, * * * if you come to them they are not asleep; if you ask and enquire of them, they do not withdraw themselves * * * They do not laugh at you if you are ignorant."

"O books, who alone are liberal and free * * * ye are the wells of living waters * * * the most delightful ears of corn, full of grain; * * * fig trees that are never barren, lamps always in readiness."

It should be observed, however, that the learned bishop meant these eulogies chiefly for old books or what he calls "the well tested labours of the Ancients," of whom he says that "whether they had by nature a greater vigour of mental sagacity, or whether they perhaps indulged in closer application to study * * * one thing we are pretty clear about, that their successors are barely capable of discussing the discoveries of their forerunners."

We have no list of the large collection of books and manuscripts which he made, but it is probable that very few of them would be read if they were in our libraries, and I think this would also apply to a considerable number of the hundred best books named by Lord Acton. We can, all of us, however, join in the eulogy of de Bury, with the simple qualification that for us it applies to *our* books, the books which we know and love.

It is, perhaps, well that in your student life you should not be oppressed by too keen a sense of the responsibilities which will weigh upon you as women in the coming years. These responsibilities will relate mainly to what you can and should do for the benefit of others. Much of what you are now learning in order to pass examinations will, for most of you, be soon forgotten because you will have no occasion to use it, but the sources of this information and the methods of finding and using these sources you will not forget. If you have acquired in this library the knowledge as to what books interest you, it will be one of the most important benefits which you can derive from your college course.

Bibliography of the Writings of John Shaw Billings

1861

1. The surgical treatment of epilepsy. *Cincinnati Lancet and Observer* 4: 334–41 (1861).

1863

2. Cliffburne Hospital, Washington, D. C. (Extract from a report). *Medical and surgical history of the War of the Rebellion.* Third medical volume, p. 910. (1888).

1865

3. Letter to Col. Thomas A. McParlin, Medical Director Army of the Potomac transmitting the statistics of sick and wounded of the Army of the Potomac for 1864. Dated Washington City, June 17, 1865. *Rebellion records,* ser. I, v. 42, pt. 1, pp. 202–3.
4. Report on the treatment of diseases and injuries in the Army of the Potomac during 1864. *Medical and surgical history of the War of the Rebellion.* First medical volume. Appendix, pp. 199–202. (1870; Second issue, 1875).

1869

5. Report of results of examinations of fluids of diseased cattle with reference to presence of cryptogamic growths. By Brevet Lieutenant Colonel J. S. Billings and Brevet Major Edward Curtis. U. S. Department of Agriculture. *Reports on the diseases of cattle in the United States.* Washington, 1869. pp. 156–70.
5A. Army medical organization. [Correspondence; signed A. B. C.]. *Medical Record* (NY) 3: 572–8 (15 Feb 1869). Reprinted in *Military Surgeon* 99: 40–50 (1946) [with annotations by Colonel Harold W. Jones].

Prepared by Adelaide R. Hasse of the New York Public Library and originally published as Appendix III, pp. 411–22, of Fielding H. Garrison's *John Shaw Billings; a memoir* (New York, Putnam, 1915). The listing in the *Index Catalogue*, 2d series, has been compared. The item numbers assigned by Miss Hasse have been retained; additional items have been indicated by following letters.

1870

6. *A report on barracks and hospitals; with descriptions of military posts.* Washington, 1870. 494 p. (U. S. Surgeon General's Office. Circular No. 4).

6A. The Marine Hospital Service. [Unsigned editorial]. *Medical Times* (Phila) 1: 97 (15 Dec 1870).

1871

6B. The medical and surgical history of the late war, and the report of the Surgeon-General for 1870. [Unsigned editorial]. *Medical Record* (NY) 5: 493–4 (2 Jan 1871).

6C. The annual report of the Surgeon-General, and the medical and surgical history of the war. [Unsigned editorial]. *Medical Times* (Phila) 1: 118–9 (2 Jan 1871).

6D. Microscopical memoranda, by Dr. Newlenz [Correspondence]. *Medical Times* (Phila) 1: 200 (1 Mar 1871).

7. The study of minute fungi. *American Naturalist* 5: 323–9 (1871).

8. The genus Hysterium and some of its allies. *American Naturalist* 5: 626–31 (1871).

1872

9. On some minute fungi. (Abstract of a paper read February 5, 1872). *Bulletin of the Philosophical Society of Washington* 1: 42–3 (1871–4).

1873

10. On the collection of a large library. (Abstract of a memoir presented December 6, 1873). *Bulletin of the Philosophical Society of Washington* 1: 92–3 (1871–4).

1874

11. Abstract of special reports by Army medical officers on the effect of mountain climates upon health. (Read at annual meeting, Philadelphia, November 12, 1874). *Public Health Reports and Papers, American Public Health Association* 2: 148–50 (1874–5).

1875

12. Notes on hospital construction. (Read at annual meeting, Philadelphia, November 10, 1874). *Public Health Reports and Papers, American Public Health Association* 2: 384–8 (1874–5).

13. A bibliography of cholera. U. S. Congress. House. *The cholera*

epidemic in the United States. Washington, 1875. (43 Cong, 2d Sess: House Ex. Doc. 95). pp. 707–1025.

14. Remarks on medical topography. (Read at the annual meeting in Baltimore, November 10, 1875). *Public Health Reports and Papers, American Public Health Association* 2: 47–54 (1874–5).

15. *A report on the hygiene of the United States Army; with descriptions of military posts.* Washington, 1875. 567 p. (U. S. Surgeon General's Office. Circular No. 8).

16. Hospital construction and organization. *Hospital plans, Johns Hopkins Hospital, Baltimore.* New York, 1875. pp. 3–46.

17. Report of Committee on the Plan for a Systematic Sanitary Survey of the United States. (Submitted at the annual meeting in Baltimore, November 10, 1875). *Public Health Reports and Papers, American Public Health Association* 2: 41–6 (1874–5).

1876

18. A century of American medicine, 1776–1876; literature and institutions. *American Journal of the Medical Sciences* 72: 439–80 (1876) Also in: *A century of American medicine, 1776–1876.* Philadelphia, H. C. Lea, 1876. pp. 289–366.

19. (Johns Hopkins Hospital.) *Reports and papers relating to construction and organization.* Nos. 1–3, 5. Baltimore, 1876–8. (No. 5: *Report on heating and ventilation.* 1878. 93 p.).

20. Medical libraries in the United States. U. S. Department of the Interior. Bureau of Education. *Public libraries in the United States of America; their history, condition, and management; special report.* Part I. Washington, 1876. pp. 171–82.

21. The rights, duties, and privileges of the community in relation to those of the individual in regard to public health. (Address at the annual meeting in Boston, October 5, 1876). *Public Health Reports and Papers, American Public Health Association* 3: 49–52 (1875–6).

1877

22. Bacteria and spontaneous generation. (Abstract of communication. February 10, 1877). *Bulletin of the Philosophical Society of Washington* 2: 109–10 (1874–8).

23. On the plans for the Johns Hopkins Hospital at Baltimore. (A lecture given to the medical profession of Baltimore, February 5, 1877). Part I. *Medical Record* (NY) 12: 129–33 (24 Feb 1877). Part II. *Medical Record* (NY) 12: 145–8 (3 Mar 1877).

24. [Course of lectures on the history of medicine, medical legislation

and medical education given by Dr. Billings at the Johns Hopkins University in the Autumn of 1877]. (Outline). Larkey, S. V. John Shaw Billings and the history of medicine. *Bulletin of the Institute of the History of Medicine* 6: 360–76 (1938). Appendix, pp. 373–6.

25. *Medical education; extracts from lectures delivered before the Johns Hopkins University, Baltimore, 1877–8.* Baltimore, W. K. Boyle & Son, 1878. 42 p. Reprinted in *Bulletin of the Institute of the History of Medicine* 6: 311–59 (1938); also *Bulletin of the Johns Hopkins Hospital* 62: 323–71 (1938).

1878

25A. Higher medical education. (Review). *American Journal of the Medical Sciences* 76: 174–89 (1878); Reprinted in *Bulletin of the Institute of the History of Medicine* 6: 287–310 (1938); also *Bulletin of the Johns Hopkins Hospital* 62: 299–322 (1938).

26. *Suggestions with regard to incorporating in the approaching United States Census statistics of diseases as well as of deaths.* (Transmitted to the Hon. S. S. Cox, M. C., Chairman Committee on Census of 1880, by Surgeon-General, United States Army. October 15, 1878). Washington, 1878. 2 l. Reprinted in *Public Health Reports and Papers, American Public Health Association* 4: 373–5 (1877–8).

26A. National catalogue of medical literature. *Library Journal* 3: 107–8 (1878).

1879

27. Introduction on hygiene. Including: I. Prefatory remarks. II. Causes of disease. III. Jurisprudence of hygiene. Buck, A. H. (ed.). *Treatise on hygiene and public health.* New York, William Wood & Co., 1879. Vol. 1, pp. 1–70. [Buck's *Treatise* was published also, with separate title page, as volume 18 of von Ziemssen's *Cyclopedia of the practice of medicine.* New York, William Wood & Co., 1879.]

28. Report of the Committee charged with making a sanitary survey of Memphis, Tenn. *Annual Report of the National Board of Health, 1879.* pp. 237–62; *1880,* pp. 416–41.

29. Address in state medicine and public hygiene. *Transactions of the American Medical Association* 30: 275–91 (1879).

30. The medical journals of the United States. *Boston Medical and Surgical Journal* 100: 1–14, 108 (1879).

31. The study of sanitary science. *Plumber* (NY) 2: 125 (1878–9).

1880

32. The National Board of Health and national quarantine. *Transactions of the American Medical Association* 31: 435–55 (1880).
33. Report of Committee on the Nomenclature of Diseases and on Vital Statistics; J. S. Billings, Chairman. *Annual Report of the National Board of Health, 1880.* pp. 537–94.
34. Report on sanitary survey of Memphis, Tenn. *Annual Report of the National Board of Health, 1880.* pp. 602–17.
35. Remarks on the sanitary condition of Memphis. *Proceedings and Addresses at the Sanitary Convention held at Detroit, Michigan, 1880.* pp. 69–72.
36. The President's address at the Eighth Annual Meeting of the American Public Health Association, New Orleans, December 7, 1880. *Public Health Papers and Reports, American Public Health Association* 6: 1–11 (1880).
37. The report of the Advisory Council on National Sanitary Legislation. *Public Health Papers and Reports, American Public Health Association* 6: 385–401 (1880).
38. The scientific work carried on under the direction of the National Board of Health. (Abstract of remarks. November 20, 1880). *Bulletin of the Philosophical Society of Washington* 4: 37–9 (1880–1).
39. The National Board of Health. *Plumber* (NY) 3: 47, 273 (1879–80).
40. National health legislation on trial. (Review). *American Journal of the Medical Sciences* 78: 471–9 (1879). Also in *Sanitarian* 7: 501–10 (1879–80).
41. The organization and operation of the National Board of Health. *Medical Record* (NY) 17: 101–3 (1880).
42. Who founded the National Medical Library? (Letter) *Medical Record* (NY) 17: 298–9 (1880).
43. Letters to a young architect on ventilation and heating. *Plumber* (NY) 3: 132, 154, 171, 191, 211, 233, 251, 271, 291, 311, 331, 351, 371, 392, 415, 432, 463 (1879–80); continued in *Sanitary Engineer* 4: 8, 37, 68, 83, 110, 131, 155, 180, 203, 228, 253, 274, 305, 329, 470, 496, 536, 554 (1880–1); 5: 6, 99, 266 (1881–2); 6: 369, 492 (1882); 7: 6, 122, 219, 339, 434, 602 (1882–3); 8: 523 (1883). [Reprinted as no. 62, infra.].
44. Yellow fever. *International Review* (NY) 8: 29–49 (1880).

1881

45. Our medical literature. *Transactions of the International Medical Congress* (7ᵗʰ, London, 1881). Vol. 1, pp. 54–70. Also in *British*

Medical Journal 2: 262–8 (1881). *Lancet* 2: 265–70 (1881). *Boston Medical and Surgical Journal* 105: 217–22 (1881). *Revue Scientifique de la France* 29: 586–96 (1882). *Geneeskundige Courant* 35: 44–8 (1881). *Vrachebniya Vaidomosti* 6: 2534, 2559, 2573, 2594 (1881). *Norsk Magazin for Laegevidenskaben* 12: 141–66 (1882).

46. The experience of the United States in recent years with regard to Asiatic cholera and yellow fever. *Transactions of the International Medical Congress* (7th, London, 1881). Vol. 4, pp. 416–28.

47. Mortality statistics of the Tenth Census. *Transactions of the American Medical Association* 32: 297–303 (1881).

48. Patents on ventilating apparatus. *Sanitary Engineer* 4: 327 (1880–1).

1882

48A. The International Medical Congress. *International Review* (NY) 12: 1–10 (January, 1882).

49. The registration of vital statistics. *Annual Report of the National Board of Health, 1882*. pp. 355–461.

50. The registration of vital statistics in the United States. *National Board of Health Bulletin* 3: 295 (1881–2).

51. On the ventilation of the House of Representatives. (Abstract of remarks. April 8, 1882). *Bulletin of the Philosophical Society of Washington* 5: 99–100 (1881–2).

52. The information necessary to determine the merits of the heating and ventilation of a school building. *Circular of Information of the Bureau of Education* (Washington). No. 2, 1882. pp. 11–19.

53. Notes on military medicine in Europe. *Journal of the Military Service Institution of the United States* 3: 234–47 (1882).

54. The vaccination question. *Nation* (NY) 34: 201–2 (1882).

55. House sanitation in large cities. *Sanitary Engineer* 5: 338 (1881–2).

56. Address to the graduating class of Bellevue Hospital Medical College. (Delivered March 15, 1882). *Medical News* (Phila) 40: 285–8 (1882).

1883

57. Medical bibliography. *Transactions of the Medical and Chirurgical Faculty of Maryland, 1883*. pp. 58–80.

58. The heating and ventilation of a school building. *Sanitary Engineer* 7: 317 (1882–3).

59. Germs and epidemics. *Sanitary Engineer* 7: 341, 387 (1882–3).

60. Papers on vital statistics. *Sanitary Engineer* 8: 418, 442, 488, 541, 588 (1883); 9: 15, 163 (1883–4); 11: 9, 80, 128, 249 (1884–5).

1884

61. *The World's Industrial and Cotton Centennial Exposition, New Orleans, La., 1884–5.* (Medical Department, United States Army, Exhibit Class 4, Nos. 5–7.) New Orleans, 1884. No. 5. Description of selected specimens from the medical and surgical sections of the Army Medical Museum, at Washington, D. C. 20 p. No. 6. Description of the microscopes and microscopical preparations from the Army Medical Museum, Washington, D. C. 15 p. No. 7. Description of the composite photographs of crania, and of crania from the Army Medical Museum, Washington, D. C. 15 p.

62. *The principles of ventilation and heating and their practical application.* New York, The Sanitary Engineer, 1884. 216 p. London, Trübner & Co., 1884. 226 p. [Reprinted from No. 43, supra.].

63. Composite photography applied to craniology. (Abstract of communication. March 29, 1884). *Bulletin of the Philosophical Society of Washington* 7: 25–6 (1884).

64. [Report of resolutions in memory of Joseph Janvier Woodward with abstract of remarks on Dr. Woodward's work, etc.] November 8, 1884. *Bulletin of the Philosophical Society of Washington* 7: 75–6 (1884).

65. The mortality rates of Baltimore; life tables for Baltimore; mortality in different wards; causes of disease. *Maryland Medical Journal* 10: 487–9 (1883–4).

1885

66. Methods of tabulating and publishing records of deaths. *Public Health Papers and Reports, American Public Health Association* 11: 51–66 (1885).

67. On composite photography as applied to craniology, by J. S. Billings, and On measuring the cubic capacity of skulls, by Washington Matthews. (Read April 22, 1885). *Memoirs of the National Academy of Sciences* 3: 105–16 (1886) 20 pl.

68. On a new craniophore for use in making composite photographs of skulls. By John Shaw Billings and Washington Matthews. (Read November 12, 1885). *Memoirs of the National Academy of Sciences* 3: 119 (1886) 4 pl.

69. Memoir of Joseph Janvier Woodward. National Academy of Sciences. *Biographical memoirs.* v. 2, 1886. pp. 295–307.

70. *Report on the mortality and vital statistics of the United States as returned at the Tenth Census (June 1, 1880).* Washington, 1885–6. 3 v. (United States Census Office, Rep. 10ᵗʰ Census, v.

11–12). [Text] v. 1. 1885. lxiii, 767 p. [Text] v. 2. 1886. clviii, 803 p. [Plates, v. 3] xvii, 19 pl., 20 maps, 38 diag.
71. Sewage disposal in cities. *Harper's Magazine* 71: 577–84 (1885).
71A. Hygiene. Pepper, William. *A system of practical medicine. Vol. 1, Pathology and general diseases.* Philadelphia, Lea, 1885. pp. 173–212. [cf. No. 112, infra.].

1886

72. Scientific men and their duties. (The President's address before the Philosophical Society of Washington, December 4, 1886.) *Bulletin of the Philosophical Society of Washington* 9: xxxv–lvi (1886–7).
73. On museum specimens illustrating biology. (Abstract of communication presented at 288th meeting of the Philosophical Society of Washington, May 22, 1886). *Bulletin of the Philosophical Society of Washington* 9: 35–6 (1886–7).
74. Medicine in the United States, and its relation to co-operative investigation. (The annual address in medicine delivered before the British Medical Association, August 11, 1886). *British Medical Journal* 2: 299–307 (1886). *Medical News* (Phila) 49: 169–80 (1886).
75. Hot water and steam compared. *Sanitary Engineer* 14: 595 (1886).

1887

76. Effect of freezing on the typhoid germ. *Sanitary Engineer* 15: 211 (1886–7).
77. Methods of research in medical literature. *Transactions of the Association of American Physicians* 2: 57–67 (1887). *Boston Medical and Surgical Journal* 116: 597–600 (1887).
78. On some forms of tables of vital statistics, with special reference to the needs of the health department of a city. *Public Health Papers and Reports, American Public Health Association* 13: 203–23 (1887).

1888

79. Medical museums, with special reference to the Army Medical Museum at Washington. *Medical News* (Phila) 53: 309–16 (1888).
80. The history of medicine. Introductory lecture (to a course of eight lectures delivered before the Lowell Institute of Boston). *Boston Medical and Surgical Journal* 118: 29–31, 57–60 (1888).
81. The Medical College of Ohio before the war. Address to the Society of the Alumni of the Ohio Medical College, delivered at the

Annual Commencement, March 7, 1888. *Cincinnati Lancet-Clinic* 20: 297–305 (1888).

1889

82. On vital and medical statistics. The Cartwright lectures delivered before the Alumni Association of the College of Physicians of New York in November, 1889. *Medical Record* (NY) 36: 589, 617, 645 (1889).
83. The plans and purposes of the Johns Hopkins Hospital. *Medical News* (Phila) 54: 505–10 (1889).
84. The United States Census in its relations to sanitation. *Public Health Papers and Reports, American Public Health Association* 15: 43–6 (1889) [Discussion, pp. 243–6].
85. Water supply for small towns. *Engineering and Building Record* 19: 235 (1888–9).
86. House drainage from various points of view. *Popular Science Monthly* 34: 310–24 (1888–9).
87. Biographical memoir of Spencer Fullerton Baird. (Read before the National Academy of Sciences, April 17, 1889). National Academy of Sciences. *Biographical memoirs.* v. 3, 1895. pp. 141–60.
87A. Rare medical books. (Remarks at the meeting of the Johns Hopkins Hospital Medical Society, December 16, 1889). *Bulletin of the Johns Hopkins Hospital* 1: 29–31 (1890).

1890

88. *Description of Johns Hopkins Hospital.* Baltimore, I. Friedenwald, 1890. 116 p., 56 pl. (Johns Hopkins Hospital Publications).
89. *The national medical dictionary.* Edited by John Shaw Billings. Philadelphia, Lea, 1890. 2 v.
90. *Vital statistics of the Jews in the United States.* Washington, 1890. 19 p. (U. S. Bureau of the Census. 11th Census. Bulletin No. 19.)
91. The relations of the physicians of the United States to the next census. *Journal of the American Medical Association* 14: 641–3 (1890).

1891

92. Ideals of medical education. (Address delivered before the Medical Faculty of Yale College, June 23, 1891). *Boston Medical and Surgical Journal* 124: 619–23; 125: 1–4 (1891). *New Englander & Yale Review* 19: 111–32 (1891).
93. [Can the reports of the sick and the sanitary statements of the different armies be arranged according to a scheme essentially

uniform for the purpose of gaining statistics of scientific worth for comparison of diseases, wounds and deaths in times of peace and war?] (Text in English). *Verhandlungen des X internationalen medicinischen Congresses, Berlin, 4–9 August 1890.* Berlin, 1891. Band 5, 18 Abtheilung, pp. 107–34.

94. American inventions and discoveries in medicine, surgery and practical sanitation. *Boston Medical and Surgical Journal* 124: 349–51 (1891).

95. A field hospital at Gettysburg. *Youth's Companion,* July 2, 1891; p. 373.

96. Modern surgery. *Youth's Companion,* October 15, 1891; p. 547.

97. *Public health and municipal government.* Philadelphia, 1891. 23 p. (Supplement to *Annals of the American Academy of Political and Social Sciences,* 1891).

98. *Social statistics of cities.* Washington, 1891. 27 p. (U. S. Bureau of the Census. 11th Census. Bulletin No. 100).

99. Mechanical methods used in compiling data of the 11th United States Census; with an exhibition of a machine. (Abstract). *Proceedings of the American Association for the Advancement of Science* 40: 407–9 (1891).

100. The conditions and prospects of the Library of the Surgeon-General's Office, and of its Index-Catalogue. *Transactions of the Association of American Physicians* 6: 251–7 (1891). *Boston Medical and Surgical Journal 125: 344–6* (1891). *Medical News* (Phila) 59: 350–3 (1891).

101. Vital statistics of the Jews. *North American Review* 153: 70–84 (1891).

1892

102. *Addresses delivered before the Mutual Aid Association of the Philadelphia County Medical Society for the Relief of the Widows and Orphans of Medical Men, December 14, 1892.* By Drs. Billings, Keen, and Willard, and George D. McCreary, Esq. [Philadelphia] 1892. 11 p.

103. The health of survivors of the war. *Forum* (NY) 12: 642–58 (1892).

104. The objects, plans, and needs of the Laboratory of Hygiene. An address delivered at the opening of the Laboratory of Hygiene of the University of Pennsylvania, Feb. 22, 1892. *Medical News* (Phila) 60: 230–6 (1892); also as Extracts, *Boston Medical and Surgical Journal* 126: 181–4 (1892).

105. *St. Augustine: Report upon her present sanitary condition.* New York, J. B. Watkins, 1892. 7 p.

106. *A syllabus of the lectures on hygiene, vital statistics, etc., at the University of Pennsylvania.* By John Shaw Billings and Alexander C. Abbott. Edited by Seneca Egbert. Philadelphia, Collins, 1892. 29 p.

107. The causes of outbreaks of typhoid fever. *Medical News* (Phila) 61: 601 (1892).

108. Prevalence of consumption in the United States. *Transactions of the New York Academy of Medicine* 9: 35–7 (1892).

109. How Tom kept bachelor's hall. *Youth's Companion*, November 10, 1892; pp. 598–9.

110. In a draft office. *Youth's Companion*, November 17, 1892; p. 610.

1893

111. *A condensed statement of the requirements of the principal university medical schools in Europe with regard to candidates for the degree of Doctor of Medicine.* Baltimore, privately printed, 1893. 25 l.

112. Hygiene. Pepper, William. *A text-book of theory and practice of medicine.* Vol. 1, 1893, pp. 1–45. [cf. No. 71A, supra].

113. *Photomicrographs of normal histology, human and comparative, prepared by direction of the Surgeon-General.* By John Shaw Billings and William M. Gray. Washington, 1893. 2 p., 76 photo.

113A. The human bones of the Hemenway collection in the United States Army Medical Museum at Washington. By Dr. Washington Matthews, [and] with observations on the hyoid bones of this collection, by Dr. J. L. Wortman. Reports presented to the National Academy of Sciences with the approval of the Surgeon-General of the United States Army, by Dr. John S. Billings. *Memoirs of the National Academy of Sciences* 6: 141–286 (1893) 59 pl. [Statement by Billings, pp. 141–2].

114. *World's Columbian Exposition, Chicago, Ill., 1892–3.* (War Department Exhibit. Medical Department, United States Army). Chicago, 1893. No. 5. Description of microscopes from the Army Medical Museum, Washington, D. C. 6 p. Description of selected specimens from the Army Medical Museum, Washington, D. C. 14 p.

115. *Vital statistics of the District of Columbia and Baltimore covering a period of six years ending May 31, 1890.* Washington, 1893. 241 p., 12 coloured maps. (U. S. 52d Congress. 1st Session. House Misc. Doc. 340, Part 8).

116. The relation of hospitals to public health. *Hospitals, dispensaries and nursing. Papers and discussions in the International Con-*

gress of Charities, Correction and Philanthropy, section iii, June 12th to 17th, 1893. Edited by John S. Billings, M. D., Henry M. Hurd, M. D. Baltimore, 1894. pp. 1–7. Also in *Lend a Hand* (Boston) 11: 168–75 (1893).

117. The population of the earth. *Chautauquan* 16: 527–30 (1892–3).

118. Effects of his occupation upon the physician. *International Journal of Ethics* 4: 40–8 (1893).

119. Municipal sanitation defects in American cities. *Forum* (NY) 15: 304–10 (1893).

120. Medicine as a career. *Forum* (NY) 14: 725–34 (1893).

121. *Ventilation and heating.* New York, The Engineering Record, 1893. 500 p.

122. Municipal sanitation in Washington and Baltimore. *Forum* (NY) 15: 727–37 (1893).

123. Municipal sanitation in New York and Brooklyn. *Forum* (NY) 16: 346–54 (1893–4).

123A. Hospital Historical Club. Rare book. (Symphorien Champier). *Bulletin of the Johns Hopkins Hospital* 4: 99–100 (1893). ["... Dr. Kelley exhibited the following book and accompanying note upon it by Dr. J. S. Billings of Washington"].

123B. The city's health. Dr. Billings explains the plan of the Sanitary League. *The Evening Star* (Washington), March 15, 1893.

123C. The city's health. Vital statistics for different sections of Washington. *The Evening Star* (Washington), November 18, 1893.

1894

124. *Bibliography (preliminary) of the literature on the physiological and pathological effects of alcohol and alcoholic drinks.* Edited for the Committee of Fifty for the Investigation of the Liquor Problem. Washington, Judd & Detweiler, 1894. 28 p.

125. Hygiene in university education. Address given to the University Extension Classes, Oxford, Engl., Aug. 7, 1894. *Boston Medical and Surgical Journal* 131: 125–31 (1894).

126. The bacteria of river waters. Presenting a paper on the bacteria of the Schuylkill River by Dr. J. H. Wright. *Memoirs of the National Academy of Sciences* 7: 419–21 (1894).

127. The influence of certain agents in destroying the vitality of the typhoid and of the colon bacillus. By John Shaw Billings and Adelaide Ward Peckham. *Annual Report of the Board of Regents of the Smithsonian Institution to the Congress of the United States, 1894.* pp. 451–8. Also in *Science* 1: 169–74 (1895).

128. The influence of light upon the bacillus of typhoid and the colon

bacillus. Presenting results of an investigation by Adelaide W. Peckham. Read April 19, 1894. *Memoirs of the National Academy of Sciences* 7: 477–82 (1894).

129. Methods of teaching surgery. *Boston Medical and Surgical Journal* 130: 535–8 (1894).

130. On the influence of insolation upon culture media and of dessication upon the vitality of the bacillus of typhoid, of the colon bacillus, and of the Staphylococcus pyogenes aureus. (Presented October 30, 1894). *Memoirs of the National Academy of Sciences* 7: 483–4 (1894) 5 color pl.

131. *Vital statistics of New York City and Brooklyn, covering a period of six years ending May 31, 1890.* Washington, 1894. 529 p., 12 maps. (U. S. 53d Congress. 1st Session. House Misc. Doc. 340, Part 13).

132. [Remarks, meeting of the Harvard Medical Alumni Association, June 26, 1894.] *Boston Medical and Surgical Journal* 131: 140–2 (1894).

133. Compulsory notification of tuberculosis. *Philadelphia Polyclinic* 3: 73 (1894).

134. A report on the etiology and vital statistics of diphtheria and croup. Presented on behalf of the American Committee to the Eighth International Congress of Hygiene and Demography at Buda-Pesth. *British Medical Journal* 2: 578–9 (1894).

135. Water supply and sewage disposal in some large European cities. *Engineering and Building Record* 30: 395–7 (1894); also in *Food* (NY) 5: 187–96 (1894–5).

136. The health of Boston and Philadelphia. *Forum* (NY) 17: 595–602 (1894).

136A. John Arderne and early English medical writers. (Read before the Hospital Historical Club, February 12, 1894). *Bulletin of the Johns Hopkins Hospital* 5: 21–2; 67 (1894). ["Dr. Billings spoke ... he showed a manuscript volume of the works of John Arderne, recently acquired by the Library of the Surgeon-General's Office, through Mr. Thomas Windsor ... The following memorandum by Mr. Windsor gives what is known of his life ..."].

1895

137. *The composition of expired air and its effects upon animal life.* By J. S. Billings, S. Weir Mitchell, and D. H. Bergey. Washington, 1895. 81 p. (*Smithsonian Contributions to Knowledge*, v. 29, No. 989).

138. The history and literature of surgery. *System of surgery*. Edited by

Frederic S. Dennis, assisted by John S. Billings. Philadelphia, Lea, 1895. 4 v. Vol. 1, pp. 17–144.

139. Municipal mortality statistics. *University Medical Magazine* (Phila) 7: 721–9 (1894–5).

140. Report of the Committee appointed by the Smithsonian Institution to award the Hopkins Fund Prizes. August 9, 1895. S. P. Langley, G. Brown Goode, J. S. Billings, and Mark W. Harrington. *Annual Report of the Board of Regents of the Smithsonian Institution to the Congress of the United States, 1895.* p. 13.

141. *Report on the insane, feeble-minded, deaf and dumb, and the blind in the United States at the Eleventh Census, 1890.* Washington, 1895. 755 p., 86 pl. (Also as: U. S. 52d Congress. 1st Session. House Misc. Doc. 50, Part 16).

142. *Report on the social statistics of cities in the United States at the Eleventh Census, 1890.* Washington, 1895. 137 p., 33 diagr. (U. S. 52d Congress. 1st Session. House Misc. Doc. 340, Part 19).

143. *Suggestions to hospital and asylum visitors.* With an introduction by S. Weir Mitchell. By John Shaw Billings and Henry M. Hurd. Philadelphia, Lippincott, 1895. 48 p.

144. *Vital statistics of Boston and Philadelphia, covering a period of six years ending May 31, 1890.* Washington, 1895. 229 p., 12 maps.

145. *Waste.* Address on Commencement Day at Miami University, Oxford, Ohio, June 20, 1895. Oxford, 1895. 19 p.

146. *The William Pepper Laboratory of Clinical Medicine.* Address given at the opening of the Laboratory, December 4, 1895. [Philadelphia, 1895]. 15 p.

147. A card catalogue of scientific literature. *Science* 1: 406–8 (1895).

148. Degeneration, by Max Nordau. [Review]. *Science* 1: 465–7 (1895).

149. The climates and baths of Great Britain. [Review]. *Science* 2: 454–5 (1895).

149A. The world's debt to medicine. *Chautauquan* 20: 668–72 (March 1895).

149B. The world's debt to modern sanitary science. *Chautauquan* 21: 18–23 (April 1895).

1896

149C. Medical statistics. *A system of medicine.* Edited by Thomas Clifford Allbutt. New York, Macmillan. Vol. 1, 1896. pp. 3–20. [Reprinted 1901; the Billings essay does not appear in the second edition, 1905].

150–1. *Report on vital and social statistics in the United States at the Eleventh Census, 1890.* Washington, 1894–6. Parts 1–4. (U. S. 52d

Congress. 1st Session. House Misc. Docs., v. 50, pt. 18). Part 1. Analysis and rate tables. 1896. 1059 p. Part 2. Vital statistics. Cities of 100,000 population and upward. 1896. 1181 p. Part 3. Statistics of deaths. 1894. 1050 p. Part 4. Statistics of deaths. 1895. 1033 p.

152. See no. 168A.

152A. [International catalogue of scientific works; letter of Simon Newcomb and John S. Billings to the Secretary of State, October 15, 1896]. *The Smithsonian Institution; documents relative to its origin and history.* Vol. 2. Washington, 1901. pp. 1770–1.

1897

153. The influence of the Smithsonian Institution upon the development of libraries, the organization and work of societies, and the publication of scientific literature in the United States. *Smithsonian Institution, 1846–1896; the history of its first half century.* Washington, 1897. pp. 815–22.

154. Some ideas in hospital construction. Report made to the Memphis City Council upon plans proposed for the new city hospital. *Memphis Medical Monthly* 17: 193, 249, 309 (1897).

1900

155. Progress of medicine in the nineteenth century. *Annual Report of the Board of Regents of the Smithsonian Institution to the Congress of the United States, 1900.* pp. 637–44.

1901

156. The card catalogue of a great public library. *Library Journal* 26: 377–83 (1901).

157. [Address at the dedication of the new building of the Boston Medical Library, January 12, 1901]. *Boston Medical and Surgical Journal* 144: 61–3 (1901).

1902

158. Biographical memoir of Francis Amasa Walker, 1840–1897. (Read before the National Academy of Sciences, April 17, 1902). National Academy of Sciences. *Biographical memoirs.* v. 5, 1902. pp. 209–18.

159. Some library problems of tomorrow. (President's address to the American Library Association, June 17, 1902). *Library Journal* 27, no. 7: 1–9 (1902).

1903

160. The military medical officer at the opening of the twentieth century. (Address to the graduating class of the Army Medical School at Washington, April 14, 1903). *Journal of the Association of Military Surgeons of the United States* 12: 349–58 (1903).

161–2. *Physiological aspects of the liquor problem.* By W. O. Atwater, J. S. Billings, H. P. Bowditch, R. H. Chittenden, and W. H. Welch. Boston, Houghton, Mifflin & Co., 1903. 2 v. V. 1, pp. 307–38: Data relating to the use of alcoholic drinks among brain workers in the United States. V. 1, pp. 339–55: Relations of drink habits to insanity.

163. The public library; its uses to the municipality. *Library Journal* 28: 293–4 (1903).

1904

164. *A discussion of the vital statistics of the Twelfth Census.* Washington, 1904. 24 p. (United States Census Bureau, Bulletin 15).

165. The Carnegie Institution. *Journal of the American Medical Association* 42: 1674–5 (1904).

1905

166–7. *The liquor problem; a summary of investigations conducted by the Committee of Fifty, 1893–1903.* By J. S. Billings, C. W. Eliot, and others. Boston, Houghton, Mifflin & Co., 1905. 182 p. Pp. 15–42: A summary of investigations concerning the physiological aspects of the liquor problem.

168. Medical reminiscences of the Civil War. *Transactions of the College of Physicians of Philadelphia* 27: 115–21 (1905).

1906

168A. The king's touch for scrofula. *Proceedings of the Charaka Club* 2: 57–71 (1906).

1908

169. Address given at the opening of the new library building at Radcliffe College, Cambridge, April 27, 1908. *Radcliffe Magazine* 10: 107–17 (1908).

1911

170. Public library systems of greater New York. *Library Journal* 36: 489–92 (1911).

171. The New York Public Library. *Century* (NY) 81: 839–52 (1911).